Growing up
with Gas

Growing up with Gas

A History of the Gas Industry

Danny and Helen Lawrence

BREWIN BOOKS

BREWIN BOOKS
19 Enfield Ind. Estate,
Redditch,
Worcestershire,
B97 6BY
www.brewinbooks.com

First published by Brewin Books 2023

A CIP catalogue record for this book is
available from the British Library.

Front cover and spine gas flame image
courtesy of sciencestockphotos.com

ISBN: 978-1-85858-764-6

Printed and bound in Great Britain
by Halstan & Co. Ltd.

Contents

Dedicated to the memory of our parents

Daniel and Ellen Lawrence (née Smith)
and
Arnold and Phyllis Wilson (née Duncan)

and

all those who worked in the UK's gasworks.

Other recent books by Danny Lawrence

The Making of Stan Laurel – Echoes of a British Boyhood
(McFarland, 2011)

Shiels to Shields – The Life Story of a North Tyneside Town
(Carnegie, 2016)

Arthur Jefferson – Man of the Theatre and Father of Stan Laurel
(Brewin Books, 2017)

The Making of Laurel and Hardy
(Ayton House, 2020)

List of Abbreviations

AA	Automobile Association
AGM	Annual General Meeting
ARP	Air Raid Patrol
BAGM	British Association of Gas Managers
BEF	British Expeditionary Force
BG	British Gas
BMA	British Medical Association
BTU	British Thermal Units
COG	Coke Oven Gas
CORGI	Council of Registered Gas Installers
	Since replaced by the Gas Safe Register
FCW	Frederick Charles Willis
FPT	Frank P. Tarratt
GLCC	Gas Light and Coke Company
GWU	The National Union of Gas Workers and General Labourers
IB	Incendiary Bombs
NCB	National Coal Board
NGB	Northern Gas Board
NGN	Northern Gas Networks
NGP	National Grid Properties

Acknowledgements

WE WOULD like to begin by acknowledging the active support of Northern Gas Networks (NGN), which made a financial contribution towards our research expenses. However, we should emphasise that the book is entirely our own work. Its content has in no way been influenced by the support we received, and we must emphasise that we and only we are responsible for any failings in the book.[1] We would like to thank the following NGN employees, in alphabetical order: Sian Fletcher, Alison Gunter, Jane Herbert, Mark Johnson, Adam Madgett, Laura McKernan and Ian Whitehead. Of these, we owe particular thanks to Mark Johnson. In addition to the encouragement and the direct assistance which we have received from him throughout, in answering our many questions, providing us with information and photographs, as well as his help with the captions to many of the images in the book, he introduced us to Prof. Russell Thomas and Neil Whalley from whom we have also received key information about the Minton Lane gasworks towards the end of its working life.

We owe debts of gratitude to several people who either spent parts of their lives in the Minton Lane gasworks house or were associated with those who lived there. We have drawn on the memoirs of Alice Ormston (née Duncan) and Lorna Brooks (née Duncan), as well as the recollections of George McDonald (the husband of Jean Duncan). We have also enjoyed the support of the wider Duncan family, particularly Lorna's daughters Hazel Iliffe, Linda Pattison, and Pamela McDonald, and Hazel's husband Alan, a former gas company employee. In addition, we have benefitted from our contact with Carol Gibson (née Jarmy) who lived in the gasworks house for some years before her marriage and was able to tell us about some of the activity at the gasworks in the period 1955-1966 when

---

1   At the time of finalising these acknowledgments in September 2022 it was reported that the newly appointed Deputy Prime Minister and Secretary of Health and Social Care, Thérèse Coffey, had instructed her civil servants not to use the 'Oxford comma' (which follows the penultimate item in a list and comes before the word 'and'). Given such insistence, we would like to make it clear that our use of the Oxford comma is a considered choice. Although taught not to use it at school, and a lifetime of compliance, we were convinced by our grandson, Jack Lawrence, that the use of the Oxford comma has merit – a view also taken by Sir Ernest Gowers in *The Complete Plain Words* (HMSO, 1954, pp.185-6).

her father was manager. Our friends Elizabeth Matthews (née Brigham) and her late brother the Rev. George Brigham, who both lived in the gasworks house for periods after they married, provided us with valuable information about the site, and the final occupied phase of the house between 1967 and 1976. Finally, we owe our thanks to our dear, late friend, George Thomson who, unintentionally, whilst filming with his Super 8 cine camera, captured the only photographic image we have of the Minton Lane gasworks house.

The local history section of North Shields Central Library, though no longer such a comprehensive research resource since being refashioned as Discover North Tyneside, has still been of considerable value to us. We are especially grateful, and wish to place on record, our thanks to the knowledgeable and unfailingly helpful Joyce Marti. We also owe thanks to the staff of the Tyne and Wear Archives (where key local gas company records, as well as the revealing several-volume journal of Thomas Taylor, a Minton Lane gasworks employee, are deposited); members of the Morpeth Local History Group (for information on the association between the Duncan family and Morpeth Gas Company); Alison Percival and Jenny Callaghan and all those involved in the comprehensive National Gas Archive in Warrington; and Janet Armstrong, the curator of the excellent National Gas Museum in Leicester.

Several North Shields' friends have been helpful, in a variety of ways. Mike Coates has been generous with his local knowledge and kind enough to let us use his map of the Low Lights area of North Shields, where the two original gasworks companies had their premises. Peter Bolger, David Morton, Jim and Mike Scott and Jim Rickard (in alphabetical order) provided us with photographs. Peter Bolger also shared his local knowledge of bombing raids on North Shields and drew our attention to the autobiographical notes of the North Shields author, Robert Westall, whose father was a foreman at the Minton Lane gasworks. Margaret Davis, a former local gas company employee, along with Stan McCrae, helped us understand how the company operated in its latter stages. Stephanie Cottis was also kind enough to explain to us how, even as late as the 1970s, her household coped without an electrical supply in their North Shields home.

Our thanks are also due to those who maintain and are continually extending the British Newspaper Archive https://www.britishnewspaperarchive.co.uk (which is also available via Findmypast https://www.findmypast.co.uk). It is a wonderful resource which has provided us with invaluable information and research leads which were not available elsewhere. This is also an appropriate place to remind readers that during the nineteenth and early twentieth centuries, the several local newspapers to which we refer were of a comparable quality to serious national newspapers today. They covered international and national as well as local events, and their editorial and letter columns were a lively forum for issues of concern to the community. Despite the limited literacy of most people at the time, local newspapers still assumed a high level of literacy on the part of their readers – but that did not mean the bulk of the population were left unaware of their content. Newspapers were 'hear read' by those who were themselves illiterate. One of the many important social functions provided by public houses was that literate workers would read newspapers to those who could not read them themselves. Some pubs hired people specifically for that purpose. It is ironic that as the level of literacy in the population has increased, the level of literacy needed to read most newspapers has decreased.

Finally, we would like to thank Alistair Brewin for the efficient way he has handled the publication of *Growing up with Gas*.

Many of the illustrations used in this book are copyright-free and in the public domain. Where that is not the case, they are acknowledged individually.

Chapter 1

Introduction

WE HAVE all grown up with gas. It is something we take for granted. Yet coal gas was a truly revolutionary fuel when introduced early in the nineteenth century, and a huge advance on the fuels available in previous millennia. Not only was the source of energy new and revolutionary but so too was the concept of delivering a fuel through a conduit to a virtually unlimited series of appliances. Today, although we use electricity for lighting, and gas primarily for heating and cooking, it was coal gas, not electricity, which first lit our streets. After the sun had set in winter months before the advent of coal gas, it was only when the moon happened to be bright that people could move around outside in anything other than darkness. Lanterns were of limited use. What little light they gave illuminated only the area immediately around them. After sunset, most people were obliged to remain indoors and, for all but the well-off, it was a dimly lit indoors. There was a heavy reliance on candles which did little to alleviate the gloom. Yet, because they were relatively expensive, most people used them sparingly. Indeed, in some social groups lit candles were a status symbol, something Elizabeth Gaskell emphasises in her 1853 book *Cranford*. It contains 21 references to candles. When guests were due during the hours of darkness, more than one candle might be used but, to be economical, they would not be lit until just before the guests arrived.

> The fire was made up; the neat maidservant had received her last directions; and there we stood dressed in our best, each with a candle-lighter in our hands, ready to dart at the candles as soon as the first knock came.

Within just a few decades of the establishment of the first gasworks in London, similar plants were built throughout the UK although, initially, most of those outside London were designed for business clients. Only subsequently were gasworks built to supply municipal areas. At first, coal gas was used almost exclusively for streetlighting. Later, it was installed in business premises, public buildings, and private households. Despite the benefits of gas streetlighting, it was not welcomed by everyone – and not just those who used the cloak of darkness to hide their criminal activities. It was not welcomed by those who lived in the shadows of the huge gasholders, or those who lived in the vicinity of gasworks.[2] Even at some distance, the air was polluted to a degree by the materials and processes involved in the manufacture of coal gas. Yet the advantages of coal gas were so great that gasworks and gasholders soon became an accepted part of the UK's urban landscape.

At the outset, we should like to emphasise what this book is, and what it is not. It is primarily a study of the UK gas industry, although its development is considered alongside the emergence of electricity as a competing fuel. For most of its history, the gas industry was based on numerous small local companies. It follows that describing its development at a national level is a necessary but far from sufficient way to understand its evolution. We also need to understand the ways it evolved locally. Too often, unfortunately, local histories, like company histories, are parochial and pay little attention to the wider world. That is why in *Growing up with Gas* we have set out to combine a national history with a detailed local case study. Obviously, a single case cannot provide a basis for generalisations, but it can identify and provide insights into the kind of issues that arose in numerous other local areas, including some of the human-interest concerns which affected directors, shareholders, employees, and customers. So, although much of the book is focused on North Shields, a town at the entrance to the River Tyne, it is much more than a work of local history. Similarly, although the book describes the origins, development, and fate of the Tynemouth Gas Company, it is not a conventional company history.

The story we tell begins not two hundred years ago, when coal gas production began, but with the origins of our use of coal as a fuel, thousands of years earlier. It continues with an account of the 'coaly Tyne', which was crucial to the development of the UK's coal mining industry and coal trade, before describing the crucial scientific and engineering breakthroughs which transformed the way the UK's streets, businesses and homes were illuminated. Only later was coal gas used to heat water, cook food, warm our homes, and power numerous appliances. Gradually, many small local companies were bought out by bigger ones. Though these takeovers were usually represented as *merely* changes of ownership, they were always more than that. Key decisions were no longer taken by people from and in the interests of local populations, but by directors and company officials, who

---

2 Early gasholders were graduated so that the quantity of gas in them could be measured. For that reason, they became known as gasometers and that term is still used interchangeably with gasholder.

might feel little or no identity with some of the areas over which they presided. Their aim was to run their companies efficiently, at a profit. Despite the takeovers, there were still over one thousand undertakings producing gas when the industry was taken into public ownership in 1949. Technological developments allowed the industry to use coke and oil as alternatives to coal to produce gas, but a much more significant development was the importation of natural gas, and then the discovery of large deposits of it under the North Sea.

At the time of writing, in 2022, the UK's use of coal is coming to an end. The coal powered steam engines that once drove the industrial revolution and made this country 'the workshop of the world' are little more than impressive curiosities. Our gasworks stopped producing coal gas after an extraordinary engineering programme which converted every coal gas appliance in the country to natural gas between 1967 and 1977. Yet those who supply us with natural gas today make use of much the same infrastructure that was created by the coal gas industry of yesteryear, and the skills of today's gas engineers are a continuing refinement of those developed, from scratch, as long ago as the beginning of the nineteenth century. It is also the case that despite the demise of the coal gas industry, it has left behind some indelible marks on the present. As trains pull into St Pancras station in London, a complex of four reconstructed gasholders have been preserved for posterity. Under impressive roof gardens, they now contain luxury apartments and event space, in addition to a park at ground level. It is estimated that there are still about 1,500 gas lamps in London. The oldest, near Carlton House Terrace, bear the initials George IV, who reigned from 1811-1830. The cloisters of Westminster Abbey are still lit by gas. The oldest, fixed to the wall in the Dean's Yard is about 200 years old, and occupies the same position as an oil lamp before the advent of coal gas lighting. The Mall, which featured so prominently in 2022 during Queen Elizabeth II's Platinum Jubilee celebration and then her funeral, has gas streetlighting on the side of St James's Palace which was occasionally visible during the TV coverage of the events.[3] Beside the statue of the Queen Mother which was dedicated in 2009, there are modern gas lamps, apparently at the request of the Royal family and, during state visits and occasions, the gas lamps around Buckingham Palace are adjusted so that they are left on throughout the day and night. There is also a recently erected row of gas lamps near Trafalgar Square and, at the express wish of the architect, the recent arcade development in Covent Garden has gas lighting. Outside London, at least one area has deliberately chosen

---

3   There is electric lighting on the other side of The Mall.

to retain some gas streetlighting.[4] Moreover, at the Fakenham Museum of Gas and Local History in Norfolk, visitors can still see the only surviving town gasworks in England and Wales, with its retorts, condenser, purifiers, and gasholder.[5]

For the families of the managers of the gasworks in North Shields, growing up with gas meant something more intimate than it did for the rest of the population. All four of the gasworks plants set up in North Shields over the years provided accommodation on site for their managers (always men) and families. The houses were built not *close* to but *within* the gasworks, albeit on their perimeters. For some of the families, that represented a marked change of environment. For example, before George John Duncan moved into the Minton Lane gasworks house of the fourth North Shields' gas plant in 1918, he had lived with his family in the nearby, then still largely rural Preston Village. Afterwards, he and his growing family, who resided in the gasworks house for longer than any of the other gasworks families, lived without neighbours, in a house over-shadowed not just by gasholders but what was a substantial chemical engineering works. Today, the Health and Safety Executive would not allow children to be brought up in such conditions. Yet, the ten Duncan children who grew up in such unusual surroundings would, in later life, recall little other than happy memories of their childhood.

Sadly, all ten children had died by 2016, when Northern Gas Networks (NGN) invited those familiar with the site to share their recollections of it before the last gasholder was removed. Fortuitously, two written accounts survive of what growing up with gas was like for the Duncans. Alice, the oldest child, and Lorna the youngest, both left us with detailed descriptions of their early lives. The sole surviving spouse of the gasworks children in 2016 was George McDonald, the husband of Jean Duncan. Still as bright as the proverbial button, at the age of 99, he was able to describe a terrifying night in 1941 when the gasworks was hit by high explosive bombs and numerous incendiary devices,

---

4   A programme to remove Malvern's 1,250 gas streetlamps began in the 1950s but came to an end with about 130 remaining. They are now protected monuments, maintained by a joint commercial and voluntary venture, the Transition Gasketeers. The surviving lamps include ten designs from five manufacturers and represent several stages in the development of streetlighting from Victorian times to the 1950s. The Gasketeers have now reduced the carbon footprint of the lamps with improvements to the original designs, and the lamps give a brighter light despite gas consumption being 70 per cent less. Running costs are now comparable to those of sodium electric streetlighting. We are grateful to Graeme Dawson for drawing our attention to these Malvern gas lamps.

5   It produced coal gas from 1846 to 1965 and is now a Scheduled Ancient Monument. The Norfolk Archaeological Society and Norfolk Historic Buildings Trust were responsible for the arrangement to lease the gasworks and convert it into a museum. It was opened to the public in 1987, ten years after the programme to convert the industry to natural gas was completed. For more information contact the Fakenham Town Gas Works Museum Trust at enquiries@fakenhamgasmuseum.com

and members of the Duncan family helped bring the dangerous situation under control.[6]

The case study element of the coal gas industry concludes with the removal of the final and largest of the North Shields gasholders in 2017. Whilst dismantling it, today's engineers were surprised and impressed with the ingenuity of their forebears. They were also astonished at the remarkable durability of the structure their predecessors had created.

However, although the gasworks may have gone, and a commitment made to make the UK carbon neutral by 2050, the gas industry is still thriving. Plans are in place, and numerous projects and trials already underway, so that the industry can move on from natural gas to the cleaner alternative of hydrogen, although possibly, for a period, blended with natural gas.

Our research has involved reading many books and articles on the gas industry, spending countless hours in several archives, many more searching through the relevant digitised newspapers in the British Newspaper Archive, as well as exchanges of messages and face to face conversations with people who had experience of the local gas industry. Since we began our investigations in 2017, we have been fortunate in also being able to draw on eye-witness accounts from several people who both lived and worked in the Minton Lane gasworks after the Duncans left it for the final time in 1941.

Outline

The Coaly Tyne (Chapter 2) describes the crucial role played by coal in the development of the UK. Without the coal beneath our feet, the ingenuity of those who learned how to mine it; the hardships endured by those who went deep underground to hew it and bring it to the surface; the keelmen who hand-loaded it into colliers, and the sailors who took it to distant markets in often appalling conditions, this country would not have become the first industrial nation and 'workshop of the world'. Coal was, as Jeremy Paxman, acknowledges in the title of his 2022 book on the history of the coal industry, the equivalent of *Black Gold*. Nor, without coal, would there have been any coal gas to illuminate our streets, businesses, and homes. But however valuable coal may have been, its use came at a price, and not only to those in the coal industry. Pollutants produced by the burning of coal have damaged our health and buildings and we now acknowledge it has been a major factor in climate change.

---

6   Sadly, George died in 2018 just days after celebrating his 100th birthday.

The Production and Significance of Coal Gas (Chapter 3) describes how engineers devised ways to make coal a more flexible, efficient, and safer fuel by harnessing the gases it generates when combusted. By doing so, they provided us with a greatly improved form of energy. Initially, coal gas was manufactured on the premises where it was used but soon community-based plants were developed, and streetlighting became commonplace. Coal gas lighting was then introduced into business premises and homes and, over the decades, the quality of the illumination it provided improved as gas burners were enhanced. Eventually, the incandescent gas mantle was invented and helped the gas industry withstand the growing competition from electric lighting. By then, coal gas was being used extensively for heating and cooking and a wide variety of other purposes and that allowed the gas industry to remain profitable despite gas lighting eventually being eclipsed by improvements in electric lighting. In addition to the production of coal gas, the distillation of coal, which produced it, gave us numerous valuable by-products, as well as coke, the virtually smokeless solid fuel, kinder to the environment than untreated coal.

Coal Gas Production in North Shields (Chapter 4) tells the story of the development of coal gas production in the town during the period when the local economy was booming, and the town and its population was expanding rapidly.[7] Coal gas production began with the establishment of the North Shields Gas Company in 1819. A rival private company, the Borough of Tynemouth Gas Company followed about 20 years later, but the two soon amalgamated. This new company subsequently extended onto a third site in the Low Lights area of the town, by the riverside, before building a much larger and technically more advanced plant in Minton Lane, then on the western edge of the town.[8] During this initial half-century, relations between the gas companies and the local Borough Council were frequently strained, as the gas company grew in its scope, influence, and financial value.

The New Gasworks at Minton Lane. Phase 1 (Chapter 5) is described and its history under the Tynemouth Gas Company discussed, from its opening in 1872 to a design by George Livesey, the premier gas engineer of the period, to a subsequent

---

7   For a full account of the markedly changing fortunes of North Shields see Danny Lawrence *Shiels to Shields. The Life Story of a North Tyneside Town* (Carnegie, 2016).

8   At the time, what is now called Minton Lane was still listed on maps as Meadow Well Lane, even though there were numerous references to Minton Lane in the press from at least the 1830s. The route between Howdon and Waterville Roads was still named Meadow Well Lane on a site map of the gasworks in 1938. In the 1970s, Geographia street maps named the section of road alongside the gasworks as Minton Lane and the upper section by Waterville Road as Meadow Well Lane. Today, the whole stretch is labelled Minton Lane.

major expansion of the works in 1903. In the course of the chapter, there is also a discussion of the sometimes-vexed divisions within the gas industry, between those manufacturing gas and those developing and selling gas appliances. From 1887, with a new chairman, that division became blurred in the North Shields area as the Tynemouth Gas Company began to exhibit, demonstrate, hire, and sell gas appliances in addition to manufacturing coal gas. The chapter also includes a discussion of the crucial changes in labour relations in the industry, as unionisation of the workforce led to an eight-hour day and companies began to introduce co-partnership schemes. Tragically, improved working conditions could not prevent a terrible accident in which six North Shields' gas employees lost their lives.

The New Gasworks at Minton Lane. Phase 2 (Chapter 6) describes the major expansion of the gasworks in 1903, during the period when competition from the electricity industry was becoming increasingly intense. It then turns to the major impact of the Great War of 1914-18 and its long-lasting repercussions which constrained all gas companies and encouraged the takeover of smaller undertakings by larger companies including, in 1927, what some local people regarded as the hostile takeover of the Tynemouth Gas Company by the Newcastle and Gateshead Gas Company. Thanks to a journal kept over several years by a senior employee of the Tynemouth company, we have been able to draw on a detailed participant observer account of this crucial event and its aftermath, in addition to drawing on documentary sources and reportage.

Under New Ownership (Chapter 7) discusses the takeover of the Tynemouth company and its implications for the Minton Lane gasworks and its workforce, as it lost its independence. Its manager was instructed to reduce the amount of gas it manufactured; and its whole future came under threat when in 1934, and subsequent years, it was obliged to shut down its retorts for the whole of the summer months. This closure of the works coincided with a depression in trade which had hit the north-east of England particularly hard. At times, over 40 per cent of the insured population of North Shields was out of work and there was widespread poverty and hardship. The chapter continues through to the desperate years of the Second World War, when the gasworks was a specific target for the bombers of the Luftwaffe.

The Duncans of Minton Lane (Chapter 8) encompasses the period from the building of the gasworks house to the Duncan family moving into it at the end of the Great War in 1918 and remaining there until after a major bombing raid on the town in 1941. It discusses the circumstances which led to the house being built, and provides information on its earlier occupants, most particularly William Hardie, its engineer and manager for 32 years, who became the Mayor of the

Borough of Tynemouth and was the chairman of its Finance Committee at the time of his death. The chapter subsequently explains how George John Duncan, born in rural Northumberland in 1877, but with family connections to the gas industry, came to start work at the Minton Lane gasworks as a boy and eventually became its manager. It relates how his children grew up in the gasworks house and treated the gasworks plant as an adventure playground, giving them a familiarity with it which stood them in good stead during the worst of the bombing of North Shields in World War Two. Thanks to the family interviews we have conducted, and accounts we have inherited, we are able to describe life on the site for the Duncans and their ten children in some detail. The chapter includes the bombing raids on the gasworks in 1941 and particularly that in April when the remaining members of the family living at home worked alongside the workers on site to prevent a major explosion and loss of gas from the gasholders. Following their deeds that night, two family members and the gasworks foreman received awards for bravery, and a radio drama-documentary based on the event was broadcast by the BBC. The script of the broadcast is provided as Appendix 4. The chapter also includes some information on subsequent residents at the gasworks house prior to its demolition.

Rationalisation, Nationalisation and Privatisation (Chapter 9) relates how the Minton Lane gasworks, along with all other gas undertakings, became part of a publicly owned industry: a transformation made primarily for pragmatic rather than ideological reasons. Long before it was taken into public ownership, it was widely accepted that the industry needed rationalisation and, although in 1949 private ownership was replaced by public ownership, it did not come under state control. On the contrary, the regional units of the gas industry, as well as the nationalised coal and electricity companies, continued to compete against one another for the raw material of coal in an open market, just as they had done before public ownership. During this post-war period, the contribution of the Minton Lane gasworks was reviewed, and, in the following decades, its role diminished. Eventually, following the discovery of large reserves of natural gas in the North Sea in the mid-1960s, and the conversion of the whole of the UK to natural gas in an extraordinary feat of engineering in the following decade, the Minton Lane gasworks was left with only a few residual functions.

Shortly after the conversion to natural gas, for both ideological reasons, and to raise revenue for the Exchequer, a Conservative government privatised and sold off the gas industry along with other public utilities. Since then, its ownership has been globalised. The buildings at Minton Lane have been demolished in stages, and part of the site is now occupied by a primary school. Fortuitously, as a reminder of the service the gasworks provided to the local community for so long, its fine brick perimeter walls have been preserved by NGN. Within them, in 2016, all that remained of the once proud gasworks was a single gasholder. It was in that year that NGN decided that the time had come for it to be removed. Its final days are recorded in both words and images in the closing pages of Chapter 9. However, the book's final Chapter, 10, is devoted not to the past but to the *future* of the gas industry, and the way in which in a revised form it will continue to make a major contribution to our energy needs in the 21st century.

The Future (Chapter 10) discusses the part that the gas industry will play in a country committed to be carbon-neutral by 2050. In response to mounting concerns about the environmental impact of the use of energy derived from fossil fuels, detailed discussions, plans, projects, and trials involving both government and industry are at an advanced stage in preparation for changes comparable in scale to those which took place when the UK moved from the use of coal gas to natural gas. This time, however, the move will not be from one fossil fuel to another, but from a fossil fuel to the cleaner gas hydrogen, both in its pure form and probably for a period blended with natural gas. The UK needs to move away from fossil fuels not only because of dangerous climate change, but because of the country's vulnerability to the vagaries of the international market for natural gas. That the UK needs to become more energy sufficient became particularly obvious in the years 2021 and 2022 in which there were unprecedentedly large increases in the price of natural gas. Such was the scale of the increases that many companies supplying gas to customers went out of business because of the discrepancy between what they had to pay for natural gas and what the government's regulator OFGEM allowed them to charge their customers. Despite such caps on energy prices, millions of UK households were plunged into fuel poverty by the increases OFGEM did allow. The inescapable fact is that at the time of writing in late 2022, gas prices and the future of gas supplies have become major political issues.

Appendix 1 James Robson's gas engine
Appendix 2 Thomas Taylor
Appendix 3 The Occupants of the Minton Lane gasworks house
Appendix 4 The Script of the 1941 BBC radio drama-documentary
Appendix 5 Alice and Lorna Duncan's Recollections of their Gasworks Home

Chapter 2

The 'Coaly Tyne'

AS THE UK's stocks of wood became depleted, the population became increasingly dependent on coal, derived from the luxuriant plants which once covered the land. Through the actions of bacteria and fungi, and high temperatures and pressure over long periods, the dead plants were gradually transformed into the different kinds of solid fossil fuels we recognize today. The first stage of the process resulted in beds of accessible peat. It was used extensively as a domestic fuel but, with a carbon content of only 60 per cent, it is of limited value. The next distinct form in the fossilization process is lignite (brown coal) with a carbon content of up to 70 per cent. After a further prolonged period of geological time, lignite is transformed into sub-bituminous and bituminous coal, with a carbon content as high as 88 per cent. With such a high-energy content, it has been burned for centuries in domestic dwellings as well as in industry. Anthracite, the least common and hardest form of coal has an even higher carbon content of over 90 per cent but has the disadvantage of being the most difficult of the solid fuels to ignite.

Coal has been burned in the UK for a long time. It has been found in the remains of Bronze Age funeral pyres, suggesting that outcrops of coal were mined as early as 3,000 BC. Much later, the Romans made use of coal when they occupied Britain, and they appear to have known the location of most of the country's major coalfields. In the north-east, coal was so plentiful that it was not always necessary to mine it. Indeed, it can still be picked up from some of our beaches, after being released from seams exposed to the sea, or washed ashore from underwater outcrops. That is why, originally, it was referred to as 'seacole' although, subsequently, that term was used for coal that had been shipped by sea rather than transported by land from inland mines.

The Coal Trade

Evidence of a trade in coal from the Tyne to London goes back to the thirteenth century, when there was a Sacoles (Sea Coals) Lane in the capital. By the fourteenth century the trade had become so significant that four officials were appointed to collect the duties imposed on coal by the City of London and Crown – and ensure buyers were not given short measure. Coal that left the Tyne was also unloaded in many locations between the north-east and the south coast, and coal was also exported to the Continent.

At this stage, coal was used only for heating. It was to be another 600 years before a way was found to generate and control the flammable gases contained in coal to produce effective lighting. Over the intervening centuries, fortunes were made by those with rich coal deposits beneath the surface of their land and those given the rights to mine and sell it. It was also a lucrative trade for the town of Newcastle (which for many centuries enjoyed a monopoly of shipping on the Tyne), and for the reigning monarchs who raised taxes on coal. For the rest of the population, the supply of coal came at a cost. It was a particularly heavy cost for the miners, keelmen and sailors who in turn hewed the coal, loaded it onto the waiting colliers and took it to distant markets. Their work was always arduous, often dangerous, and never well-rewarded. For centuries, they paid the price whilst the rest of the population appeared to reap the benefits of our abundant coal deposits, but we now know that we have all paid a heavy price for the profligate way we have burned coal in open grates for centuries. Things began to improve a little when in the nineteenth century coal gas became available to light our streets, illuminate and heat our buildings, cook our food, and provide the energy for numerous specialized appliances. But it is only as recently as 2019 that the UK government has set a target (of 2050) for ending our dependence on fossil fuels.[9]

The huge amount of coal shipped from the Tyne is one way to illustrate the extent to which we became dependent on it. Even as early as the end of the sixteenth century, about half a million tonnes of coal were shipped from the Tyne each year.[10] Indeed, coal and the River Tyne were by then so synonymous that Milton used the term 'coaly Tyne' in a poem he wrote in 1628. By the end of the nineteenth century, over two million tonnes were being extracted from the mines in and around North Shields alone. In the UK as a whole there were by then over 3,000 deep mines, employing almost 700,000 miners, producing more than 200 million tonnes of coal annually.

---

9   Despite that pledge, in 2021, Cumbria County Council and central government subsequently agreed to a proposal for a new coal mine, although opposition to it continued because it plainly undermined the UK's commitment to reduce its reliance on fossil fuels. The perceived advantage of the mine is that it would reduce the need for Russian coking coal for the UK steel industry, following the introduction of sanctions against Russia after its invasion of Ukraine in 2022.

10 A metric tonne is 1,000 kilograms compared to an imperial ton which is the equivalent of 910 kilograms.

As the demand for coal increased, there was an incentive to improve the way it was transported from the mines to the waiting colliers. Wooden wagonways were introduced as early as the seventeenth century. By road, a horse could pull about 900kg of coal but on wooden rails and, after 1768 iron-capped or entirely iron rails, it could pull more than twice that much. In time, a series of wagonways were constructed in and around North Shields. They included the Whitley wagonway which took coal to the staithes at the Low Lights by the riverside. A wagonway from the mines around Backworth ran down to Northumberland Dock a little further upstream. Initially, horses were the source of power. Fixed steam engines powered by coal then replaced horses and pulled the waggons along the rails by rope. Later still, they were replaced by steam locomotives, also powered by coal.

By this time, the primary focus of mining operations on Tyneside had moved away from Newcastle towards the coast, to gain access to the better-quality seams of coal in demand for residential properties.

By the nineteenth century, industrial manufacture had developed at an extraordinary rate, and it was the use of coal-fired machinery which earned the UK the description 'workshop of the world'. Coal-fired steam engines also revolutionised transportation, as locomotives took freight and passengers round the country on the vast network of railways that were built in an astonishingly short time. During the same period, the introduction of coal gas brought about a major change in the way in which we illuminated and heated our homes and commercial buildings. Not long after, coal provided the energy for the generation of electricity. It was the cumulative significance of these developments which led to the nineteenth century being dubbed 'the great age of coal'.

The Disadvantages of Coal

The Dangers for Miners

Extracting coal was always dangerous and accidents were common. The biggest and most remembered disaster in the vicinity of North Shields, took place at the Hartley Pit, six miles away in January 1862. The beam of the pumping engine snapped and by the time rescuers reached those who had survived the initial accident, no one was left alive. In all, 204 men and boys died. The youngest were John Armstrong and John Duffy, both ten years old. The tragedy was so momentous that Jeremy Paxman begins his book *Black Gold: The History of How Coal Made Britain* with a lengthy account of it (Collins, 2022). Hartley was by no means the only major mining disaster in the area around North Shields. In addition to the countless unrecorded small accidents that were disastrous to individual miners and their families, there were at least 30 major disasters in

Durham and Northumberland in the nineteenth century which together cost more than 1,500 people their lives. The records maintained by the Durham Mining Museum show that the scale of mining fatalities increased markedly in the nineteenth century. This was in part because inexperienced workers were recruited as the demand for coal grew but also, ironically, because of the very safety lamps designed by Humphrey Davy and George Stephenson to protect miners' lives against poisonous and explosive gases. Safety lamps were treated by many mine-owners as a cheap alternative to improved ventilation. Once equipped with them, miners were required to work at greater depths and to 'rob' (i.e. reduce in size) the coal pillars that at an earlier stage had been left behind to support tunnel roofs. In 1852, the first President of the North of England Institute of Mining Engineers said he was appalled by the number of fatalities since Davy's lamp had been introduced. In the north-east alone they ran into thousands. The indifference of mine-owners to such a great loss of life shocked those who conducted the 1842 government inquiry into the conditions in coal mines. It reported that in Northumberland, there were no accident records and that the 'colliery medical men' refused to provide them with information on accident levels.

Miners were not only at risk from accidents. They succumbed to respiratory conditions such as emphysema, chronic bronchitis, and pneumoconiosis. Yet, it was not until 1831 that Dr Stratton of North Shields, after dissecting the body of a 70-year-old coal miner, identified the condition 'black spots on the lungs', and labelled it as a dust disease which he called *anthracosis*. Such occupational diseases did not always result in death but greatly affected the quality of life of those suffering from them. As well as lung related illnesses, many miners developed the eye disease *nystagmus.*, caused by working underground for long periods.

Conditions in coal mines were particularly brutal for children and it must never be forgotten that at the time the UK population was beginning to enjoy the advantages of coal gas, the lives of numerous young children were being ruined to provide the coal to generate it. An 1842 Royal Commission reported that in Northumberland about a third of underground workers were children. Some began work underground at the age of four as 'trappers', which involved opening a flap or door when a coal cart passed, and closing it immediately afterwards, to maintain the flow of the limited supply of air. Trappers had to be at work from the opening of mines each day, which could mean leaving home at 1am or 2am in time to start a 12-hour shift at 4am. From the age of six, children took hewed coal to the surface on carts called corves, which might weigh as much as 227kg (500lbs). These child 'putters', as they were called locally, pushed corves an average of about eight miles daily, whilst often ankle-deep in water. The minimum height in which they were supposed to work was 114cm (3.7 feet), but witnesses admitted to having seen children pushing corves in even more confined spaces. Sometimes children were allowed 15 minutes to eat their 'bait' but often their break from work was even shorter. In winter months, many young children did not see daylight for months on end. It was dark when they went down the pit and dark when they returned to the surface for a few hours' relief from their monotonous life underground. Other than a day away from work on Good Friday and sometimes Easter Monday, the only break child mine workers were allowed was two weeks over the Christmas period. Inevitably, the health of such young children was damaged in many ways. Working in cramped conditions

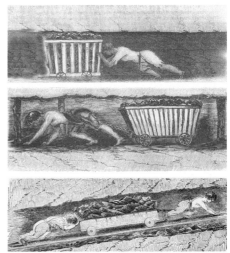

Illustrations of child putters in coal mines derived from the UK's 1842 Commission on Children (pp.78-82). The mode of putting varied depending on such factors as the depth and incline of the seams.

stunted and deformed their normal physical development. Many became crippled as part of the normal routine of their daily work. In addition, they were exposed to the coal dust which led to serious respiratory problems in later life.

The Dangers for Seamen

In the process of taking coal to market by sea, large numbers of sailors lost their lives. Ships were sometimes damaged even before they left the River Tyne. Their keels could be damaged by the Shields Bar, the shifting bank of sand, shingle, and rock across the river mouth from North Shields to South Shields. At low water mark, there might be no more than 1.2m (less than four feet) of water above it. Hitting it could create leaks that would sink a vessel several days later. In the eighteenth and nineteenth centuries, colliers and other sailing ships were shipwrecked on a scale that would be unimaginable today. The weather was responsible for many losses but, often, ships were lost because they were in poor condition or badly loaded. Steam-driven colliers, when introduced, were safer as well as more reliable and economical to run. Unfortunately, to try to compete with them, the owners of traditional colliers often cut back on the maintenance of their ships. That, in turn, led to a greater number of losses. Many wooden colliers became known as coffin ships because they went to sea with bad gear, rotting timbers and inadequate crews.

Ships entering the Tyne had to contend not only with the Shields Bar but also the Herd Sands and infamous Black Middens, an area of rocks close to the northern riverbank. Although the risks of going aground were reduced with the advent of powered vessels, and then the building of piers at the entrance to the Tyne, a few ships still foundered on the Black Middens well into the later decades of the twentieth century.

The Gaseous Pollutants of Coal Combustion

The most obvious problem in burning coal is that it gives off unpleasant gases in the process. Its growing use by smiths, lime-burners, brewers, dyers, and other trades, as early as the thirteenth century proved unpopular amongst those who lived nearby. Whereas woods have long been ranked not just by how well they burn but how pleasantly they smell, no one enjoys breathing in the fumes given off by coal. The concern became so widespread that in 1306 a royal proclamation prohibited people in such trades from using coal in their furnaces. Although the ban seems to have been widely ignored, for at least another three centuries coal continued to be regarded as an objectionable fuel by the upper classes, at best unpleasant and at worst a danger to health.

The fumes given off when burning coal in open grates is why houses were constructed with chimneys. They were there not only to improve combustion by drawing air into a fire, but also to take the offending smoke away from residents. Although the dangers of 'choke damp' and 'fire damp' in coal mines was understood, it was assumed that if fumes from coal were drawn up chimneys and dissipated into the atmosphere, the problem was solved. The cumulative effect of the gases on the earth's atmosphere seems not to have been considered. Only recently, have we come to realise that what seemed like a neat and cheap solution to a minor immediate inconvenience, has over the years contributed to a major long-term problem which now threatens the very existence of mankind.

By the middle of the twentieth century, most houses in the UK were heated by one or more open coal fires. Taking care of them was a time-consuming and messy business. Coal had to be shovelled into sacks; loaded onto horse-drawn carts and later lorries; delivered regularly to houses and stored in coal houses. From there it had to be carried, often upstairs, in small quantities to one or more fireplaces. Each morning, the residual ashes from the previous day's fires had to be cleaned out and put in a bin (or perhaps, in the case of the better-off, their garden). Paper and kindling wood was needed to ignite the fresh coal and then, throughout the day, the fire had to be topped up with coal to keep it going. In addition to the disadvantage of the amount of time and energy that had to be devoted to an open fire, its naked flames were inherently dangerous. Fenders, fire guards and tongs, as well as pokers and other paraphernalia, usually surrounded domestic fireplaces. They were necessary to protect the area around the fire from falling coal and naked flames. One of the Duncan family to be the subject of Chapter 7, fell victim to such an accident. He survived the nasty burns to his head but carried the scars for the rest of his life.

This image shows how sacks of coal used to be delivered to domestic households in the UK. The standard measure of a sack was one hundredweight (112 pounds), the equivalent of about 51kg. The 'coal man' is Percival Folland, and the image is reproduced courtesy of his great-nephew Brian Huxtable.

An illustration of the smoke that once poured from domestic dwellings, in this case in York in 1960 even after the Clean Air Act of 1956. See: https://www.yorkpress.co.uk/news/18226940.york-rooftops-1960/ Courtesy of York Press and Stephen Lewis.

Domestic coal fires were not only labour intensive but wasteful. Only about 20 per cent of the energy derived from the burning coal heated the room in which it was located. Those who can remember the days of coal fires will tell you that though they were attractive, and even mesmerising, it was not unusual in winter to have an unacceptably hot front but an uncomfortably cold back. Leaving a room containing a fire to go to bed usually meant going from a warm room to a cold one. Few households could afford to light more than one coal fire.

Smoke disappearing up domestic and factory chimneys may have helped reduce the immediate inconvenience of the gases given off by the burning of coal, but the smoke did not always disappear high into the atmosphere. When it remained at a low level, it endangered the immediate health of the public. On occasions, when the smoke combined with particles of water and settled at ground level like fog, it became dangerous to breathe. It was then known as smog [sm(oke)+(f)og]. For many years, it was accepted with resignation. There are reports of smog in December 1813, and in December 1873 when deaths were 40 per cent higher than normal. There were also big jumps in the death rate associated with smog in January 1880, February 1882, December 1891 and November 1948. However, the authorities found it impossible to ignore such occurrences after the Great London

Smog of 1952. During a spell of unusually cold weather, larger quantities of coal than usual were burned. That, unfortunately, coincided with anti-cyclonic weather conditions, in which air was pushed down, making it impossible for the smoke particles and gases emitted from houses and factory chimneys to escape into the upper atmosphere. It has been estimated that, in this brief period, perhaps as much as 1,000 tonnes of smoke particles, 2,000 tonnes of carbon dioxide, 140 tonnes of hydrochloric acid, and 14 tonnes of fluorine compounds were discharged from chimneys into the atmosphere and trapped near to the ground. In addition, 370 tonnes of sulphur dioxide were converted into 800 tonnes of sulphuric acid. The pollutants were so concentrated that at least 4,000 vulnerable people are known to have died after inhaling these toxic gases.

The Clean Air Act of 1956 followed shortly afterwards. That, and further legislation in 1968, required the residents of urban areas and owners of factories to switch to using smokeless fuels. The change did not come soon enough for the estimated 750 Londoners who died in 1962 before the legislation had taken effect, but undoubtedly it has had a beneficial effect in the UK in subsequent decades. Tragically, as is so often the case, government legislation can do nothing about the legacy of what has gone before. Clean Air Acts have not been able to undo the damage already done to our health and environment. In the past, the smoke from domestic fires and factory chimneys in industrial areas was so great that it reduced the available sunlight by as much as 40 per cent. The soot which escaped from the chimneys did not remain in the air forever. Much of it returned to earth

An image illustrating the deadly London Smog of 1952, reproduced under a Creative Commons licence.

and, in the worst affected areas, as many as 500 tons of soot might fall on a single square mile each year. It did not just make freshly washed clothes drying in the open air dirty again. It contributed towards the development of chronic and serious respiratory diseases, as well as damaging the surfaces of buildings. They became blackened by the soot, and the nitrogen oxide and the sulphur dioxide in the smoke later fell as acid rain, harmful not only to stone and brick buildings but also metal structures and vegetation.

We now realise that the human cost of mining and burning coal is unacceptable. But long before we came to that conclusion, we are fortunate that chemical engineers devised ways to transform coal into a more flexible and environmentally friendly form of energy and, at the same time, produce coke, a smokeless solid fuel, and valuable by-products for a wide variety of purposes. Coke had never been popular with the public because it was more difficult to burn than coal, but it did mean that when the Clean Air Acts were introduced, in addition to coal gas (and electric) fires, there was a smokeless substitute to burn in open grates.

By the closing decades of the twentieth century, the UK was using a greater variety of energy sources than ever before. Oil, natural gas, nuclear power, and wind power were utilised in addition to coal to meet our growing demand for energy. Then, for political as well as environmental reasons, the UK's coal mining industry went into a terminal decline. Yet, despite these dramatic changes, as late as 2016, 40 per cent of UK electricity was generated in coal-fired power stations. Thanks primarily to a remarkable advance in the use of wind power, the use of coal has fallen dramatically. However, in the meanwhile, during the periods we were closing our own coal mines, we were instead importing substantial quantities of coal. Ironically, in 2011, instead of dredging the River Tyne to aid the *export* of coal, it was deepened to receive the *Alam Penting* which brought a record 75,000 tonnes of coal *into* the Tyne from New Orleans. By then, the centuries-old expression 'it's like taking coals *to* Newcastle', to signify an activity that was utterly pointless, had lost its meaning.

Chapter 3

The Coal Gas Industry

Early Experiments in Producing Gas from Coal

Coal miners were only too aware that coal contained gases that could be released into the air – even without combustion. They nicknamed them *choke damp* and *fire damp*.[11] Choke damp, a mixture of mainly nitrogen, carbon dioxide and water vapour, has such a low oxygen content that breathing it can prove fatal. It was choke gas which suffocated those who survived the initial Hartley Pit disaster. Fire damp is a loose term used for the inflammable gases found in coal, and the Davy and Stephenson safety lamps were invented to detect it and avoid what could be catastrophic explosions.

It was small-scale uncoordinated experiments producing gas from coal, which culminated in the astonishing development of a widespread coal gas industry in the nineteenth century. There were many pioneers but there is only space here to mention a few. The earliest documented case of the controlled use of coal gas in Europe appears to be that of Jean Tardin in France in 1618. In the UK, the initial credit for discovering the potential of coal gas is usually credited to Thomas Shirley in 1659. He noticed a stream of gas bubbles coming from a spring and found that he could ignite them. He speculated that the inflammable gas must be seeping from coal below ground. About 15 years later, Dr John Clayton, a Yorkshire clergyman, investigated Shirley's surmise. He dug down and found that the inflammable gas was being released from a bed of coal about 45cm (18 inches) below the surface. He then followed that up with a real-life experiment comparable to Tardin's, in which he generated gas by heating coal. Their experiments convinced both men that a useful gas could be produced from coal.[12]

---

11 Choke damp is sometimes known as black damp.

12 It should not be a surprise that Clayton was a clergyman rather than a scientist or engineer. In the days before the professionalisation of science and engineering, many advances in those fields were made by people without formal training but with enquiring minds and enough leisure time to pursue their interests.

Carlisle Spedding is another interesting British pioneer. On his return to the north-west from a visit to the north-east to learn about its more advanced coal mining, he began work at the Saltom Pit near Whitehaven. Sunk to 139m (152 yards), it was then the deepest *undersea* mine in the country. After reducing (but not solving) the problem of flooding by installing an early Newcomen steam engine, he then turned his attention to the dangers of fire damp, which had killed 23 men in an explosion in the pit in 1737. He made a study of the dangerous gases in conjunction with a local doctor, William Brownrigg, who, from time to time, was obliged to treat Spedding when exposure to the gases made him seriously ill. Their work included feeding fire damp to a laboratory for further study, and to an office where Spedding used it to provide lighting. There was such a ready supply of the gas that Spedding even offered to supply Whitehaven with fire damp for streetlighting. His offer was declined. Tragically, Spedding died in a mine explosion in 1755, caused by the very fire damp he had been working so hard to tame.

In 1778, the ninth Earl of Dundonald tried to restore his family fortunes by finding additional uses for the coal deposits on his Scottish estate. He subjected coal to great heat and used the gas given off to give a demonstration of coal gas lighting at Culross Cathedral. Despite that, he does not appear to have pursued the commercial potential of coal gas in the way he did with the other main derivatives of his process. He sold the coke left behind to a Falkirk ironworks, and tried, albeit unsuccessfully, to persuade the Admiralty to buy the residual coal tar to protect the hulls of their wooden ships.

Around the same time, George Dixon used coal gas to light a room in his own house in County Durham.[13] His early experiments were described by a friend some years later.

> I remember being much amused when a little boy by his filling an old tea-kettle half full of coals and setting it on the fire and luting [attaching] a tobacco pipe with clay to the spout, and to this several others round the end and side of the room. After a certain time, he put the flame of a candle to the end of the furthest pipe, and immediately a bright flame issued from it, where nothing was perceptible. He then made small holes with a pin through the clay that luted the pipe heads and shanks together, and applying the flame of the candle to each, there were as many flames as pipe heads. … This mode of lighting rooms was for a long time a favourite project with

---

13 Dixon was a polymath. As well as being a chemist and engineer, he was something of a mathematician, geologist, engraver, and painter on china.

him, and he had thought of lighting his collieries with them, but was cured of it by the following experiment, at which I was present. Wanting to know the quantity of tar produced by a ton of coals, he erected a furnace with a large cast-metal boiler, and to this fixed two large cast-metal 'pumps' (iron pipes). One of them passed through water in order to condense the oil and tar. The end of this was filled by a wooden plug, with a small hole to let out the tar etc. Towards the conclusion of the experiment he placed the flame of a candle to this hole, and the inflammable gas immediately burned with a large bright flame. To extinguish this, he struck at it with his hat, the flame was driven inwards, the gas in the inside of the apparatus took fire as quickly as gunpowder and exploded with a report like a cannon, driving out the wooden plug to a great distance and exhibiting a cylindrical body of fire several yards in length. The heavy cast-metal pumps were removed from their places. From this time, he considered his project of lighting collieries and rooms with gas lights as very dangerous, and I record this experiment with a view that it may probably be a useful hint to those who are at present engaged in similar projects of lighting manufactories and great towns with a material so subject to explosion (Macfarlan, pp.53-54).

After this experience, it is perhaps not surprising that Dixon turned his attention to other matters.

On the continent, several scientists were experimenting with inflammable gases. Their work was encouraged by the craze for ballooning in this period and some explored the possibility of inflating them with the gases produced from the distillation of coal. Foremost amongst them was Jan-Pieter Minckelers at Belgium's University of Louvain. He went on to develop an elementary form of gas lighting and lit a lecture hall with it in 1785. Unfortunately, because of political turmoil, he had to leave Louvain in 1790 and his work did not develop beyond that point. Nevertheless, his and similar work, meant that by the end of the eighteenth century there was sufficient familiarity with the gases produced by coal for them to be described in the most readily available texts of the period. Tomory also maintains that by this stage 'all the basic elements for a gaslight apparatus could be found in embryonic form in the best-equipped chemical laboratories' (Tomory p.35).

In the UK, none of the early pioneers in gas lighting patented their work and credit for the manufacture of coal gas is usually attributed to the Scottish engineer William Murdoch.[14] Whilst working in Cornwall for the Birmingham company

___

14 Sometimes spelled Murdock.

of Boulton and Watt, installing steam-powered pumps in copper, tin and lead mines, he began to experiment with coal gas. According to Barty-King, around 1786, he produced coal gas from a small iron retort and stored it in bladders which he mounted on the steam carriage he had designed for himself. The gas was fed through tubes to lamps on either side of the vehicles which he lit when he was driving at night. In 1792, Murdoch took his idea one crucial step further. He used a variety of portable containers to store the coal gas and utilised it to illuminate both his house and office in Redruth. At this stage, it seems that Murdoch had not thought of exploiting his idea commercially. However, two years later, after he had moved back to the Midlands, his employer (James Watt Jnr.), who was familiar with earlier experiments with coal gas in Scotland, suggested that Murdoch take out a patent on his idea and encouraged him to try it out in their factory in Ayrshire. Murdoch did so by filling small bladders with coal gas and attaching them to light fittings. Despite that, it was only after Murdoch and one of the Watt family visited Paris and witnessed the progress Philippe Lebon had made with gas lighting that, in 1802, he was encouraged to provide gas lighting for Boulton and Watt's own works in Birmingham. The workers were soon enjoying what Murdoch called his 'strong and beautiful light'.

The Beginnings of the Coal Gas Industry

Single v Multi-customer Gasworks

Murdoch was soon offering similar lighting systems to other companies. His single-customer approach was to design and provide a bespoke engineering solution for a commercial customer prepared to pay for it. Technical issues were resolved as he went along. For example, his early retorts were not of an optimum design. They had to be lit shortly before each occasion gas was required, which was inconvenient and inefficient. It was his colleague, John Southern, who suggested storing gas in large containers so that the furnaces and retorts could be operated continuously. Murdoch then developed what is believed to be the world's first (albeit small) circular gasholder in 1805. In 1808, his paper to the Royal Society on 'The Application of Coal Gas to Economical Purposes' was so well received that he was awarded its prestigious Rumford Gold Medal. However, because of the limitations of Boulton and Watt's business model, and despite that company being the first to manufacture and install coal gas systems, it lost its lead within ten years to specialized companies like Samuel Clegg's.

Although Clegg is often described as Murdoch's pupil at Boulton and Watt's, it seems to have been Clegg who designed the installation for Henry Lodge's cotton mill at Sowerby Bridge near Halifax, the first major such installation in

Britain. Once satisfied with the lighting in his mill, Lodge asked Clegg to install gas lighting in his home. That was an additional challenge because Lodge insisted on a further purification of the coal gas. Clegg achieved this by introducing lime into the kiln from which the gas was led, in piping, to jets in Lodge's home. Another industrialist, George Lee, adopted the opposite approach to Lodge. He insisted that the coal gas system was trialled in his own home before it was installed in his Salford cotton mill. Had he not taken such a precaution, his might have been the first major factory installation of gas lighting. He later testified to a Select Committee of the House of Commons that gas lighting was not only cheaper but made working conditions more congenial, safer, and more efficient. Previously, mills like his had been lit by tallow candles or oil lamps. Knocking one of them over could sometimes lead to fires, which could put a whole mill out of action. Lee's insurance company agreed that gas lighting was safer. His premiums were cut by a third after he introduced it into his factories, which helped to offset the cost of installation. It was following Lee's experience in his Salford Mill that Chapel Street in Salford became the first street in the world to be lit by gas, in 1806.

Despite Murdoch's early success in the design, manufacture and installation of coal gas lighting whilst working for Boulton and Watt, it remained just a side-line for the company. Their core business remained the manufacture of steam engines. That gave Samuel Clegg the opportunity to set up his own, specifically *gas* company with the help of his wealthy father. In that respect Clegg may have been an opportunist but his subsequent record indicates that he was also an innovative engineer. He improved on his initial methods for generating and purifying coal gas and continued to do the same after 1812 when he moved to London. He also worked hard to overcome the still widespread concern about the danger of gas explosions. In one spectacular attempt to reassure the public, he instructed one of his workmen to drive a pickaxe into the side of a gasholder. He then lit the escaping gas to demonstrate that it would not explode.

By this time, Murdoch must have also felt that he was being upstaged by the flamboyant German, Friedrich Albrect Winzer, the most prominent of those who advocated centralised gasworks supplying multiple customers. He came to the UK, then the most dynamic of the newly industrialised nations, to seek support for his proposal. He anglicised his name to Fredrick Albert Winsor (a century before Britain's royal family adopted the surname Windsor) to make it more publicly acceptable. From the outset, and unlike Murdoch, he focused his attention on London rather than the industrial north and set out to win public support for his venture. He began his marketing drive, like a showman, with entertaining demonstrations of the use of coal gas at London's Lyceum Theatre in 1804. Although he employed an English narrator to read his script from the orchestra pit, he himself demonstrated a variety of gas appliances for heating and cooking as well as lighting. Winsor had no difficulty in pulling in the crowds to his entertaining demonstrations. However, with the UK again at war with Napoleon's France in 1804, he had no comparable success persuading capitalists to invest in his project. What he did succeed in doing was register a patent for piped gas.

Centralised gasworks supplying multiple customers was a new business model which required heavy capitalisation and the support of central and local government, not least because it necessitated laying gas pipes under streets, close to properties owned by people who might not want to use coal gas but were concerned about its explosive potential. Long before any income could be earned from gas lighting, manufacturing plants had to be built to produce the gas and gasholders constructed to store it. Gas mains and smaller pipes had to be installed to agreed standards so that third-party suppliers of gas products could be confident that they would operate safely and efficiently. In addition, a centralised multiple customer business had to develop ways to measure the amount of gas used by individual customers, as well as establish a system for collecting payment from those who had already used it (because pre-payment meters did not come into regular use until the 1890s). Once all these elements were in place, a maintenance system had also to be introduced, not only to ensure the centralised system operated smoothly but to guard against the dangers from gas leaks which could develop without warning and have catastrophic consequences.

In pursuing his more ambitious dream, Winsor benefitted from a stroke of good fortune. In 1805, the Prince of Wales asked him to mount gas-lit illuminations on the wall which separated his Carlton House home from The Mall, as a way of celebrating the King's birthday. Winsor was more than happy to oblige. He produced the coal gas in two furnaces in his own nearby Pall Mall home and led it underground through iron pipes to the garden of the Prince of Wales. It represented a major publicity coup for Winsor. Thousands of Londoners flocked to see this revolutionary method of lighting which had the support of the heir to the throne. The following year, Winsor persuaded Westminster Council to let him erect 13 lamp posts each with 3 gas-jet globes on a stretch of Pall Mall. The gas was produced and channelled in the same way as in 1805 and his three-month demonstration of streetlighting attracted large crowds and considerable press publicity.

Despite Winsor's showmanship, and Murdoch and Clegg's pioneering work, the London brewery, Whitbread, installed its own system of gas lighting without help from any of them. The company then obtained permission to install 11 gas lights in two surrounding streets, as a trial. Although it appears to have been successful, the responsible local authority chose not to extend the system, or make it permanent, and Whitbread's early venture came to nothing.

Winsor, meanwhile, encouraged by the publicity generated by his Pall Mall streetlighting experiment, applied to Parliament for a Bill to set up a company with the ultimate aim of supplying the whole country with coal gas. Although it seems that many potential investors were already persuaded that gas lighting had a promising future, they had doubts about Winsor himself. Despite his name change, he was still regarded as a foreigner with an imperfect grasp of English who made exaggerated claims about what returns investors could expect. He even made the mistake of making the preposterous and easily refuted assertion that coal gas was 'more congenial to our lungs than vital air'! These failings may help to explain why Winsor's first application for the incorporation of the New Patriotic Imperial and National Light and Heat Company to the Chancellor of the Exchequer was not accepted. The matter was referred to the Privy Council who, in turn, referred it to the King. He referred it to the Law Officers, who advised that an Act of Parliament was required for such a venture. The first such application was made in 1809 for the more modestly named Gas Light and Coke Company and was discussed at length by a Parliamentary Committee of Inquiry. Murdoch who, like Clegg, was continuing with his more modest piece-meal approach, opposed the application. He objected on the grounds that, if it was successful, it would create a virtual monopoly and undermine his own pioneering work in the field. He also maintained that the application of the limited liability principle to a company planning to raise as much as £1 million (a colossal sum in 1809), and which promised huge investment returns, was comparable to creating the same kind of 'bubble' which had led to the collapse of the notorious South Sea Company in 1720. Winsor's application failed but a second more modest proposal to provide gas to London was successful in 1810, with the proviso that half of the now more limited £200,000 capital was raised before the company's Charter was granted, and that the remainder was raised within three years. A second stipulation, that gas streetlighting had to be provided for no more than the cost of oil lamps, was no great problem for the new company because, given that no limit had been set on the price that could be charged to private customers, it was possible to subsidise the public provision of streetlighting with revenue raised from private customers. In any case, much the most important concession which the company had won was the right to dig up roads and pavements to lay gas mains.

Winsor's Gas Light and Coke Company (GLCC) received its Royal Charter on 30 April 1812 and from then on was often known as The Chartered Company. Its first gasworks were built on the Crown Wharf on Cannon Row, Westminster, just across the road from Big Ben. Winsor's idea was that a non-stop supply of Tyneside coal could be off-loaded from barges to continually fuel his retorts. The location proved less than ideal, and Winsor and his collaborators found it more difficult to scale up gas production than they had anticipated. The site of the original gasworks was abandoned.[15] However, a second gasworks built at a bigger site on Great Peter Street, also in Westminster, was successful and in 1813 the company secured its first contract to light several streets near Parliament, including Downing Street. Shortly afterwards, the pioneering Clegg, with his experience of bespoke single user systems, joined the GLCC despite it being committed to the multi-user business model. Only then did the company build its first major storage facility. By the end of the year, Clegg had also supervised the installation of gas lamps across Westminster Bridge.

Sadly, for Winsor, his association with his company was short-lived. He was ousted the following year, fell into debt, and returned to the Continent to escape his creditors. But there can be no doubt about his importance in the development of the gas industry in the UK.

Winsor may not have succeeded in establishing the nationwide company he once envisaged but what did follow was the setting up of numerous local multiple customer gas companies. In that key respect, Winsor's vision won out over Murdoch's more limited approach. Based on his own experience trying to persuade Lancashire and Yorkshire businesses to install gas lighting, Murdoch had assumed it would take a long time for gas lighting to win universal acceptance. He was mistaken. There was still some unease about escapes of gas and the potential for explosions but, by the mid-1820s, with few exceptions, all towns with a population of over 10,000 had at least one gas company. North Shields was amongst them. Its first gas company was established in 1819.

Murdoch's business model, in which gas was manufactured for the exclusive use of a single industrial or commercial unit, did not disappear with the advent of multiple customer gas companies. In 1847, for example, a survey established that most of the UK's largest mills produced their own gas, as did many institutions and some railway companies. Nor did the rapid and widespread setting up of local gas companies mean that the bulk of the population had access to gas in their homes. Initially, gas companies did little more than provide limited streetlighting which

---

15 The site later became the location of the National Liberal Club.

gave them only a small return on their considerable investment. The real value of municipal contracts was that it gave companies the authority to dig up the streets to lay their 'gas mains', i.e. the main pipes from which smaller pipes took the gas to the customers from whom significant profits could be made. Even then, until the second half of the nineteenth century, most of the customers of gas companies were factories, shops, railway stations and institutions of various kinds.

In many respects, the development of the gas industry paralleled the development of the railway industry. George Stephenson built the Stockton to Darlington railway using iron rails and a coal-steam locomotive in 1821, coinciding in time with the initial wave of local gas companies. By the time the more significant Liverpool to Manchester railway was running in 1830, using Stephenson's Rocket, gasworks had already been opened in numerous towns and cities around the country.

Laying pipework from gasworks to streetlights, businesses and homes around the country may not have required the sometimes spectacular feats of engineering needed by the railway network but it was still a major achievement. What is different about the two industries is that for the first few decades the railways made more money from passengers than freight, whereas the gas industry made more from supplying gas to businesses and municipal corporations than to domestic consumers. During the period from about 1835-1850, which has been dubbed the period of 'railway mania', lawyers were busy drawing up Acts of Parliament for gas as well as railway companies. In both instances, the government adopted a generally *laissez-faire* policy and intervened only when the workings of the free market had implications for public safety, or when a degree of standardisation was essential, with respect to minimum coal gas quality and the dimensions of railway tracks.

Although in its early decades, the gas industry was relatively free of statutory regulation, the situation changed significantly when the illumination of the new Palace of Westminster with coal gas began in 1847. It was then in the immediate self-interest of the members of the Lords and Commons to introduce statutory safeguards. The Gasworks Clauses Act, passed in that year, was the first of several pieces of legislation which, in time, would control almost every aspect of the industry.

The Use of Gas in Private Households
The provision of coal gas to other than large private homes did not develop on a significant scale until the second half of the nineteenth century. Gas lighting then seems to have become a middle-class 'must-have'. A contributor to the

Englishwoman's Domestic Magazine insisted that parties 'must always be given by gas light … if it be daylight outside, you must close the shutters and draw the curtains, the better to show off your gasoliers'!

This growing adoption of coal gas made possible a marked improvement in people's ability to read, write and undertake other tasks in the evenings. That is not to say that early coal gas lighting did not have drawbacks. It gave off black deposits as it burned and reduced the oxygen content in the air. It has even been suggested that the depleted oxygen content of gas-lit drawing rooms, along with tight-laced corsets, explains the propensity of middle-class ladies to faint whilst indoors. It is also one of the reasons why aspidistras became such a popular indoor plant in Victorian households. They coped well with lower oxygen levels in gas-lit homes.

The Coal Gas Production Process

The coal gas industry was always innovative and, because gas engineers designed such a variety of improvements to manufacturing techniques, it is difficult to describe here in other than general terms. The process began by loading coal into retorts and heating it to an extremely high temperature. Most original retorts were round, made of cast iron with an airtight door at one end and an 'ascension' pipe for the gas to escape at the other. At an early stage, these were replaced with horizontal D-shaped 'through retorts'. Doors at each end allowed coal to be pushed in and the residual coke raked out. The retorts were heated from below for between 8-12 hours during which the gases given off were collected and the coal was converted to coke. Methods of heating the retorts improved over the years and led to an increased gas yield and improvements in the quality of by-products. Initially, charging and discharging the retorts was done manually. It was very hot and uncomfortable work. For that reason, the roofs of retort houses were often louvred to try to stop working conditions becoming unbearably hot. From the 1870s, in larger gasworks, the process of loading and discharging the retorts was mechanized. In the early twentieth century, *continuous vertical retorts* were introduced in some gasworks although smaller companies tended to stick with horizontal retorts until they closed.

Hydrogen and methane made up about 85 per cent of the gases given off by coal distillation. Of the others, carbon dioxide was considered for many years to be harmless, although we now understand that it is a greenhouse gas with a major impact on global climate change. Other gases given off have always been known to be dangerous, for example ammonia, carbon monoxide, cyanogen, and hydrogen sulphide. They had to be removed from the final product. So, after the gases left the retorts, they were fed through condensers and then washers (to remove the remaining coal tar). Typically, by then, still only about half of the soluble impurities had been removed and further washing and 'scrubbing' was required. As a final stage, the gaseous material had to be purified to remove the remaining poisonous substances. Various forms of lime were used for this until around 1850, when the use of iron oxide became more common.

In addition to the gases, the distillation process generated both liquid and solid by-products, primarily coal tar, ammoniacal liquor and coke. Initially, coal tar was regarded as little more than a waste product but, as early as 1823, Charles Macintosh patented a method to waterproof fabrics with substances derived from coal tar. In the 1840s, creosote was distilled from coal tar and sold as a wood preservative – at a propitious time given the vast number of wooden 'sleepers' used in our expanding railway system. Then, from the 1850s, coal tar became a key feedstock for the huge range of products made by the UK's burgeoning chemical industries. The ammoniacal liquor produced during the distillation process was used as a fertiliser. The solid residues from the retorts were also valuable. We have already noted that coke is a virtually smokeless solid fuel with a substantial calorific value. It was used like coal in open grates and, although more expensive, enjoyed a new popularity after the introduction of Clean Air Acts in the latter part of the twentieth century. Even the spent oxide from the furnaces was of value. It was sold for use in the manufacture of sulphuric acid.

Large cylindrical gasholders, which were closed at the top but open at the base and set in a tank of water which acted as a seal, were in use from an early stage. The first telescopic gasholder was introduced in Leeds in 1824. As coal gas was pumped into the container, it would rise inside the frame. When the inner vessel of a telescopic gasholder was fully extended, it would engage with the next container and so increase the capacity of the gasholder. The biggest telescopic gasholders contained as many as six containers. A later design did not require external columns and guide frames because they were fitted with spiral rails. As the volume of gas increased or decreased, the gasholder moved up and down like a screw. All such telescopic gasholders had the major advantage of being able to hold large quantities with a small footprint.

Gas Appliances

Lighting

Once the equipment and processes needed to manufacture and store coal gas became established, it was not long before numerous companies began to devise a multitude of ways to make use of it. Initially, the focus was predominantly on lighting. Given that for tens of thousands of years previously, people had been dependent on oil or spirit lamps and candles, this new form of lighting was truly revolutionary.

Igniting a wick placed in animal, vegetable or mineral oils stored in containers of some kind has a history lasting thousands of years during which a vast range of designs emerged. The earliest lamps were probably shells or stones which held animal fat, with moss used as a wick. Later, ceramic and metal containers were used with a fashioned wick. Unfortunately, the most readily available oils gave off the least light, worst smell, and most smoke. Better quality oils were too expensive for ordinary people to use on a regular basis. The most important advance in such lighting was the brainchild of the Swiss chemist Aime Argand. His 'Argand lamp'

of 1780 had a cylindrical wick which produced a much larger flame. It was covered by a glass cylinder which not only made it safer to use but allowed for a flow of air over the flame to make it brighter. A typical Argand lamp would provide illumination which was the equivalent of about six to eight candles. It was a major advance but can still be regarded as an evolutionary rather than revolutionary development. From about 1850, paraffin (derived from petroleum) lamps were introduced and were both brighter and simpler to construct.[16]

A few examples of the many kinds of oil and spirit lamps that were developed.

Because of their portability, such lamps are still widely used and pressurised versions, fitted with incandescent gas mantles, of the kind manufactured by the British company Tilly, are particularly effective. Nevertheless, for regular use in permanent buildings, they cannot match either gas or electricity for convenience and efficiency.

The simplest candles were made from rushes. After they had been cut and dried, lengths were coated with layers of hot fat and set in holders. Easy to make and cheap to buy, they were in use in the homes of the poor until the late nineteenth century. Ordinarily, they would be lit at only one end but, for extra illumination, they could be lit at both ends – which seems to have given rise to the expression 'burning your candle at both ends'. Lit at just one end, a rush candle could still

---

16 Paraffin is also known as kerosene.

last for as little as 20 minutes. Even a 70cm (28 inch) length of rush would last for less than an hour.

Tallow candles made from rendered animal fat were also in common use for a long time. They provided poor illumination and gave off an unpleasant smell. Moreover, when lit, tallow candles needed their wicks trimmed every few minutes to minimise the smoke given off. That required a deft touch and, in the days before safety matches were invented in the nineteenth century, re-lighting an extinguished candle took time and effort unless there was an open fire close by. Beeswax candles were preferable to tallow but only the rich could afford them more than occasionally, and even fewer could afford to amplify the light from such candles with mirrors and chandeliers. Significant improvements in candle manufacture followed in the nineteenth century but they were still only modest, evolutionary advances on an old basic design. Those made from coconut oil, palm oil and paraffin wax became popular and, for those who could afford them, candles made from the spermaceti oil found in the head cavity of sperm whales. The latter candles burned with a bright white light and were odourless, compared to lamps using whale blubber oil. Because of its superior quality, spermaceti oil, and the candles made from it, commanded a high price and helped justify the difficult and dangerous practice of whaling. For ports such as North Shields, whaling made a significant contribution to the local economy and was the main reason why some influential people resisted the introduction of gas lighting. Sperm candles were so highly regarded that even in 1860 a 'British Parliamentary Standard Candle' made from spermaceti oil was adopted as the standard light intensity against which gas lighting was rated – ironically around the very time that sperm whaling was declining.[17]

Tallow Candles

Sperm whale candles

THE WHITEHALL SPERM CANDLES

The British Parliamentary Standard Candle

A few examples of the many kinds of candles that were developed.

Candles did not go out of use when gas lighting became commonplace. In later sections of the book, we shall draw on the journal of Thomas Taylor, a senior member of staff at the North Shields gasworks, who was reading by candlelight in his bedroom well into the 1930s.

The earliest gas lights were primitive. Their burners were essentially pieces of iron with pinprick-sized holes through which the escaping gas was lit. To

---

17 It is estimated that over 200,000 sperm whales were killed in the 19th century alone.

protect the flames from the danger of being extinguished, they were enclosed by a glass container. Initially, the principles which determined the luminosity of the flames were not well understood. In time, engineers learned both that there needed to be a supply of carbon within the flame (because it was by making the carbon incandescent that light was given off), and that the flame needed to be hot (because the hotter the carbon particles the brighter they glowed). Although a variety of burners were soon on the market, and 'bats wing' and 'fishtail' burners were more efficient than simpler forms, the first notable advance did not come until the principal of the cylindrical Argand oil burner was adapted to burn gas. What made it distinctive is that air was drawn into the flame as it burned (the same principle used in 'Bunsen' burners). However, whilst a notable improvement, critics maintained that it consumed too much gas at a time when gas was still an expensive commodity. One development which did help to bring down the overall cost of gas installations was the introduction of burners which did not corrode. Until 1858, the slightest obstruction, such as rust, reduced the efficiency and reliability of gas burners. The William Sugg Company then developed burners made of the mineral soapstone, which not only did not corrode but produced a better light. That advance came at a propitious time because the discovery of petroleum fields in the USA had cut the cost of paraffin and candles made from paraffin wax, making gas seem relatively more expensive than previously.

The first major advance in gas burners came in 1887 when Welsbach, an Austrian chemist, invented the gas mantle. In due course, British companies were able to follow his example and supplied customers through local ironmongers. Although delicate and easily damaged, these textile cups, soaked in the oxides of rare metals such as thorium, produced a brilliant incandescent light. Their adoption was slowed initially by the company's monopoly but in time prices fell and the use of mantles allowed the gas industry to compete with the developing electricity industry for longer than would otherwise have been the case. Indeed, the *Financial Times* declared that with the incandescent mantle 'the gas engineers have turned the tables on the electricians.' Fortuitously, the gas mantle arrived on the scene around the same time as the first reliable pre-payment gas meters and together they prompted a substantial increase in the amount of gas used by households. For a time, gas also enjoyed a revival in some parts of the theatrical world. Ellen Terry, Sir Henry Irving's leading lady hated the illumination provided by early electric lighting and persuaded him to go back to using gas. In her 1933 memoirs, she referred to 'the thick softness of gas light' but the 'naked trashiness of electricity.' Stan Laurel's father, Arthur Jefferson, who was planning to use electricity in his new Blyth Theatre Royal, changed his mind

The Evolution of Gas Lighting Burners

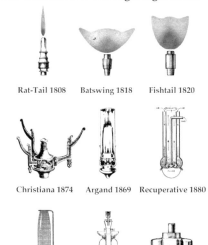

Rat-Tail 1808   Batswing 1818   Fishtail 1820

Christiana 1874   Argand 1869   Recuperative 1880

Incadescent 1890   Inverted 1900   Cluster 1909

The development of gas lighting burners. Based on information provided on the William Sugg history site: https://williamsugghistory.co.uk/lighting/burners/

An example of an incandescent gas mantle in situ, on display at the National Gas Museum in Leicester: www.nationalgasmuseum.org.uk

and at considerable extra cost reverted to using gas (Lawrence, 2017, p.168).

Living in a world that has progressed through several types of electric lighting to today's efficient LED lamps, it may come as a surprise to some readers to know that gas remained in extensive if diminishing use until the 1950s for both street and domestic lighting. Indeed, in North Shields, as late as the 1950s, about half the streetlights were lit by gas. Moreover, even as late as 1970 there were houses without electricity. Stephanie Cottis was kind enough to respond to our request for information on this topic and explained that in Burdon Main Row, just a short distance from the Minton Lane gasworks in North Shields, her family had gas lighting but no electricity supply. To watch TV her family bought a 12-volt portable set, powered by a car battery.

The Vaux Borough Arms pub in Camden Street, North Shields, in 1963 when it was still lit only by gas.

Gas Fires, Water Heaters, and Other Domestic Gas Appliances

It was because for many years coal gas was used predominantly for lighting that, originally, its quality was rated in terms of its illuminating power. Winsor had anticipated gas would also be used for heating, but it was only in the 1880s that it began to be used widely as an alternative to coal. That was in part because gas was relatively more expensive. Early gas 'fires' were essentially convector heaters. Air drawn into the base of the heater was heated by the gas burners. A current of warm air was then released into the room from the top of the heater. Later gas fires incorporated ceramic elements which were heated until literally red-hot. Simulated burning logs were also considered fashionable in the 1880s.

Examples of early convector gas fires on display at the National Gas Museum in Leicester: www.nationalgasmuseum.org.uk

Examples of early ceramic gas fires on display at the National Gas Museum in Leicester: www.nationalgasmuseum.org.uk

During the nineteenth century, when a supply of safe, cold water direct to a tap in houses was still considered a luxury, having hot water on demand was beyond the imagination of most families. However, in time, gas did provide a growing number of houses with instant (or near instant) hot water. The well-known 'Ascot' water heater, in its numerous iterations, was eventually installed in many working-class homes and provided hot water when there was no prospect of a fully plumbed supply. Later, gas-fuelled boilers provided not only hot water but also whole-house central heating.

Gas also powered boilers for washing clothes, irons, and refrigerators: which today we think of only as electrical appliances. In workshops and factories, gas was used not only to heat the premises but to fuel specific appliances such as soldering irons, welding, and brazing tools, and irons used in commercial laundries.

Examples of early gas water heating appliances on display at the National Gas Museum in Leicester: www.nationalgasmuseum.org.uk

An unusual, combined gas washing machine and dish washer on display at the National Gas Museum in Leicester: www.nationalgasmuseum.org.uk

An example of one of the many domestic gas irons on display at the National Gas Museum in Leicester: www.nationalgasmuseum.org.uk

Cooking

Gas cookers were made as early as the 1820s and, by 1834, were used to prepare meals at London's Reform Club. However, despite such early innovations, and several companies designing and marketing gas cookers, the public at large continued to cook with coal. It was not just the cost and inconvenience of installing gas in kitchens that acted as a deterrent. Coal gas was not cheap and maintenance costs not insignificant. Even in the 1870s when cooking by gas became more common, gas cookers were often hired rather than purchased. Some of the early gas cookers were little more than gas rings, of the sort that later became popular amongst those who lived in 'bed-sits'. But it was about this time that the now familiar gas cooker design emerged, with gas rings on the hob and an oven below. Earlier concerns that burning gas would taint the food, or be a danger to health, were overcome and cooking by gas became commonplace. Nevertheless, even until the second half of the twentieth century, many people had to be persuaded to switch from the versatile large black-leaded ranges, heated by coal fires, which were already installed in a huge number of houses. As well as heating the room, they could be used for frying, boiling, braising, baking and roasting food, and provided a place to help dry clothes, keep kettles, pans and flat irons, along with a mantlepiece for ornaments and other odds and ends. It is noteworthy that the winning entry in a 1905 postcard competition organized by the Newcastle and Gateshead Gas Company to draw attention to the claimed advantages of cooking on a gas stove rather than on a black-leaded coal-fired range, ignored the versatility of the traditional stove, drawing attention only to its disadvantages, and in the case of the gas cooker, its advantages but not limited functionality.

The winning entry in a 1905 postcard competition organized by the Newcastle and Gateshead Gas Company draws attention to the claimed advantages of cooking by gas rather than on a traditional black-leaded coal-fired range. The image (originally in colour) is reproduced here courtesy of Billy Embleton.

Examples of the many early gas cookers on display at the National Gas Museum in Leicester: www.nationalgasmuseum.org.uk

Gas Engines

Most people associate the internal combustion engine with petroleum derived fuels. However, it was coal gas which powered the first successful internal combustion engines. In some cases, it was used to generate steam. In other instances, it was used as the direct source of energy. Although four-stroke (cycle) engines are credited to French and German engineers, the more compact two-stroke engine is credited to the North Shields born and raised James Robson (1832-1913).[18]

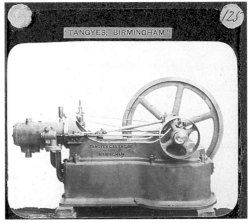

An image of Robson's patented gas engine taken from a Tangyes of Birmingham projector slide. More details of Robson's work are provided in Appendix 1.

The First Half of the Twentieth Century

The First World War

The First World War was such an immense event that it had an impact on all industries and sections of the population. Gas companies were no exception. There was a reduced demand from previously regular customers, most obviously

---

18 He was not the only North Shields engineer working on gas engines. For example, in May 1886, Leighton Mills of 1 South Preston, North Shields, applied for a patent for what he described as an 'improved gas engine'.

the Germans who, prior to the war, had bought large quantities of UK-produced coke, tar, and other products. Local authorities also used less coal gas because streetlighting was reduced to make towns less visible during air raids. Fortunately, for gas companies, there was an increased demand from other British customers. Coal tar was the source of the phenol and toluene used to make explosives. Ammonia was used to manufacture the nitric acid needed to make gun cotton and nitrogenous fertilisers.[19] Coal gas was used to power some motor vehicles (by attaching gas bags to their roofs). Charcoal used in gas masks was made by carbonising wood in the furnaces of a small number of gasworks with spare capacity.

Key workers in the gas industry volunteered for or were later conscripted into the armed forces, and in many companies, women took over the work that traditionally had been done by men. As the then chairman of the National Gas Council put it:

> Nearly all the jobs done by women within the gasworks are of a fairly arduous nature – ordinary navvying, for instance, trucking coal and coke, loading breeze [dust, ash, cinders and coke] and clinker [the stony residue], handling tar barrels and weighing sulphate. Their heaviest task is to empty and recharge purifiers. They have to use a pick and shovel on the spent oxide at the bottom of the tanks, carry it away on their backs in three-quarter hundredweight [c.40kg] sacks, stack it and then continually turn it over so the air can reach and revivify every part of it for future use.

During the First World War, the cost of producing gas rose enormously. For instance, between 1914 and 1918, the cost of coal rose by 80 per cent and freight charges by 600 per cent. The increased costs could not be passed on by raising prices because they were tightly controlled by central government. As a result, some companies went bankrupt, and their gasworks closed. Others, particularly smaller gas companies, struggled to survive. Gas supplies then had to come from usually larger plants further afield. Other companies survived the difficult war conditions only by merging.

It was only following the war that the government decided it was time to oblige gas companies to use a uniform measure to sell their gas. Until the Gas Regulation Act of 1920, customers had been charged by the volume of gas they

---

19 Nitrocellulose in the form of gun cotton was used as a propellant in firearms, and for low order explosives.

consumed, irrespective of its quality. From then, they were obliged to charge by the heat content of the gas, measured in terms of British Thermal Units (BTU).[20] The calorific value of a company's gas was the number of BTUs produced by burning 1 cubic foot of it. Charging by calorific value rather than illuminating power made more sense because of the changing uses to which coal gas was being put.

The Inter-War Years

Between 1920 and 1937, the amount of gas supplied for public use doubled and, by the mid-1930s, the British *coal gas* industry may have been the largest in the world with 11 million customers. The USA may have had 17 million gas customers, but it used much more *natural gas* than manufactured *coal gas*. It was not just the consumption of coal gas that increased in those years. There was also a growing demand for some of the industry's by-products. Road builders, for example, were making extensive use of coal tar on road surfaces.

British gas companies employed about 125,000 people in the supply industry, spread across 1,200 separate gas undertakings.[21] It was the widespread belief that this resulted in higher costs that encouraged the Board of Trade to recommend, in 1933, that adjacent companies consolidate their resources. The recommendation was made despite a 1932 analysis which showed that larger undertakings did not necessarily enjoy economies of scale. On the contrary, it showed that smaller companies were producing gas slightly more cheaply than larger companies, and the best performer of all was the smallest undertaking in the sample! Nevertheless, the consolidation of gas undertakings became marked in the 1930s, encouraged by the fact that the government did insist, from 1934, that all gas had to be supplied at a uniform pressure. It became common for a holding company to own several undertakings. By 1938, for example, 18 holding companies owned 242 separate gas undertakings between them. But, overall, the gas industry remained fragmented and even after 120 years there was still no national gas grid. Indeed a 1930 Board of Trade Committee had explicitly decided against having one even though by then there was a national grid for electricity.

It was not just the manufacturing side of the gas industry that was fragmented. The same held true of its national bodies. No single organization enjoyed

---

20 One BTU was the amount of gas needed to raise the temperature of 1 pound of water by 1°F with 1 Therm being the term used for 100,000 BTUs.

21 A further 30,000 people were employed in the manufacture of gas plants and gas appliances. New houses were increasingly built with gas appliances already installed and a wide range of increasingly efficient and attractive products were available for heating houses and water, and for cooking food. Less common, but growing in popularity, were gas fridges, gas washing machines, gas irons and even gas hair curling tongs.

executive authority over the industry. The nearest thing to that was The British Gas Federation which tried to reach a consensus on policy between five separate bodies (The Institution of Gas Engineers, The Gas Companies Protection Association, The Society of British Gas Industries, The British Commercial Gas Association, and The National Gas Council of Britain and Ireland). In addition to The British Gas Federation there was a Federation of Gas Employers which had been set up in 1919 specifically to act as a collective bargaining agency for the gas industry.

During the inter-war years, about 65 per cent of the coal gas produced was used by domestic consumers: by then, predominantly for cooking and heating. The lead the industry had once enjoyed in household lighting was by then lost to the electricity industry. Yet, despite the popularity of electricity for domestic lighting, more than half of Britain's streetlights still used coal gas at the outbreak of the Second World War.

The Second World War

Gasworks were prime targets for the bombers of the Luftwaffe but just as important to maintaining gas supplies were the 68,000 miles of gas pipes which connected gasworks to their customers. Little could be done to reduce the risk to gas plants, other than try to remove the visible glow that usually emanated from retort houses. What was possible were measures to minimise disruption when gasworks or gas pipes were hit. One of the dangers was that the continued use of gas would draw air in from broken mains, creating an explosive mix of gas and air. To reduce that possibility, valving systems were installed so that, when mains were damaged, they could be isolated for repair. Special mobile repair teams were organized to act quickly in emergencies and, where practical, adjacent undertakings prepared plans to connect their systems should it prove necessary. To ensure that skilled personnel were available for all this vital work, the government ordered that no technically qualified gas employee should be allowed to enlist, or be conscripted, without the permission of the Ministry of Labour.

In these difficult circumstances, it is remarkable that, *overall*, by the end of the war, the gas industry had expanded production by almost 20 per cent, and that much of the work was undertaken by women without any previous experience. The increase in production was also achieved despite often inadequate supplies of coal; major problems with transportation; and a requirement that gasworks produce hydrogen (for barrage balloons), as well as the coal gas and by-products that were more in demand than ever. Operating under such conditions made it difficult for companies to remain commercially viable and some ran for a time at a loss because, although costs had risen, the government exercised strict control over prices.

The Second Half of the Twentieth Century

'Nationalisation' and Privatisation

As part of the prosecution of the war, a Ministry of Fuel and Power was created in 1942 during the days of the coalition national government. In 1944, its minister appointed a committee to 'review the structure and organization of the gas industry'. Although its 1945 report did not recommend public ownership *per se*, its conclusions did form the basis for taking the industry into public ownership in 1948. The fragmentation of the industry, with its large number of small undertakings, was judged inefficient and the experience of the Second World War convinced the members of the committee of the need for a national fuel policy. As Alf (later Baron) Robens put it when introducing the gas bill for its third reading:

> The gas industry's own report in 1943 came down heavily on the need for integration and co-ordination, the Heyworth Report did the same, and the fundamental difference between hon. Members opposite and hon. Members on this side of the House as to how that should be achieved, either by some form of private enterprise, municipal enterprise, or public ownership, was decided at the General Election of 1945 (Hansard, 16 June 1948).

In short, the post-war Labour government which had been elected with a huge majority in 1945, favoured the third approach but it was not taking the gas industry into public ownership for primarily political reasons. The overwhelming case for it was based on the need for greater operational efficiency. Moreover, most of those within the industry had long since been reconciled to a reorganization of this kind, not least because they were conscious that footing the bill for the long overdue modernisation of the industry was not attractive to private investors. In taking the industry into public ownership, the government was also doing what the French government had already done the year before and the UK government had already done with the electricity industry. As Robens reminded the House:

> (This) is really a twin of the Electricity Bill. Indeed large parts of the Gas Bill, particularly some of the most controversial parts, such as that dealing with the compensation provisions, were lifted bodily from Part II of the Electricity Bill and put into the Gas Bill almost word for word (Hansard, 16 June 1948).

In the event, over a thousand gas undertakings were taken into public ownership but then reorganized into twelve *largely autonomous* area boards. The newly established Gas Council did not determine industry policy. It existed to liaise between the Ministry of Fuel and Power and the independent area boards. Public ownership subsequently brought with it a huge programme of much-needed investment. Old and inefficient gasworks were closed, and the remainder modernised. Public ownership also made it easier to organize advertising, and by the 1960s more nationally coordinated campaigns were underway. The significance of the *High-Speed Gas* campaign was that it emphasised that, unlike cooking with electricity, gas was available instantly, and was visible and so easily controlled. Burners on electric cookers, in contrast at that stage, were slow to heat and slow to cool down and not so easily controlled. Over the same period, gas appliances became not only increasingly easy to use but also smarter in their appearance. *Flavel*, for example, advertised its *Debonair* as, 'the first heater designed to go with your furniture.' At about the same time, gas-fired central heating grew in popularity, which required additional skills to install and maintain, not least because of the electrical and electronic controls fitted to gas boilers. It was in part for this reason that, in accordance with increasingly strict government regulations, the Confederation for the Registration of Gas Installers (CORGI) was set up in 1969 to ensure that the then 9,000 independent installers were as competent as their equivalents in the publicly owned part of the industry.[22]

Chapter 8 is devoted to a more detailed discussion of the rationalisation, 'nationalisation', and subsequent privatisation of the gas industry in the decades following the end of the Second World War. It also includes a discussion of the conversion of the industry to natural gas during the period it was in public ownership.

Employment in the Gas Industry

There was no organized career guidance in the nineteenth century. Most young people went into work that was readily available in their immediate neighbourhood or followed in the footsteps of their parents or other family members. Initially, those who went into the gas industry were either employed to do labouring work for which only limited training was necessary, or already had relevant skills, for example as plumbers. Thomas Duncan, whom we will introduce in Chapter 7, is a good example of this route into the industry. He was trained as a plumber before becoming a gas fitter. However, by the 1860s, the notion of occupational

---

22 Replaced by the Gas Safe Register in 2009.

choice was sufficiently in currency for the major publisher Routledge to release *The Boys Book of Trades* – though it seems unlikely that the boys who finished up in the trades described in the book conceived of their employment in the same terms that the authors described it in the Preface.

> Our daily work, however common or humble it may seem, is our daily duty, and by doing it well we may even make it a part of our daily worship.

The book described the nature of 33 skilled occupations in some detail, including the tools used as well as the work involved. Amongst them, in consecutive chapters,

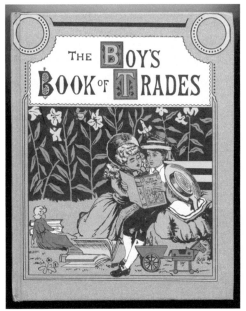

Front cover of The Boy's Book of Trades *which, in consecutive chapters, describes in some detail the kind of work expected of Plumbers, Gas Fitters and those involved in* The Manufacture of Gas *(Routledge 1865, reprinted by Pryor Publications, 1999).*

were Plumber, Gas Fitter, and Manufacture of Gas. Interestingly, the same sequence of employment was followed by Thomas Duncan. After serving his apprenticeship as a plumber, he went on to become a self-employed gas fitter before going to work first for the Morpeth Gas Company and then the Tynemouth Gas Company.

At a more senior level, there was no formal training for gas engineers for several decades. They learned on the job, effectively as apprentices. That was not just true in the early years, when Samuel Clegg was pupil to William Murdock, and George Livesey was apprenticed, aged 14, to his father at the South Metropolitan Gas Company in London. It was also true in the decades that followed. Despite the huge importance of the coal gas industry, its engineers were slow to seek and gain professional recognition. The obvious need for consistent training, and standardised manufacturing and commercial practices, had led to the establishment of *The Gas Gazette* in 1847, which was succeeded by the *Journal of Gas Lighting* in 1849 (later renamed the *Gas Journal*). 'Best practice' was also available to novice and experienced gas engineers and managers in the form of Thomas Newbiggin's *Handbook for Gas Engineers and Managers* which was first published in 1870 and was so popular it went into eight editions. It covered everything from building a gasworks (including the design of the retorts, purifiers, and gasholders); testing coal for its gas-producing properties, and laying pipes (including their diameter, thickness, depth to be buried in the ground, and ways to test for leaks). The *Handbook* was above all else a practical, 'how to do it' manual but it would also have been invaluable to those embarking on the first examinations in gas manufacture introduced by the RSA in 1874.

Newbiggin did acknowledge that those designing and running gasworks also needed to understand the theoretical aspects of gas manufacture but there were no university courses in gas engineering in the nineteenth century. Nor was there a single established professional body for gas engineers. The British Association of Gas Managers (BAGM) was not founded until 1863 and its early years were fraught with problems. The body changed its name to the Gas Institute in 1881 but fell victim to an internal dispute which led to the resignation of the President, Secretary, and most of the Institute's Council. By the time a new body, the Institute of Gas Engineers, was established in 1890, there was another specialist journal in circulation, *Gas World*, which had been founded in 1884. Despite initial opposition from the original Institute, the new body received official recognition so, for a time, there were two competing professional bodies in the gas industry. It was not until 1912 that there was a reconciliation and they amalgamated. The result was the Incorporated Institution of Gas Engineers formed in 1903. Although the industry was now represented by a single professional body it was still not until 1929 that it received a Royal Charter.

What is noteworthy is that the Institute set up in 1881 did not follow the example of the Royal Institute of Chemistry (established in 1877) and become the qualifying body for the industry. The formal education of gas engineers did not receive the systematic attention it enjoyed in continental Europe and, despite its pioneering position in the gas industry, the UK was slow to develop systematic technical education in this and other areas of engineering. It was not until 1903 that the Institute of Civil Engineers invited its eight sister institutions to discuss the future of technical training for engineers in conjunction with the City and Guilds Institute. That led to the formulation of agreed syllabuses for gas engineers, but all still below degree level. It was not until 1906 that the University of Leeds became the first to establish a department specifically related to fuels; and not until 1908, the year of Sir George Livesey's death, that a Chair in his name was endowed and the first professor of coal gas and fuel industries appointed.

The individuals represented by this sequence of professional bodies constituted only a tiny proportion of the industry's work force. For the main body of workers, the niceties of professional recognition were of no consequence. What mattered to them were their day-to-day working conditions and wage levels. The light at the end of the process for which they were responsible might have been dubbed 'beautiful' but there was nothing beautiful about their work. It was hard and heavy. The hours were long even by the standards of the day and a contemporary observer once remarked that 'a more fatiguing, dirty, uncongenial occupation scarce exists in the whole round of manual labour, nor one that soon makes old men out of young ones.' Originally, manual workers in the gas industry 'enjoyed' a break from work on Sundays but that was only achieved by not providing gas on Sundays. Once the demand for coal gas was established, a seven-day week became the norm, and each day was divided into two twelve-hour shifts. Although for those who worked in the retort houses there might have been spells of inactivity between each bout of shovelling coal into the retorts, and the removal of coke and other products from them at the end of the distillation process, those involved were still obliged to remain in or close to the very hot, dirty and unhealthy atmosphere for the whole period. In the Westminster gasworks of the GLCC, in 1859, The Gas Stokers' Protection Society called a strike in protest at the seven-day week and twelve-hour shift but after four months the strike was broken by the dismissal of the workers along with some assistance from other gas companies. Although improvements were secured outside London, it was not until 1889 that significant concessions were negotiated in London with the National Union of Gas Workers.

Constraints on the Gas Industry

Problems of Cost and Quality

Much of the gas that was produced in the early years failed to reach customers. An internal investigation in London in the mid-1850s found that about 25 per cent was lost, most of it through leaking pipes into the surrounding soil. Given that in the area, at the time, there were 23 gas plants owned by 15 companies, with 1,800 miles of piping and 38,000 streetlights, finding and repairing leaks was not the only problem. It was also sometimes difficult to determine which company was responsible for rectifying any given problem. Another issue, more so for the consumers of gas than the producers, was that as late as 1860 there was no agreed standard for either the purity or illuminating power of gas. Even then, the first steps in that direction appear to have been unsuccessful. The quality of the gas produced was in part related to the quality of the coal burned in the furnaces and, in part, what individual gas engineer-managers deemed appropriate.

Government Regulation

Until 1856, any English company which raised capital by selling shares was, in law, only a partnership. Should it become insolvent, all those who held shares were liable for the company's debts. If necessary, their private assets could be seized to pay those debts. The only way to avoid this risk was to secure a private Act of Parliament (or a Royal Charter) and in the initial decades of the industry there were a plethora of such applications from gas companies.

Even though the nineteenth century was a period of competitive capitalism and relatively *laissez-faire* economics, in which state intervention was kept to the minimum, politicians could not avoid regulating industry. In doing so, they had the architect of competitive capitalism, Adam Smith, on their side. He recognized that the government had a responsibility to protect the public from unscrupulous entrepreneurs and to ensure that the benefits of competition were not lost by the emergence of monopolies. Somehow, public authorities had to strike a balance between competitive freedom on the one hand, and regulation to protect the public on the other. That was not easy to achieve in the case of the gas industry. The conventional wisdom of the day was that a company with a monopoly could exploit its customers and, in the absence of competition, become prone to inefficiency. However, an 1847 government commission concluded that the assumed benefits of competition did not seem to apply in the gas industry. It reported that having rival gas companies in the same area did not benefit consumers. In practice, either one company went out of business and the other raised its prices once its monopoly position was secured; or a monopoly was achieved by a merger of the competing companies. The study led to the Gasworks Clauses Act of 1847. To try to prevent gas companies from making excessive profits, dividends were not allowed to be more than 10 per cent, unless it was to compensate for a lower dividend in an earlier year. As gas companies entered a new phase of amalgamating in the 1870s, the government stepped in to protect consumers by introducing a standard price and a standard dividend. The dividend could be increased only if the price charged for gas fell below the standard price. Conversely, if dividends were paid to shareholders above the standard level, then there had to be a corresponding drop in the price charged to customers. From 1877, it also became mandatory to sell new stock by public auction, to prevent existing shareholders buying it at face value. This practice continued until 1934. Thereafter, the issue price of new stock was determined by the Board of Trade.

For the first four decades of the gas industry, companies were free to choose which customers they supplied with gas. That degree of freedom was curtailed for most companies after 1855 and removed after 1871. To be given statutory status, companies had to provide gas at a minimum level of illumination to any customer who demanded it, provided the customer was prepared to bear the cost of connecting the installation to the gas mains. In return, the companies enjoyed local monopolies. By 1882, there were 500 *authorised* undertakings. Of these, 70 per cent were private but 30 per cent were municipally owned. In addition, there were still non-authorised companies, but their number can only be estimated because, as non-statutory bodies, they were not obliged to provide statistics to the Board of Trade. It has been estimated that in this period, and in the early decades of the twentieth century, they numbered 100-200. By 1937, there were over 500 but together they provided less than 4 per cent of the overall gas supply (Goodall, pp.249-50).

Inevitably, there was a potential tension between private gas companies and municipal gas undertakings. The profit regulations described above did not apply to the latter because they had no shareholders. So, to protect private gas companies, municipal undertakings were banned from supplying private customers in areas that already had an established gas company. What was made explicit, from 1875, is that in areas where there was no statutory-based private company, municipal authorities could establish their own gasworks or purchase an existing company.

Competition from Electricity

The advent of electricity in the late 1870s posed a major threat to a gas industry that was only just beginning to make serious inroads into supplying gas for heating and cooking. Fortuitously for gas companies, electricity was expensive, and the early generators did not produce a uniform output. The fact that towns had differing power supplies made it difficult for manufacturers to develop standard light fittings for a national market. That was not finally achieved until the National Grid was established in the 1930s.

Initially, electric lighting was produced by the carbon-arc process. Although effective for some purposes, it was dismissed by many as too bright and painful to the eyes. The electric filament lamp was received with more enthusiasm yet the first two towns to use it soon reverted to gas. That was in part because the inroads of the electricity industry into what had previously been gas industry territory, prompted the latter to take marketing more seriously. As a result, between 1882 and 1912, the number of gas consumers increased from just under 2 million to almost 7 million. Even so, the industry realised that more needed to be done and the British Commercial Gas Association was set up in 1912, with the specific task of further promoting the use of gas, although that was made difficult when the outbreak of war in 1914 brought about the suspension of all advertising.

Alternatives to Coal

Despite these advances, the coal gas industry was still facing serious problems. Unlike the electricity industry, its furnaces needed good quality and expensive coal. The processes involved were labour intensive at a time when virtually full employment had led to increased labour costs and made it more difficult to recruit workers. Thirdly, there was a fall in the demand for coal tar because the chemical industry was increasingly using petroleum as its principal raw material. Three main responses were available. The first was to find ways to use cheaper coal but the research undertaken found that even using intermediate-grade coal necessitated such an expensive process that it would defeat the object of the exercise. The second option was to follow the example of the chemical industry and use petroleum instead of coal as the basic raw material. That had significant advantages. Petroleum-based plants were smaller, more efficient and the gas produced was cheaper, with a lower poisonous carbon monoxide content. However, these ventures were eclipsed by the third option, which was to use natural gas instead of coal or petroleum-generated gas. That process will be described in detail in Chapter 8.

Chapter 4

Coal Gas Production in North Shields

THE VERY concept of providing energy to a specific geographical area was unheard of in the eighteenth century. Nor was it welcomed by all at the beginning of the nineteenth. In North Shields, only a few oil lamps alleviated the darkness after sunset. Yet even this minimal illumination had met with resistance from some residents. They were so vociferous in their opposition to the proposal that they succeeded in thwarting it when it was first suggested.

> The project [to provide some oil lamp streetlighting] was thought most revolutionary, and a crowded meeting was held to oppose it. Eloquence might be lacking amongst the opponents of change, but strength of lungs was present in full force and the stragglers for light were howled down. One worthy stood upon a form, waving his arms and shouting 'Nee leets! Nee leets!' (Boyce, p.119).

The earliest known advocacy of *gas* lighting in North Shields came in a letter to the *Tyne Mercury* newspaper in May 1816, just three years after Winsor's London company installed its first streetlighting.[23] The writer set out, in detail, the savings which Lee had achieved using coal gas in his Manchester cotton mill and argued that, especially in a coal mining area, moving from oil to gas streetlighting would be both cheaper and more efficient.

Not everyone agreed. A public meeting was held to discuss the introduction of gas lighting in September 1817. The vote was split, and a decision left to the casting vote of the chairman, John Motley. Apparently, in voting against the proposal, he remarked that his grandfather had carried a lantern, and his

---

23 The *Tyne Mercury*, which covered issues on both sides of the river, was founded in 1802 and continued until 1846 when it merged with the *Newcastle Guardian*. North Shields' news was also carried by Newcastle newspapers, as is still the case today. From 1849, the *Shields Daily Gazette* became available with a specific focus on North and South Shields (though published in South Shields). From 1864, North Shields had its own *Shields Daily News*. These were all serious newspapers covering national and international issues as well as local news.

father had carried a lantern, as he had also done 'these 40 years or more', and he did not see any necessity for gas. Subsequently, 'a number of freeholders and inhabitants of North Shields' presented him with 'an elegant silver snuff box to acknowledge what they regarded as the successful outcome of the meeting.' However, the proponents of gas lighting did not give up and continued with their campaign. In response, in January 1819, the chairman of the 1817 meeting (now using the pseudonym Will Watch) circulated a handbill making a case against the introduction of gas streetlighting. Unlike the opponents of gas elsewhere, he did not base his case on the inconvenience of having pipes installed outside properties which would not use the gas, or the risk of gas explosions. His main reservation related to the potential impact of coal gas on the local whaling industry which consisted of five ships and provided employment to about 500 local people, as well as supplying the town with additional indirect economic benefits. As we explained above, at the time, whale oil was used for both oil lamps and to make candles. Will Watch further argued that, in contrast to those involved in the local whaling industry, those advocating the building of a gasworks were concerned only with 'their own PROFIT'. He dismissed gas lighting as 'a novelty' which 'has a direct tendency to stop the source from whence a great proportion of the prosperity [of our town] flows.' He maintained that the light from 'oil lamps was sufficiently vivid for every purpose of tradesmen' and, though he conceded that gas lighting was superior, insisted that 'even this is more than counter-balanced by the noxious and unwholesome stench produced by it.'[24]

These local opponents of coal gas lighting did not prevail. Six months later, in July 1819, an advertisement in the *Tyne Mercury* invited proposals 'for making two Cylindrical Gasholders of sheet iron, with iron framing'. The advertisement added, 'Wanted immediately, a Mechanic, who understands the fixing of gas pipes, and who can be well recommended.' By 1820, with the legal formalities completed, North Shields had its own, *private*, gas company. The timing was fortunate for the shareholders of the new company. Had the decision been delayed, the outcome might have been different because in a gas explosion in Newcastle in January 1820 a child was killed, several people seriously injured, and a house half demolished. Moreover, the coroner concluded that the explosion was due to 'the gross carelessness of the gas managers'. Gas company workmen had visited the house after a gas leak had been reported but it had been concluded that, because the leak appeared to be small, it could safely be left until the following morning.

---

24 A copy of the handbill was displayed on the wall of the North Shields' Library's newsroom until at least the 1930s.

Tragically, the gas company's workmen had underestimated the scale and nature of the leak, and, with hindsight, it was clear that the house should have been evacuated. The explosion occurred when a child took a lit candle into her bedroom. The leak was eventually traced to a defective joint in a pipe: a not uncommon problem in those early days when the gas industry was in its infancy. The decision to delay tracing the leak until the morning is indicative of a fundamental problem with gas installations in those early days. Trying to trace a gas leak in the dark was obviously dangerous as well as difficult given that the only forms of illumination available required naked flames that would increase the risk of an explosion.

The North Shields Gas Company

Little information has survived about the early years of the North Shields Gas Company. Thirteen names are listed on the original deeds but we know from later documentation that there were 70 shareholders in all who, between them, owned 177 shares.[25] At that stage, the company had capital of £5,000. Although there is no one way to calculate what that sum would represent today, the Economic History Association considers that it is appropriate for this kind of purpose to use the *economic cost* indicator of inflation i.e., treat the sum as a proportion of the total output of the economy, because that is an indication of the significance of the project to the society at the time. Based on that measure, the corresponding sum today would be in the region of £23 million. The scale of the investment is indicative of the strength of the local North Shields' economy in the early nineteenth century, and the fact that there were enough local people with sufficient surplus income to invest in the new venture.

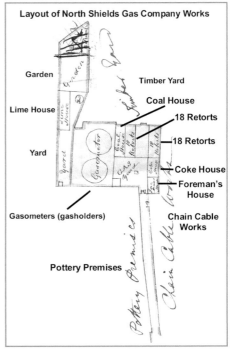

1854 hand-drawn site plan of the original North Shields gasworks (of the North Shields Gas Company) in the Low Lights area of the town.

---

25 The original names listed were William Wingrave, Thomas Thompson, George Scott, John Matthews, Robert Laing, Richard Beall, William Downie, Robert Hall, George Hall, Foster and Pearson, Alexander Russell, and John Wilkinson.

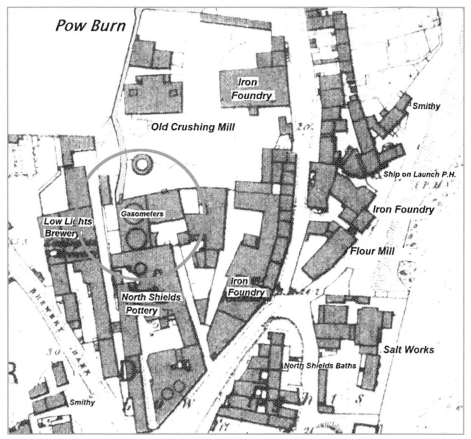

1861 map showing the location of the North Shields Gas Company site in relation to the other main industries in the Low Lights area of North Shields, courtesy of Mike Coates.

In keeping with most industrial developments at the time, the gasworks were constructed in the Low Lights area of the town, close to the riverside. A hand-drawn plan of the original Low Lights gasworks shows two gasholders containing the gas produced by two retort houses, each with 18 retorts. The plan also shows that the gasworks foreman lived in a house on the south-east corner of the site, with only the coke house between his home and one of the two, noisy and dirty retort houses. It was not the most congenial place to live especially given that the other side of the house butted up against a chain cable manufacturer.

Although the gasworks was at the eastern extremity of North Shields, by June 1820 pipe-laying had advanced as far as the western end of the town, about a mile away. We know that because 'the workmen digging in the streets … to lay gas pipes in a place called the Bull Ring [on the Low Road at the foot of Coach Lane], came to a large, flat square stone in which, on being turned over, were found, greatly corroded, the iron bolt and ring to which bulls had been made fast when baited there in old times.' The land above the Bull Ring was then known as Milburn Place and had been sold off in plots for expensive houses, so the likelihood is that the gas pipes were being laid not only to provide streetlighting but also in anticipation of the well-off residents of Milburn Place paying to have their houses lit by gas.

Evidence that the company was doing well by its shareholders is confirmed by a report in the *Civil Engineer and Architect's Journal* which reported that in its first ten years it was paying a dividend of 12.5 per cent, 'more than companies generally'. Another indication is that when William Horner's estate came up for sale in January 1829, the list of items to be auctioned off included not only his dwelling house; 'very large, elegant, and commodious shop' but also, in a bold typeface, 'ONE SHARE in the NORTH SHIELDS GASWORKS'. At the time, there were only 74 gas streetlights in North Shields.

By then, the North Shields Gas Company was operating in a town with a new system of local government and a growing sense of civic pride. Until 1828, the public affairs of the town had been managed by the traditional 'parish vestry', commonly referred to as the Four and Twenty because it was made up of 24 prominent, unelected local individuals. However, this form of local government proved increasingly inadequate as the town developed and it was abandoned during the first few years of the North Shields Gas Company's existence. An Improvement Act, passed in 1828, replaced the Four and Twenty with an appointed 92-strong Board of Commissioners. They were charged with responsibility for 'paving, lighting, watching, cleansing, regulating, and improving the town of North Shields' and authorised to level charges on the local population to pay for those services.[26] The gas company then had no other option but to enter into a contract with the Commissioners, which meant that its performance was monitored more closely than it had been in the past.

The officials and shareholders of the gas company, though making a healthy profit, did not consider that they were not in an entirely secure position. Before pre-payment meters came into common use in the latter half of the nineteenth century, ensuring that their customers did not use more gas than they had contracted to buy was a problem for all gas companies. That is why, in a public newspaper notice in 1831, the North Shields Gas Company, drew attention to the fact that 'the rules of the Company having of late been much infringed, the Committee request that consumers be punctual to the hours agreed'. That was not the only kind of

---

26 Shortly afterwards, in a further boost to civic pride in the town, North Shields became the major part of one of the new parliamentary constituencies established by the 1832 Reform Act.

infringement which concerned the company as an 1832 local court trial revealed. It involved a case brought by the company against a local grocer. To understand the significance of the company's action, it must be remembered that, in that period, a victim of crime had to bear some of the cost of apprehending a criminal and bringing him or her to trial. In court, the company was able to establish that in November 1829, the accused had paid a local brazier to install an unauthorised gas burner in his cellar. The gas company explained that it was unaware of the additional burner and so he was not charged for it. It was discovered only by chance when the manager of the gasworks visited the premises a considerable time later. Although common sense indicated that the burner had only been installed to be used, because the company could not provide incontrovertible evidence that it had been used to burn the company's gas, the case against the grocer was dismissed.

The lease on the gasworks site was renewed in 1832 for a further 21 years and the company stock 'thrown open' in 1837, which increased the number of shares to 885, valued at £11 each. Such a sum may seem trivial today but in terms of average earnings, £11 then was the equivalent of over £8,000 in 2022. The annual cost of having *the use of* a single time-limited bat-wing burner in 1820 was £1.11s. 6d. In 1831 it was £1.8s.0d although, by 1844, after continuing criticism, lower at £1.3s.0d. Using the same inflation index of average earnings, the equivalent 2022 cost of having a gas burner at those three dates would be £1,250, £1,330, and £909. With average *annual* earnings at those dates only about £33, the installation of gas fixtures was beyond the means of most ordinary workers. There were also frequent complaints about the cost of the coal gas itself. For example, in a letter to a local newspaper in August 1833, a gas consumer complained that 'our liberal gas proprietors' had gulled [tricked] consumers into believing that they were getting a better deal from the company when they reduced their prices in 1831. The reality, it was claimed, was that the actual gas supply had been reduced so much, at the same time, that the 'real' price of gas had gone up! He wrote:

> Tonight, now nine o'clock, I am writing this with a bat-wing [burner] at full cock, and I really have not so much gas as a common jet will consume. If the present Company cannot give the consumers a sufficient supply, the sooner we have another company the better. There is no lack of capital, and I think you might find sufficient consumers to subscribe the capital wanted in a week (A Subscriber, *Northumberland Advertiser*, 20 August 1833).

John Robinson, the then superintendent of the company was quick to reply. He insisted that 'there is as great a supply now as ever there has been' and added that 'if you give me your name and where you use the gas – I will try to remedy it, as the fault may be within your own premises.'

To the stated disapproval of the newspaper's editor, the complainant declined to give his or her name and address but replied in such terms that it was clear that he or she was determined to raise the stakes. The person using the pseudonym 'A Subscriber' was plainly not just a dissatisfied customer but someone trying to discredit the gas company in the hope that another company would emerge to compete with it.

> Is he not aware that the very liberal managers have twice reduced the size of the burners, which at least makes a difference of 30 per cent in consumption in favour of the company? If he is not aware of this, I am, as well as the managers. I am also desired to give my name, that the Superintendent may call upon me. In reply to that I would say, call upon every consumer, beginning at the low end of North Shields up to Milburn Place, and ask them if they have a sufficiency of gas, *or* if they have it at a proper time. Messrs W.W. and H.C.T. know to the contrary, and if they intend to make a 'cat's paw' of the Superintendent [i.e. cynically use him to cover their own guilt], I will let them know more than perhaps they wish. The public require more gas, and at least two hours earlier; if I am wrong, I am willing to be set right by the public or 20 respectable consumers – not being shareholders (A Subscriber, *Northumberland Advertiser*, 3 September 1833).

The complaints that followed were of such a nature that it is difficult to draw any conclusion other than that they were part of a concerted campaign to undermine the North Shields Gas Company. It is not possible to determine if the complaints were warranted. What is plain is that the campaign against the company became nasty. At the beginning of 1834, handbills, allegedly written by the superintendent of the gas company, were distributed throughout the town. They were couched in language designed to discredit both him and the gas company. Several critical letters were then sent to the *Northumberland Advertiser* on the assumption that he really was the author of the handbills. The only one of the letters printed in the newspaper was accompanied by a statement from the editor, commiserating with the superintendent 'for the liberty taken with his name'. The following week, the editor added this.

> A second handbill, addressed to us, made its appearance last week, bearing the same signature of 'John Robinson' as the one we noticed in our last.

They are too contemptible for us to waste a moment's consideration upon, nor will we abuse the time, or patience of our readers by offering a single comment. We can but pity the silly man who is thus led, either by his own temper or the cunning of another (now pretty well known), to do that of which he may repent hereafter at his leisure (*Northumberland Advertiser*, 14 January 1834).

Criticisms of the gas company did not end at that point. In 1839, someone describing himself as 'An Old Inhabitant' wrote as follows to the *Port of Tyne Pilot*.[27]

In your paper of the 4th you observe that when it was first proposed to introduce gas into North Shields it was strongly objected to by some old inhabitants in the Low Town. ... You ask, who now carries a lantern! ... The inhabitants never stood more in need of lanterns than they did for several nights after the gas was put out in the streets this spring for the summer season, which nights proved to be much darker than any we had during the winter, and I assure you many made use of lanterns. Now Sir, I for one wish you, through your useful paper, to make the inquiry why the good people in Shields were left so soon in the darkness this spring, and why so many of the streets are so imperfectly lighted; if the inhabitants are to be taxed for this gas why are they deprived of it when most wanted! (*Port of Tyne Pilot*, 11 May 1839).

In this instance, the newspaper editor did not adopt a neutral stance but lent support to the campaign for an improvement in the town's streetlighting.

We have had many complaints besides that of our present correspondent, of the pitchy, palpable darkness which enveloped our streets during the last week – when not a single light was to be seen, except as we must believe, this ancient illumination of the lanterns. Divers odd accidents happened we know. ... one gentleman of our acquaintance had his legs very near carried away by a sort of chain shot, formed by two sailors carrying a sea chest between them. It is no uncommon matter for the captains of foreign vessels to complain that the inconvenience of coming ashore in the dark and filth, from landing places and quays, is so great as to induce them not to leave

---

27 Another of many newspapers on Tyneside which had what has been described as a 'print-rich culture'.

their vessels.[28] As to the taxes of which your correspondent complains, we doubt they are, however heavily felt by many, totally inadequate to effect the purposes required; and we believe the utmost economy and vigilance is exercised by the Commissioners. Believing this, however, we think that in justice to themselves, as well as to satisfy those who furnish the funds, a statement of the accounts should regularly be made public. The fact that South Shields is in regard to light, so much better managed than North, has made many of the inhabitants of the latter place sore on this subject. We are convinced if it were proved that with economy the funds were inefficient, the people of North Shields would spontaneously increase the rate. Some liberal commissioner should propose to make the accounts public; and if no one else does it, we ourselves promise to have the proposition made to the commissioners, and get the matter put to the vote (*Port of Tyne Pilot*, 11 May 1839).

In view of the mounting criticism, it may not be a coincidence that the day before this editorial appeared, a new superintendent of the gas company was appointed. Ralph Mather, who had moved from the Newcastle Gas Light Works seems to have been held in high regard by those who had worked with him, and for him. It was reported in the local press that the workmen at Newcastle had marked his leaving by clubbing together to buy him 'a piece of plate as a testimonial of their personal esteem, high admiration of his talents, and respect for his general character.' (*Port of Tyne Pilot*, 11 May 1839).

In addition to vociferous criticism of what the gas company was offering the people of North Shields, the new superintendent soon had to confront the possibility of a local competitor. It came not from another coal gas company but from Wallsend Colliery. A proposal was mooted for it to supply gas to North Shields and Newcastle, 'at a cheaper rate and purer quality' by drawing on a huge supply of underground 'natural' gas from the mine, along pipes to 'artificial receptacles at each terminus'. The idea was not new, but the proponents of the scheme maintained that it was now practicable because the gas pipes could be laid alongside the new railway line between Newcastle and North Shields, much more easily and less expensively than would have been the case before. The claimed advantages of the scheme were that 'the price of gas will probably be lowered one-half, the supply will be more ample, and ... in quality will be very much superior

---

28 Readers need to know that during this period North Shields was without a proper sewage system and refuse was allowed to build up on the streets. (Lawrence, 2016, pp.228-238).

1856 map of North Shields to illustrate the inadequacy of the c.150 gas streetlamps installed at the time.
Source: Heritage Cartography Victorian Town Map Series based on the Ordnance Survey of 1856, copyright
and courtesy of Peter J. Adams (www.ancestralmaps.com).

to that now supplied' (*Port of Tyne Pilot*, 25 July 1840). Whilst in the end nothing came of the proposed scheme, the potential threat from it further weakened the bargaining position of the North Shields Gas Company.

It had responded to earlier criticism by increasing the number of streetlights to 134 by 1844, but that was not nearly enough to satisfy the local population. Just a glance at the town's mid-nineteenth century street map makes it obvious that, however the gas lights were distributed, large areas of the town would still be in total or near total darkness.

The town's Commissioners negotiated with the gas company to try to secure an improvement in the terms and conditions of their contract, to make it comparable to those in other local towns. In time, however, it became clear that the differences between the directors of the North Shields Gas Company and the Commissioners were irreconcilable. Deadlock was reached, and the town plunged back into darkness as the winter of 1843 approached. The Commissioners issued an ultimatum in September 1843: 'At present, the town is without lights [and] unless the terms are agreed to, a new gas company will be the result' (*Newcastle Journal*, 9 September 1843). In a defiant response, the company raised more capital and spread its shareholder base by dividing its stock into 1,300 shares at the relatively modest price of five shillings each (equivalent to £188 in 2022). It rationed them to lots of no more than ten shares to any individual gas consumer. At the same time, the company reduced the price of its gas. Despite these moves, the company could not stop the tide of public opinion running against it. From then on, things moved quickly. At a public meeting of gas consumers in October 1843, the stance of the Commissioners was endorsed. A decision was taken to form a new *private* company called, confusingly, the Borough of Tynemouth Gas Company, and 1,595 shares sold to gas consumers, and a further 433 to non-consumers. It was also determined at that crucial public meeting that, when the new company began to produce gas, the price would be fixed at a level to compete with the reduced price then being charged by the existing North Shields Gas Company.

The Borough of Tynemouth Gas Company

The choice of name for the new company requires a word of explanation. North Shields, despite its size and significance, and the fact that it was the powerhouse of the local economy, was located within a local government unit called the Borough of Tynemouth. In time, the same name, Tynemouth, was used for several other administrative units, with differing boundaries. However, despite the official sounding name of the new company, and the active role of the Commissioners in its establishment, it was not a municipal undertaking. It was as much a private company as the original North Shields Gas Company. However, the name did have the advantage of signifying that although the new company was located in, and run from, North Shields, it envisaged supplying gas to the whole of the Borough of Tynemouth. At this stage, the areas beyond the town of North Shields were predominantly agricultural or moorland, containing only a few small villages but, later in the nineteenth and twentieth centuries, they developed rapidly into residential suburbs of North Shields.

But, to return to the public concern that led to the formation of the new company, what is clear is that there was an inherent conflict between the public body charged with lighting the streets on the one hand, and the private company (or companies) in a position to provide that service on the other. The public interest was to have the streets lit as extensively and brightly for as long as possible, for the least possible cost. The primary concern of the private company was to make as much money as possible for its shareholders, consistent with retaining its contract with the public body.

At the time, the prevailing assumption was that the provision of services such as gas lighting should be left to the private sector. That view was based on Adam

Smith's notion that through the 'invisible hand' of market forces the pursuit of self-interest would lead to the common good. However, market competition depended on customers being able to choose between suppliers and in the case of the supply of gas in North Shields, there had been a monopoly. Elsewhere, some public bodies chose to set up municipal undertakings to ensure that the public interest was protected: a type of initiative that came to be known as 'gas and water socialism'. In North Shields, the approach was different. The town's Commissioners, in effect, actively contrived to introduce private competition into the local gas market.

A week after the public meeting, tenders were invited to supply the new company with gas mains and other pipework. By December, the company was inviting tenders for a 'barrel and other small drains' at its new premises, also at the Low Lights, just a short distance from the premises of the North Shields Gas Company. In the same month, the new company advertised for 'a professional person' to take charge of its gasworks. 'He must be competent to superintend the erection of the works, and the most approved plan of manufacturing gas, the laying of pipes, and conducting an establishment for the lighting of the town.' Other tenders were invited for retorts, and for 7-inch, 5-inch, 4-inch and 2-inch piping. The following year, a tender went out for a gasholder to be built to a depth of 20 feet and:

> … constructed in such manner as to admit hereafter, of a lower and outer part of equal depth and 53 feet 6 inches diameter, on the telescopic principle. The gasholder to be suspended from, and guided by, cast iron columns, at three equidistant points, and secured to the stonework of the tank in the usual manner (*Newcastle Journal*, 13 April 1844).

A flurry of other tenders went out in June 1844 for ½-inch, ¾-inch and 1-inch 'roundway cocks' with brass ferrules; ½-inch, ¾-inch and 1-inch lead piping; and fire bricks and clay. Not everything went entirely smoothly for the new company. In October 1844, the Commissioners expressed concern at the way in which it was laying its gas pipes and wrote to it (and also the original gas company and the town's private water company) 'requesting' them 'to avoid whatever was likely to deteriorate the quality of the water supplied to the inhabitants' (*Newcastle Courant*, 4 October 1844). Nevertheless, things were sufficiently advanced for the company, in the same month, to offer its output of coke, tar and ammoniacal liquor for sale.

By August 1845, the new company had agreed terms with the town's Commissioners, although the public would have been disappointed that initially

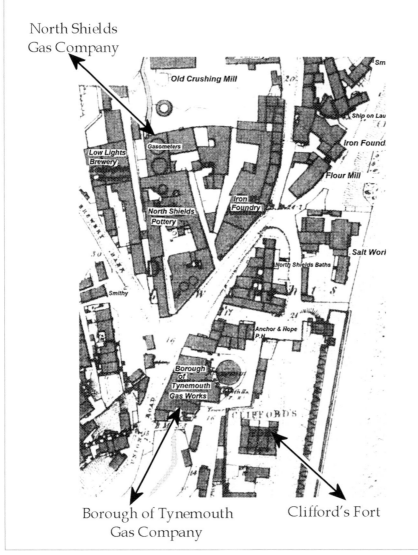

Locations of the North Shields and Borough of Tynemouth Gas Companies in the Low Lights area in 1861

The locations of gasworks of the North Shields Gas Company and Borough of Tynemouth Gas Company in the Low Lights area of North Shields, based on an 1861 map, courtesy of Michael Coates. The location of Clifford's Fort is also shown to help identify the two locations.

only ten additional streetlamps were planned. By December, at the first annual general meeting (AGM) of the new company, a dividend of three per cent was declared, much less than had been received at the same stage 20 years earlier by the shareholders of the original gas company.

Merger

Within a few years, the board of the original gas company realised that its days were numbered. On 6 May 1848, it agreed to merge with the Borough of Tynemouth Gas Company.[29] So the period of competition was short-lived. Monopoly was once again the order of the day. This was precisely what had been predicted by the government commission the year before. The assumptions of competitive capitalism were not applicable in the gas industry. Rival gas companies in the same area did not benefit consumers. Either one company forced the other out of business or they merged. Either way, a monopoly was restored.

What must have been disappointing to the residents of North Shields was that, even after three years, the new company had installed only 60 more streetlights and the 194 in total did not provide anything like blanket coverage for a town which had been developing rapidly in the meanwhile. The streets were still illuminated only between September and April each year and even then, as a wit put it in a letter to the editor of a local newspaper in 1849, 'we are as much indebted to the moon as the light we enjoy from the gas providers' (*Newcastle Journal*, 24 November 1849).

However, the big issue in North Shields in 1849 was not streetlighting. It was that a Charter of Incorporation had been granted to the Borough of Tynemouth on 6 August. This was regarded as a great local achievement and shops and businesses were closed to celebrate the event. With the town's incorporation, the days of the Improvement Commissioners was over. The new Borough Council was made up of a mayor, six alderman and eighteen elected councillors representing three wards. The first election was held on 1 November 1849, although it needs to be emphasised that the then electorate consisted only of those who had lived in the Borough for at least three years and were sufficiently well-off to contribute to the poor rate. The newly elected councillors took over the building on the north side of Saville Street, between Howard and Norfolk Streets, which had been designed by the architect John Dobson for the Improvement Commissioners in 1845. Just days after the election, 'A Subscriber' picked up his or her pen again and wrote to the *Newcastle Journal* expressing the hope that now that 'North Shields is possessed of a Corporation *and* Gasworks, would it be too premature to ask will the inhabitants have the pleasure of seeing their borough properly lighted!'[30]

---

29 Unfortunately, newspaper reporters, and other people, sometimes used the shorthand term *North Shields Gas Company* for one or other or both of the original companies as well as the amalgamated company.

30 The term Corporation was often used as an alternative to Council.

The fact that the new company was selling gas at a significantly lower price than the original company did not stop people defrauding it in the same way they had done its predecessor. A virtually identical case to that brought against a grocer in 1831 was brought against another shopkeeper, in 1851. It was regarded as a test case and for that reason widely reported nationally. The prosecution brought against the shopkeeper, like the earlier case, failed on a legal technicality. On this occasion, there was no doubt that gas had been used without the knowledge of the company. The shopkeeper had been caught in the act and had been using the company's gas fraudulently for four years. The case against him collapsed because he had been accused of a *felony* and whilst he had obviously been less than honest, the magistrates were not prepared to brand him a felon, an elastic legal term open to different interpretations. Today, there seems little doubt that the shopkeeper would have been found guilty of theft. Here are the details of the case for the reader to judge!

NOVEL APPLICATION OF GUTTA PERCHA[31]

A novel charge of felony was heard before the Tynemouth Borough Bench on Wednesday – a case of considerable importance to gas companies. The Borough of Tynemouth Gas Company supply their customers with gas by meters, the company furnishing the meters and the piping from the street leading thereto; the consumer the pipe to the burner. Of course, the company only receives payment for that quantity of gas consumed, as indicated by the meter. A person of the name of … … ., a small shopkeeper, residing in the low town, but having failed in business, the employees of the gas company went on Monday to fetch away a meter, and cut off the supply. They removed that instrument, and broke off the piping within the shop, which extinguished a light there, but to their astonishment they observed a light still continuing to burn in the back premises. They looked about them, and at last discovered that the gas burnt at that light was conveyed by a gutta percha tube [a natural latex used for many things at the time] from the company's pipe to which it was attached. Upon further search it was found that an upper room could be lighted by the same means, and that by an ingenious contrivance gas could be turned from the meter, and the light in the front shop be furnished by the gas abstracted from the company's pipe. The men reported to the directors, and that body determined to

---

31 Gutta-percha is a purified, coagulated latex obtained from both wild and cultivated trees in Malaysia and Indonesia. It is collected in a similar way to rubber, although it flows less freely. It has been used for a variety of purposes including as a filling for teeth.

institute a charge of felony against … … ., as they must have been cheated to a considerable extent by the ingenious device. He was accordingly given into custody, but on Wednesday, after hearing the case, and considerable legal discussion between the gentlemen who appeared for the prosecution, and the Magistrate's Clerk, the Bench came to the conclusion that the charge did not amount to felony and dismissed it (*Worcester Journal*, 27 November 1851).

It seems the magistrates, for some reason, did not want to label the shopkeeper a felon even though he had been caught systematically stealing gas from the gas company. Inevitably, one wonders if that was because one or more of the magistrates, or others they knew, were doing the same! A Londoner charged with 'stealing gas from the Commercial Gas Company, by means of a surreptitious pipe' in 1855 was not so fortunate. He was sentenced to a year's imprisonment (*Newcastle Chronicle*, 5 October 1855).

The Borough of Tynemouth Gas Company chose to expand its operations and open another site between Hudson and Northumberland Streets in 1852, when it invited tenders for the excavation and building of a water tank, 62 feet in diameter, to a depth of 21 feet, ready for the erection of another gasholder. Also newsworthy in 1852 was a strike by some local gas workers:

> … the result of which was that the public lamps in various parts of the town bobbed and blinked and left darkness visible. The villagers of Tynemouth complained that their lamps are not lighted in time enough; the inhabitants of the higher parts of North Shields that they are put out too soon (*North & South Shields Gazette*, 24 September 1852).

It was not the most auspicious time for the arrival of a new superintendent of the gas company. He was Finlay Mitchell, a Scotsman who came to North Shields about 1853. He lived with his wife and five children in Northumberland Street, indicating that the house provided for the manager was, again, on site or very close to it.

In August 1854, the Borough of Tynemouth Gas Company, now with a monopoly, raised the price of gas by 20 per cent. The town's Watch Committee resolved not to accept the increase and prepared (but did not release) an announcement to explain why the streetlights would not be lit as usual on 1 September. Before it was released, the Mayor called a special meeting of the Council. During it, a spokesman for the Watch Committee (not the chairman who

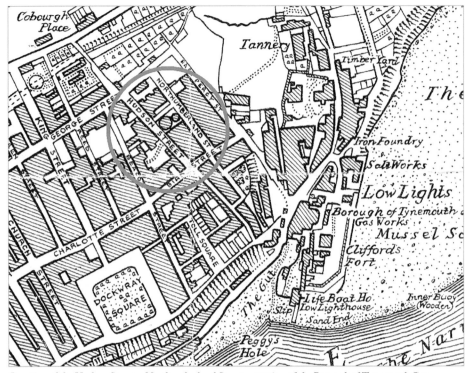

Location of the Hudson Street – Northumberland Street extension of the Borough of Tynemouth Gas Company, from the North Shields map in the Heritage Cartography Victorian Town Map Series based on the Ordnance Survey of 1856, copyright and courtesy of Peter J. Adams (www.ancestralmaps.com).

was a shareholder in the gas company) reminded the Council that the Borough of Tynemouth Gas Company had been formed to break up the monopoly which the North Shields Gas Company had enjoyed. He pointed out how this aim had been compromised by the merger of the companies. It had involved the new company buying the plant, pipe work and equipment of the old company although much of it was neither needed nor used. That, he asserted, was why the town's inhabitants were being charged more for gas than in other towns. He concluded that, as the shareholders of the gas company had not suffered because of their business blunder (having received a dividend of 5 per cent and a bonus of 20 per cent the previous year) they could not 'in conscience' propose to charge their customers more than their counterparts elsewhere. His specific proposal was that the Council should offer to pay only the average of the gas prices charged in neighbouring towns. However, with four of the seven people on the committee also being shareholders of the gas company, there was only a majority for the amendment that an increase of seven per cent for streetlighting should be accepted. The fact that most of those voting for the amendment were company shareholders, did not go unnoticed by the local newspaper.

> The feeling meanwhile continues strong against the Gas Company, and the public are all the less satisfied with the advance that it has been assented to by a majority made up of shareholders (*Newcastle Journal*, 26 August 1854).

It was announced a few months later that what was described as the Old Gasworks would be leased to the adjacent pottery firm of John Carr for a term of 21 years. We shall never know how much difference relinquishing the site made to the company's finances, but, from that point on, concessions were made by the merged company. For example, in 1855, it agreed to light the streetlamps for an additional 15 days each year. In 1856, that concession was extended, and the streets lit for nine rather than eight months, along with a price reduction of about 10 per cent, 'with the sincere desire of meeting the wishes of the Council in this respect.'

A further reduction of 10 per cent followed in April 1857. Then, in July, the Council announced that it had entered into a three-year agreement with the company for streetlighting. Given that the price of the company's coke was also reduced in 1857, it would seem the company was doing relatively well at this point – and sufficiently so to ask for and be given permission by the Council to increase the size of its site by 'inclosing a portion of the ground adjoining the east end of the company's works at the Low Lights'. Despite the price reductions, the company declared an 8 per cent dividend for shareholders in 1857, followed in the next two years by dividends of 7.5 per cent.

The 1859 AGM of the Borough of Tynemouth Gas Company was presided over by its retiring chairman William Wingrave, the very same William Wingrave who was the first signatory of the deeds of the original North Shields Gas Company. Given his key role in both companies, it is not surprising that he said that he 'rejoiced' that the new company was doing so well! He explained that it was now 40 years since, along with others, he had set up the original North Shields Gas Company and that the capitalisation of the new company was now four times that of the original and that the consumption of gas was still growing (*Newcastle Daily Chronicle*, 1 April 1859).[32]

The retiring chairman may have been happy with the company's financial performance but not all its customers were happy with the service it provided. For example, someone from the western end of the town in September 1859 complained that 'for the last three weeks and especially on Saturday nights, we

---

32 Although considerable strides had been made in lighting the streets with coal gas over the previous 30 years, gas was still not universally accepted as the best form of illumination. Lighthouses, for example, were still lit with oil rather than gas. In 1858, a proposal was made to the Admiralty and Board of Trade to switch to gas. Those bodies, in turn, referred the proposal to Trinity House. The Brethren, however, declined to grant permission for a test of the proposal, even at the proposer's own expense.

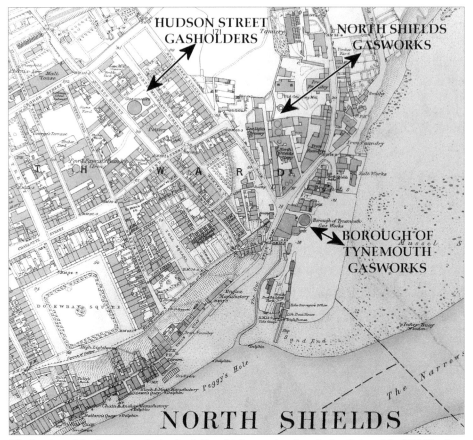

The locations of the three gasworks sites in the Low Lights area based on the 1st edition of the 1861 North Shields and Tynemouth Ordnance Survey map, Copyright and courtesy of the Northumberland County Archives at Woodhorn. For security reasons, Clifford's Fort and other military buildings were not displayed on the map.

have been in a state of comparative darkness, having to light up with candles, paraffin lamps etc, causing very great annoyance in the transaction of business. Several complaints have been made at the company's office, yet we are not a whit better for it' (*Shields Daily Gazette*, 26 September 1859). Those who were unhappy with the gas company's performance may have subsequently been encouraged by the national legislation introduced in 1860, to standardise the units in which coal gas was sold. Following its adoption (in the case of the Borough of Tynemouth, in February 1860), gas was sold only by the cubic foot, and local councils were required to employ inspectors (not related to the supplying gas companies) to ensure that gas meters were accurate.

Concern that the gas company's monopoly position enabled it to be complacent came to a head again in January 1863. The Town Council discussed streetlighting and passed a motion that the Town Clerk should write to the gas company to complain about the quality and price of the gas. One alderman expressed concern about its quality and maintained that this was an issue acknowledged even by many of the gas company's shareholders. Another councillor asserted that the streetlights were 'really most disgraceful'. He claimed that 'when they went to other towns they could see the gas lights in the streets, but in the Borough of Tynemouth half of them were obscured. The burners were extremely small, while the glass was so dirty that the gas could not shine through with any degree of brilliance'. The final complaint was about the price of the allegedly poor-quality gas. In Newcastle, it was 25 per cent cheaper than in North Shields (*Shields Daily Gazette*, 29 January 1863).

Despite such complaints, the consumption of gas continued to increase and required the construction of another gasholder. At the same time, the company decided to sell off some land at the original gasworks site. In March 1864, it offered for sale 'the whole of the materials composing several dwelling houses on the Brewery Bank, North Shields. The purchaser to take down and remove the same off the ground before the 4th April'. The company had already agreed to construct the new 82 feet in diameter gasholder, and so all that was necessary at the AGM was to seek confirmation on how the cost of it would be met. What the shareholders agreed was that the funds would be obtained by increasing the company's share capital by one-third (*Shields Daily Gazette*, 16 March 1864). The gasholder was constructed in due course by a specialist Birmingham firm.[33] The following year, one of the company's original gasholders was offered for sale along with the 'metal columns, chains, balance weights and pulley system', with the demanding proviso that the purchaser 'take down and remove the whole within one month from the time of the acceptance of the offer' (*The Shields Daily News*, 5 August 1865).

The 'new' Borough of Tynemouth Gas Company

At the company's AGM in March 1866, the annual report was largely upbeat. The company was now operating from the prestigious premises of 97 Bedford Street. The new gasholder was producing cost-savings; there had been a marked increase in the consumption of gas and the company planned to lay a larger gas

---

33 Whilst the new gasholder was being painted, a North Shields man, George Axford, fell and broke a leg in two places. The local newspaper, in reporting the incident, deplored the fact that, after having been seen by a local doctor who ordered him to be taken to a Newcastle hospital, the injured man had to remain in an open cart for three hours whilst being taken there. 'Surely if any argument is needed for the long talked of hospital at Shields, the above, amongst similar cases, is sufficient (*The Shields Daily News*, 21 October 1864). However, the foundation stone for Tynemouth Jubilee Infirmary was not laid until 1891 and was the result of a voluntary initiative.

main to Tynemouth so that it could in turn extend its pipes further along the coast to Cullercoats, Whitley and Monkseaton, a distance of about four miles.[34] However, it became evident that there was no room for complacency after the 1866 amalgamation of the Willington Gas Company and the Walker and St Anthony Gas Light Company, which supplied the area that lay to the west of North Shields. Initially, North Shields had been limited to a narrow stretch of land alongside the river, and the steep bankside rising from it, at the south-eastern tip of Northumberland. From the 1760s, there had been a rapid development on the 'bank top', the land on the plateau above the original town. Expansion thereafter was possible northwards, along the coast towards Whitley; north and north-west in the direction of the township of Preston, or westwards in the direction of the township of Chirton. By 1865, there had been little development to the west of the town although it was obvious that it would happen in time. That probably explains why the combined Willington Quay and Walker Company applied to Parliament for authority to sell its gas beyond its existing area into 'the township of Chirton, in the Parish of Tynemouth'. Although express permission was needed to do that, there was ample precedent. In fact, to try to mitigate the impact of local monopolies, the legislation covering gas companies did, in principle, allow gas supply areas to overlap, or for a second undertaking to be established within the area of an existing gas company.

The Tynemouth company opposed the proposal by inviting the Court of Referees in the House of Commons, to recognize that it enjoyed *locus standi* in the township of Chirton. In other words, the company argued that it was already the established supplier to that area and would be damaged if the new company should be allowed to encroach on its territory. Although the company's argument was dismissed, it was rescued from competition by Tynemouth Council who made

The Bedford Street offices of the Borough of Tynemouth Gas Company as they looked in 1912. Note that Bedford Street was cobbled and that the building had an elaborate cupola and roofline balustrade that have since been removed.

---

34 The town was known officially as Whitley until the 1940s but unofficially as Whitley Bay from at least the 1860s and, in 1899, the North-Eastern Railway Company informed the Whitley Urban District Council that it was changing the name of its station to Whitley Bay. The response of the Council was that the company could do what it wanted but that they would continue to call their town Whitley. In that respect, they were swimming against the proverbial tide as the double-barrelled name had been used extensively in local newspapers and elsewhere since the closing decades of the nineteenth century.

it clear that they would not pay what the new company proposed to charge for streetlighting. As a result, the new Willington Quay and St Anthony Company withdrew the reference to Chirton from its Bill. However, the threat from the new company was enough to stir the Tynemouth Gas Company into a major new phase in its development. Its first response was a formal legal one. During the Parliamentary deliberations, it had been noted that, legally, the Tynemouth company was a partnership i.e. collection of individuals and not a properly incorporated company enjoying full Parliamentary recognition. By November 1866, the Tynemouth company was at an advanced stage to remedy this weakness. It proposed to dissolve the existing company and reincorporate it, whilst at the same time establishing a new manufacturing base on undeveloped land at the western end of the town, adjacent to what had been (in terms of the supply of gas) the contested township of Chirton. The proposals were drawn up by specialist Parliamentary agents and a detailed, 12-paragraph Bill was subsequently introduced into Parliament, designed to give the company full legal support for anything which its directors and managers could conceivably want to do in the future, along with as much protection as possible for any conceivable contingency that might arise.[35]

Although the Tynemouth company already enjoyed an *effective* local monopoly, members of the Council were concerned that the scope of the Bill was so great that it would change it into a *state-sanctioned* monopoly. So, to safeguard the public interest, they insisted on several changes. If they were not accepted, the Council announced that it would formally oppose the gas company's Bill. The key stipulations were that the maximum price for the gas supplied should be 26 per cent less than that proposed; that there should be a scale of discounts from 10 per cent to 25 per cent depending on how much gas was consumed; that the gas company should 'provide, maintain, and light the public lamps' on the terms the Council decided, and that the quality of the gas should be about 16 per cent brighter than proposed in the Bill, equivalent to the light of 14 sperm candles instead of 12. These conditions presented the Council's Town Clerk with an obvious conflict of interest. He was one of the solicitors who had drawn up the gas company's Bill! As a result, the Council felt obliged to pay for the services of a separate firm of Parliamentary agents to safeguard the public interest (in addition to that of a technical gas expert).

---

35 The Parliamentary agents were Fearon (John Peter), Clabon (John Moxon) and Fearon (Francis). Fearon was a distinguished Parliamentary lawyer who, amongst other things, acted for the major railway companies at that time. Clabon was equally distinguished and, like Fearon, became solicitor to the Charity Commissioners. In addition, he was President of the Incorporated Law Society, and the first Editor of the Solicitors' Law Journal.

The meeting held between the company and Council members to try to reach a compromise, produced only deadlock. Further concerns were raised in Parliament by the Walker Gas Company (which argued that the Bill would give the Tynemouth company a monopoly position in relation to the township of Chirton); and the local private water company (which claimed that it had a *locus standi* interest in the issue because its water pipes might be affected), but both claims were dismissed. So, the only remaining opposition to the Bill came from the Council. Just before its third reading, concessions were made on both sides. The company agreed to the higher quality of gas demanded by the Council and some price reductions. In return, the Council agreed to pay for the lamps in the Low Town all year round, and at least half of the other streetlights for not less than nine months in the year. And so, on 2 April 1867, The Tynemouth Parish Gas Bill was read in the House of Commons for the third time – and passed. It received Royal Assent on 8 July 1867. That formality was very much welcomed by whoever wrote the column on local public companies for *The Shields Daily News*. This is how he or she explained the commercial significance of the Act to the newspaper's readers.

PUBLIC COMPANIES

The annual transfer of share in the public undertakings of this and other localities is announced to be held on Wednesday evening next, by Mr Jackson, at the Commercial Hotel in North Shields. The auction embraces a large amount of stock, amongst which are shares in Gas, Water, Railway, and other undertakings. As many of our readers may intend to be purchasers at the sale, it will be handy to have before them a resume of the dividends paid by, and a few notes concerning, the respective companies. ... In Gas Shares there are only those of the Borough of Tynemouth ... the shares in it are esteemed a first-class investment, and very few indeed ever reach the public market. A public undertaking, protected by an Act of Parliament, may be compared to Freehold Property, whereas a Company without one is regarded as a less sure affair. On these grounds, we, with pleasure, congratulate the Shareholders of The Borough of Tynemouth Gas Company on the Act of Parliament they are now obtaining. ... Everything augurs a brilliant future in store for this already favourite company (*The Shields Daily News*, 13 April 1867).

At the AGM, in March 1868, the report on the company's financial situation was again more than satisfactory but not all aspects of the business were doing

ANNO TRICESIMO & TRICESIMO PRIMO

VICTORIÆ REGINÆ.

****

Cap. cliii.

An Act for incorporating the *Tynemouth* Gas
Company, and defining the Limits of Supply of
Gas by them, and regulating their Capital; and
for other Purposes.   [25th *July* 1867.]

WHEREAS "the *North Shields* Gas Company" and "the
Borough of *Tynemouth* Gas Company" were amalgamated
in the Year One thousand eight hundred and forty-eight,
and formed a new Company for supplying the Borough of *Tynemouth*
and Places adjacent thereto with Gas, under the Name of "the
Borough of *Tynemouth* Gas Company," which Company was provi-
sionally registered under the Provisions of the Act Seventh and
Eighth *Victoria*, Chapter One hundred and ten, and a Deed of Settle-
ment of the said Company was made and executed on the Twenty-
ninth Day of *March* One thousand eight hundred and forty-nine, and
the said Company was completely registered under the Provisions of
the said Act on the Twenty-fourth Day of *December* in the same
Year: And whereas on the Twentieth Day of *May* One thousand
eight hundred and sixty-three the said Company was registered under
"The Joint Stock Companies Act, 1862:" And whereas the Capital
of the said Company at its Formation was Fourteen thousand five
hundred and seventy Pounds, divided into Two thousand nine hundred and fourteen original Shares of Five Pounds each, and by the
[*Local.*]   27 R   Deed

*Front cover of 1867 Tynemouth Gas Company Act
(dated 25 July 1867).*

well. Sales of gas were up but the demand for the other derivatives of the manufacturing process were down. That was an obvious problem for the company because as the demand for gas increased so too did the surplus of the derivatives. In answer to a question at the AGM, the chairman admitted, 'We have difficulty in getting any person to buy it [coke] … we have been obliged to sell it at almost any price.' Much the same situation was reported in March 1869. The sale of gas had continued to increase but the mild winter had reduced the demand for coke still further. The company still had a 'very large stock in hand … although the price has been reduced.' Similarly, revenue from tar had dropped, not least from 'the great fall in its market value'. That would suggest that the occasional donations of coke to worthy causes, and of tar to repair the playground at Jubilee School, were not as generous as some people might have imagined. However, overall, the company was doing well and continued to enhance its gasworks. A new retort house was built to hold four beds with seven retorts and two beds with 14 retorts. Gas mains were extended to the township of Chirton, and new 12-inch pipes laid to Tynemouth, along with additional service pipes to new public and private customers. It was also planned to do much more in that respect, to meet the expected demand from the new streets that were being laid out and developed in Tynemouth, Cullercoats and Whitley. The company's ambition was to supply customers from Percy Main, through North Shields, Tynemouth and Cullercoats, as far as 'the convalescent home at Whitley'. As part of that plan, tenders were invited in 1870 'for the formation of a road from Tynemouth to Cullercoats, and for the laying of a 7-inch gas main along the same' (*The Shields Daily News*, 17 May 1870). By the 1871 AGM, the company were able to report that the work had progressed further and that mains had now been laid in all the new streets in Tynemouth, Cullercoats and Whitley.

At that point, the company anticipated that the existing works could cope with the growing demand for gas for another two years but, in anticipation of the need for a much greater capacity in the years beyond that, it had already purchased a tract of land from George Otto Trevelyan, on the then western edge of the town, between Waterville Road and what was then known as Meadow Well Lane.[36]

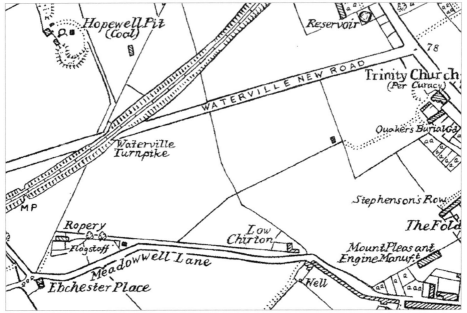

A section of the Ordnance Survey map showing the site of the proposed Minton Lane gasworks, from the Heritage Cartography Victorian Town Map Series based on the Ordnance Survey of 1856, Copyright and courtesy of Peter J. Adams (www.ancestralmaps.com). Note that although there are references to Minton Lane as early as the 1830s, on this map and others up until the 1930s, it is still known as Meadow Well Lane. Note too that Howdon Road had not yet been constructed.

---

36 Trevelyan, or to give him his full title, Sir George Otto Trevelyan, 2nd Baronet, OM, PC, FBA (1838-1928) was the Liberal MP for the constituency of Tynemouth and North Shields between 1865-1868. He had a ministerial career lasting almost 30 years and was also admired as a historian, writing several books on a variety of topics.

Chapter 5

The New Gasworks at Minton Lane (Phase 1)

AT THE Borough of Tynemouth Gas Company's AGM on 24 March 1869, a resolution was adopted to build the new gasworks at the western end of the town at the earliest opportunity. A group of directors then visited recently built gasworks in the south of England and held talks with their managers. They returned with a clear recommendation that they should enlist the services of George Livesey, of the South Metropolitan Gas Company, to design their new works.[37] He was no ordinary engineer. He had been promoted to the post of General Manager at the South Metropolitan Gas Company at the age of 23 and was its chief engineer at 28. Shortly after taking on the responsibility for designing and building the new gasworks for the Tynemouth Gas Company, he became President of the British Association of Gas Engineers. He went on to be knighted. In his memory, the gas industry established the Livesey Chair (i.e. a professorship) at the University of Leeds in what was then the Department of Coal Gas and Fuel Industries.

At the monthly meeting of the company's directors on 6 May 1869, the following letter from Livesey was read into the minutes.

> South Metropolitan Gasworks
> 589 Old Kent Road
> London
> 29 April 1869
>
> Dear Sir
> In response to your conversation with me this day about your proposed New Works at North Shields I have to say that I shall be glad to undertake to prepare drawings and specifications and design the works for your Company for 2½ per cent of the cost but, should it amount to upwards of £20,000, I would be content with a lump sum of £500.

---

37 George Livesey was the son of Thomas Livesey, the Secretary to the South Metropolitan Gas Company from 1839 to 1871, and the older brother of Frank Livesey.

I think from what Mr Williamson [the company chairman] told me this morning that it will be necessary to get a portion at least of the New Works ready for use before the winter of 1870 and if the work is set about at once I consider there will be no difficulty in executing in that time.

As I presume the greater part of the work will be done by Contract it would be necessary in addition to occasional inspection by myself (if the Directors entrust it to me) to have a competent man constantly on the spot to see that my plans are properly carried out and for this purpose I would suggest that my brother who has been brought up as a railway engineer and has had considerable experience should be engaged at a salary at the rate of £200 a year while the work is being done. I think that an arrangement of that sort would be found to work well.

Should the work be placed in my hands I am prepared to begin at once and it will be my endeavour for the sake of my own reputation as well as to do the best I can for you to make the Works as complete and perfect as possible with the least expenditure of capital.

I am Dear Sir, yours truly

George Livesey

(Borough of Tynemouth Gas Company, Directors' Minutes, 6 May 1869)

Livesey's terms were accepted, including his suggestion that his younger brother Frank should oversee the day-to-day construction of the new gasworks. Why the Borough of Tynemouth Gas Company was keen to employ the pre-eminent gas engineer of the period to design a 'state-of-the-art' gasworks and invest what was at the time a huge sum of money, needs explanation. Using the *economic cost* indicator recommended by the Economic History Association, £20,000 in 1870 is equivalent to about £37 million in 2022. The key point is that, though still a relatively small town, North Shields was expanding rapidly. After centuries of being held back by the bullying tactics of its much bigger neighbour, Newcastle upon Tyne, the local economy was booming. Particularly because of this unusual history, North Shields' business and civic leaders had, in addition to their self-interest, an unusually strong local identity, with an evident desire to put *their* North Shields on the proverbial map. When it came to the design of public buildings, and to churches, functionality was not enough. The structures were often larger and more impressive than necessary because they were not just utilitarian buildings but statements about the people behind them. It was thinking in this vein which lay behind the directors of the Borough of Tynemouth Gas Company commissioning such a splendid new gasworks. They were proud of their company's success. Its shareholders regularly received high dividends. Its orbit was extending daily. What it lacked was a modern gasworks which could be recognized as a visual statement that the company meant business and was in it for the long run. Livesey's design meant that its new gasworks was not only as technically advanced as possible at the time but was built with capacity to spare and scope to expand. It had been designed and built by the best to be the best.

The association of the Livesey brothers with the company was further strengthened in 1870 after Mr Mitchell, the manager of the existing gasworks gave notice of his intention to resign (to set up his own business). He had been with the company for 18 years. He was replaced by the 25-year-old Frank Livesey, a King's College, London University graduate, at a time when very few people went to university and education was not yet compulsory in the UK. His initial salary was £200 per annum which from 1872 was increased to £300 (the equivalent of about £170,000 in 2022). His salary matched that of the Company Secretary, who was effectively its CEO. Livesey was appointed on the basis that he would continue to supervise the construction of the new gasworks 'and give what time he can spare to the old works so long as they continue working'. The construction appears not to have gone as well as George Livesey's anticipated but, by September 1871, the work had progressed sufficiently for the directors to issue instructions to Frank Livesey to open it as soon as possible. His brother George then spent a week in North Shields examining the new gasworks and on 4 October issued the following written report to the company.

London
October 4th 1871

The Directors of the
Tynemouth Gas Company

Gentlemen
On the 18th September 1871 I visited Tynemouth and left on the 22nd, the whole time having been spent in examining and starting your New Works.

I did not expect everything would be quite right at first but having taken the precaution to try each part separately and finding all in perfect order, excepting some leaks in the purifier which were stopped by midday of the 20th, the first charge of coals was put into the retorts on the afternoon of the same day and the New Works started and has continued working without hindrance or mishap. For the first few days 'the make' of gas was small which was owing to leaks in the retorts and to working without an exhauster. As to the leaks, they always occur on charging a new bed of retorts. The joints between the bricks are not perfectly gas tight until gas has been made for a few days when, all the interstices being filled up, the brick retort beds are more sound and less able to crack than the ordinary clays. These leaks would have stopped sooner had the exhauster been working but I did not consider it safe to work the exhauster at first. There might have been some serious leaks in the pipes between the retorts and the exhauster and in that case a dangerous proportion of air would have been into the gas. Working without the exhauster enabled us to detect and stop the leaks in question which I am glad to say were very few and trifling in amount.

The result of this is that in the first week about half the gas made was lost in blowing out the air from all the pipes, scrubbers, purifier and gasholder and in working under pressure to find out and stop leaks which being done, and the exhauster started, the New Works at once went into full work, I believe without a single drawback. I have every reason for thinking that every week will give you increasing satisfaction and that your business will now and for many years to come be carried on under exceptionally favourable conditions.

In proportion to the gas required to be made I do not think there are works in the Kingdom with pipes, condensers, scrubbers, purifiers and other apparatus comparatively as large as yours, the result of this being that the gas meets with scarcely any resistance in its passage from retorts to gasholder. The proof of this being that there is only ½ inch [c.1cm] more pressure on the hydraulic main than on the gasholder instead of, in some cases, as much as 12 inches. As 'the make' of gas increases the pressure will rise but not to any notable extent. In consequence of laying out the works on this large scale the cost has been greater than if everything had been smaller but, had I to do the work again, I would not reduce any one part, so convinced am I that you will find the truest economy in them as they stand.

The retort house when in full work, but allowing three through beds of retorts to be out of use for repairs, is capable of making 1,200,000 [cubic feet] in 24 hours and the rest of the apparatus is quite equal to the task of dealing with this quantity – and to do this all that is required in addition to what you have is to fill up the house with its complement of retorts so that for years to come no further outlay of capital will be required. Considering the capabilities of the works the cost at which they have been erected (without sacrificing any essential point either of strength or convenience) has been extremely low. The Great Beckton Works has cost over £60,000 of capital for each million feet to be made per day.[38] The Metropolitan cost about £30,000 for the same while the cost of yours does not much exceed £20,000 for a million.

My original estimate of the cost of the Works was from £20,000 to £22,000 and the result I am not ashamed of – I feel I have not wasted one pound of the moneys you have entrusted to my spending and I feel that it has all been productively laid out and I am further convinced that the enlightened policy you have pursued from the first in the desire you have expressed so often to have the Works made perfect and complete and large enough to meet all requirement for the next 10 years or so will bear fruit to your shareholders in the shape of increased or permanently full dividends and to your consumers in a reduced price. I hope and believe that next year's working will fully bear out all I have stated. I cannot conclude this without expressing to you as a board, and to each member including the Secretary individually, thanks for the uniform kindness and confidence you have shown me and I trust, though business relations will soon cease, the kind feeling mutually engendered may continue to exist for many years to come.

I am gentlemen, yours truly

George Livesey

Later in October 1871, Frank Livesey was able to report that gas was now being produced at both the Low Lights and at the new gasworks. Beyond the new site, 18-inch gas mains had been laid in the streets of North Shields, amongst other things, to take gas from the new gasworks for storage at the company's gasholders in Hudson Street and at the Low Lights. Fortuitously for us, the *Newcastle Daily Courant* provided its readers with this astonishingly detailed description of the new gasworks. It is indicative of their impressive nature that the account was provided for the readers of a newspaper produced primarily for those living in the much larger town of Newcastle, eight miles from North Shields.[39]

TYNEMOUTH NEW GASWORKS

The ground on which the old works of the Tynemouth Gas Company were built long ago and found to be getting too small and, after pulling down

---

38 This was a major London gasworks completed in 1870 for the Gas Light and Coke Company on a huge site with colliers from the north-east delivering coal to two piers built specifically to receive coal for the gasworks.

39 Readers not interested in technical detail can skip this detailed account but should register the significance of the *Newcastle Courant* providing it.

a gasholder, and building retorts in its place, and then not having room, as well as the knowledge of the term of lease rapidly drawing to a close, it was determined to erect entirely new works. ... In order to save the trouble and expense of carting coals, land adjoining the North-Eastern Railway was selected. ... The retort house, 210 feet in length by 77 feet in width, outside dimensions, which also includes the coal stores under the same roof, is arranged for 20 double benches of retorts, capable of making at their best, 1,200,000 cubic feet of gas in 24 hours, still allowing for two to three double benches of retorts to be out of use for repairs. This winter, seven of these benches, or 49 through and through retorts have been used. The coal stores before mentioned runs the whole length of the house on each side and are capable of storing opposite each setting of retorts, eight days' supply. The railway waggons run direct into the retort house and drop the coals into that part of the store where wanted, allowing the coals to pass on to the retort house floor in the exact position required without any casting or trimming.

The gas on leaving the retort house passes through an elongated spiral worm condenser of 18-inch pipes. This form of condenser is novel and is believed by Mr Livesey to be not only the cheapest but the most easily erected, and the most effectual – and thence through a water-cooling tank – the temperature of which can be regulated – to the engine house and exhausters. The engines are used to pump the gas from the retorts, to force it through the various purifying apparatus, and fill the gas holders. Engines, boilers and Beal's exhausters are all in duplicate to avoid the great loss of working without them for however short a time. Next in its course come the scrubbers or apparatus for taking out the ammonia. There are two of these large circular wrought-iron vessels 25 feet high, 11 feet diameter, filled with boards ¼ inch thick, 9 inches deep, 1 inch apart, placed on their edges tier above tier. Water, by means of a self-acting spreader (the common 'Barker's Mill') is distributed over these boards in such a manner as to completely wet the whole surface, which in each vessel amounts to nearly 40,000 square feet. This is a speciality of Mr Livesey's, first introduced into the South Metropolitan Gasworks, London, in 1866, where it has worked very successfully ever since, his object being to expose the greatest possible wetted surface to the action of the gas which, by contact, parts with the whole of the ammonia so freely soluble in water. The principal object attained by these scrubbers is to use the least quantity of water and still free the gas from ammonia, which is now so valuable a residual product for the manufacture of sulphate of ammonia. It is only fair to say that about the same time that Mr Livesey first adopted the idea of filling up scrubbers with this arrangement of thin boards, Mr Warner, of South Shields, invented and has used ever since a somewhat similar arrangement.

The sulphuretted hydrogen is next taken from the gas by means of oxide of iron, in what is known as the Purifying House, a building 90 feet by 50 feet, containing four purifiers 20 feet by 15 feet, which can be charged either with lime or oxide of iron. After this, it passes to a meter to be measured, and thence to the gasholder, of telescopic production, 100 feet diameter, 28 feet deep, Messrs. Piggott's of Birmingham being the maker.

Remarks have been made upon the strange idea of erecting gasworks in the highest part of the town, or nearly so, but a question of this sort is of little consequence when works are properly constructed, certainly so in this case, as it is a fact that the gasholder at the Low Lights is now filled every day from these works, giving less pressure, represented by nine inches of water, than it did to fill from the old works, on the spot, entirely owing to improved construction.

There are capacious tanks underground for tar and ammoniacal liquors, an efficient apparatus for converting the latter into marketable sulphate of ammonia, a very pure white salt being produced. The sulphate plant was erected by Mr Hathaway, late manager to Mr R. Laming, so well known in connection with gas purification. There are also commodious workshops and stores. The works have been constructed to allow for future extensions without altering any of the present arrangements, which really only form part of a much larger works. The quantity of gas now made could be trebled without any addition to present buildings.

The retorts of these works are built of bricks, made specially to pattern by Messrs. J. Cowen and Co., whose name is quite sufficient guarantee for the quality. The life of these brick retorts is generally five seasons or more, against three only of clay retorts. In the hottest part of the furnace a red fire brick is used, which is found most efficient, merely glazing over on the surface, and going no deeper when exposed to the greatest heat required in a gasworks. The brick is made at Ewell, near London.

The men here are not required to work on Sundays, sufficient gas being made during the week for the Sunday supply, an advantage which is fully appreciated by them.

The works in cost will most favourably compare with any others that have been lately built. The great gasworks of the Chartered Company, recently erected at Beckton, for the supply of the city of London, have cost over £60,000 for each million [cubic] feet of gas they are capable of making each day, while these come out at considerably less than half that rate. They are substantially built, without any useless ornament, which is out of place in a gasworks. Mr George Livesey, of the South Metropolitan Gasworks, London, is the engineer, and his brother Mr Frank Livesey, has had entire charge of their erection and the working is now under his management (*Newcastle Daily Courant*, 16 February 1872).

A further indication of the impressive nature of the new gasworks is that in the months that followed, requests were made for visits to the site by engineers and directors from the gasworks in Newcastle, Sunderland, and South Shields. However, the honeymoon period for the new gasworks did not last for long. Frank Livesey's association with the company ended much more quickly than the directors would have wanted. He gave them three months' notice in November 1872 and then moved to the South Metropolitan Gas Company, as assistant to his brother, eventually succeeding him as chief engineer in 1882.[40] Before leaving, he oversaw the construction of a well and reservoir for the new gasworks, to reduce its dependence on the supply of water from the troubled North Shields Water Company. The directors made it clear to Livesey, that they accepted his resignation 'with regret'. They were to regret it even more in the years that followed. His departure was followed by two unhappy appointments. Within seven years, two managers were appointed and sacked.

After the initial design for the new gasworks had been submitted, the directors had resolved that, 'a manager's house be erected on the south side of the works and that George Livesey be requested to furnish plans for one of a suitable size and description' (BTGC DM, 26 Sep 1870). However, that decision was not acted upon and one, inevitably, wonders if that was a factor in Frank Livesey's resignation. At the time of the 1871 Census, he was lodging with a shipowner and his family in Northumberland Terrace in the village of Tynemouth. It was not until April 1873, after he had left the company, that an on site manager's house was next on the agenda. Given the 'no expense spared' approach to the building of the Minton Lane gasworks, the directors' approach to the associated house was decidedly niggardly. They did not like the estimates put forward and resolved that the new manager and company secretary 'get a plan and specification of a house on a smaller scale to lay before the directors.' Their decision seems mean-spirited

---

40 Like his brother, he proved to be an innovative gas engineer.

given the c.£700 estimates were less than three times the new manager's annual salary and not much more than twice the salary that had been paid to Frank Livesey. Without a house for the manager to move into, the directors agreed to pay Livesey's replacement, Henry Hathaway, £26 per annum 'house rent' in addition to his salary. There were other signs at this stage that the directors were being mean towards their employees. Contrary to what had been agreed originally, the directors instructed Hathaway to make the stokers work on Sundays. At their next meeting, he advised them that the stokers had told him that if they were obliged to work on Sundays they would hand in their notice. It was only for that reason that the directors agreed to leave things as they were. At the time, the stokers received just over 5 shillings for a shift of extremely hard labour. The directors received twice as much for a two-hour meeting and were soon to have their attendance fee doubled to one guinea (£1 1s). What the company did do, by way of a little extra for its employees, was provide each of them with a piece of beef at Christmas.

By the second part of 1874, the directors were concerned by a marked drop in the gas yield from the new gasworks and wrote to George Livesey to ask if he could offer any explanation. In a lengthy reply, he confirmed that, provided the figures with which he had been supplied were correct, the plant was now making 2,000 cubic feet less gas for each ton of coal than previously. Livesey refused to believe the new manager's suggestion that the difference could be explained by the quality of the coal being supplied by the Pelton Colliery in Chester-le-Street. 'Nothing but rubbish, to be condemned at a glance, could account for such a falling off.' The obvious implication was that the new gasworks was not being properly maintained and Livesey speculated that the retorts may have been neglected, or that there might be a stoppage between the retorts and the exhauster. His strong recommendation was that, in future, all aspects of the gas-making process be logged and carefully monitored. His surmise, about the quality of maintenance, seems to have been correct. The directors' minutes of October 1874 record that the Minton Lane manager had breached the terms of his contract 'not at any time to act or engage or be employed in any other business or profession or calling whatsoever'. In short, he appears to have been moonlighting. He was given the stark choice, resign or be dismissed, and was replaced by James Kemp.

It was only against this background that the directors appear to have reconsidered the merit of having the manager live in his own house 'on the job' rather than in rented accommodation over a mile away. On 6 May 1875, at the company's AGM, it was agreed that a manager's house should be built on Meadow Well Lane, 'as it was the desire of the directors for the manager to be within call of the works.' In anticipation of that, in October 1875, a house the company owned in Stephenson Street was sold to Tynemouth Council for £650, just short of the price the directors were unwilling to pay for the proposed on site house two years earlier.

Unfortunately, for the company, the fall in gas yield coincided with growing pressure from Tynemouth Council to reduce the price charged for gas. For example, in November 1875, its Trade and Commerce Committee recommended that the Council send a deputation to the company's directors 'to lay the information obtained from other places as to the price of gas before them'. In January 1876, a small reduction was made in the price of gas, but it was not sufficient to silence the critics.

Monochrome reproduction of a portrait of Sir George Livesey by William Mainwaring Palin in the Southwark Art Collection.

The directors became the target of further criticism after the 1876 AGM, when they awarded themselves a substantial increase in their fees, which was not in any way related to the amount of time they spent on company business. The increase was justified with the same kind of comparability argument in use today to justify the high salaries paid to top executives.

> The chairman referred to the subject of remuneration to the directors for their services to the company and remarked that the directors in the company were paid less by £100 than in any other gas company, and he had to propose the sum of not less than £250 per annum (equivalent to about £110,000 in 2022, BTGC AGM 1876).

Although the shareholders welcomed a dividend which was the largest allowed by law, those present rejected the enhanced attendance fee proposed for the company's chairman. Whilst they agreed to directors receiving, in addition to an annual 'salary', an additional attendance fee of one guinea (£1.1s) per meeting (equivalent to c.£500 today), they rejected the proposal to give the chairman even more. However, at the next meeting of the board, the directors simply ignored the wishes of the shareholders and doubled the attendance fee of the chairman to two guineas (equivalent to about £1,000 today). Coincidence or not, days later, a letter appeared in the local newspaper which was critical of the company and made the case for the municipalisation of gas supplies, in which the public interest would be put ahead of the interests of shareholders.

Sir,

Your report of the annual meeting of the Tynemouth Gas Company ought to make gas consumers think seriously whether an article of such importance and of such constant demand ought to be made the sport of so much profit and complimentary payments, as that meeting exhibited. The directors take immense credit for reducing the price of gas from 4s to 3s 6d and yet you read of 10 per cent dividend ... and not less than £250 per annum to the directors for smoking their pipes over the works occasionally ... Gas has become such a powerful element of our social life, the very sunshine of order and security, that it ought to be in the hands of the lighting authority, and ought to be produced at the least possible cost to the community ... Beyond the grievous taxation on trade involved in these heavy profits of gas companies, it keeps our domestic cookery in a costly and barbarous condition; scorching and burning our meat over great coal fires is as wasteful as it is unscientific and cooking by gas, even at the present high rates, is adopted by all thoroughly intelligent households, and if gas were supplied to the community at the mere cost of production, it would soon produce a great domestic reform, and economise our coal supplies (*Shields Daily News*, 3 April 1876).

Shortly after a complacent 1877 AGM, the Tynemouth company was completely upstaged by its South Shields counterpart. An exhibition of gas appliances was organized by its engineer, W. K. Warner, a leading light in the gas industry, who had been instrumental in setting up the British Association of Gas Managers (BAGM) in 1863. He believed that the gas industry had reached a turning point and so had organized what was the first such exhibition in the country, to demonstrate how much more the gas industry had to offer than street and domestic lighting. Exhibitors were attracted from all round the country, and Warner had laid on gas supplies for the appliances so that the public could see them working. What the exhibition demonstrated, was that there were now numerous other kinds of appliances available other than those related to lighting. As well as the wide range of cookers on display, there were gas fires; appliances to heat water (from small gas kettles to elaborate systems for piped hot water); gas engines, and numerous 'fancy articles' which included fire lighters for coal fires, irons, coffee roasters and cigar lighters. The exhibition was opened by R. P. Spice, the President of the BAGM, who congratulated the South Shields company on what he described as a 'very important event' which 'would make itself felt in the annals of gas engineering.' He was convinced that comparable events would follow elsewhere but 'everybody would remember that the movement was started at South Shields.' In responding, after a luncheon cooked with the appliances on display, R. Wallis, the chairman of the South Shields company made some prophetic remarks. He declared that 'in his humble opinion, gas for the purpose of lighting would someday be superseded – although that day might be a long way off' but that shareholders 'need have no alarm when they saw that gas could be applied to such numerous purposes.' Perhaps in anticipation of the changes ahead, the many gas managers from the north of England at the exhibition decided to establish the North of England Gas Managers' Association, with W. G. Warner as its first President.

By the time the next AGM of the Tynemouth Gas Company was due, the editorial of the local newspaper echoed the words of the chairman of the South Shields company about gas lighting and suggested that the holders of gas shares 'cannot be said to have a perfectly pleasant prospect before them when they consider the progress which the electric light is making.'

> Lord Rosslyn, writing from Naples, adds his testimony to that already given with respect to the excellence, steadiness and clearness of this light, with which the Puerto del Sol was illuminated at Madrid during the recent Royal marriage festivities. The place, he says, was at midnight as light as day. … There was really nothing new in what Lord Rosslyn saw at Madrid and experiments have already been made not only in London but in every large provincial town. There can be no question about the illuminating power and the space-penetrating range of electric light. But a means of producing the light cheaply has yet to be devised. … As soon as the electric light can be made cheaper than gas it will supersede gas, but not till then (*Shields Daily Gazette*, 16 March 1878).

That day was still some time off and at the 1878 AGM the company again declared the maximum dividend of 10 per cent allowed by law and agreed a further modest reduction in the price of gas to customers, which it could accommodate from the surplus income still available after the dividends and other expenses had been paid. The report also contained reassuring information that the gas yield continued to be satisfactory, and that the quality of the gas was higher than that required by law. One thing which did trouble one shareholder was the scale of outstanding payments shown on the balance sheet. He was reassured that the total amount was not a cause for concern. Nevertheless, in January 1879, the company took the Tynemouth Aquarium and Winter Garden Company (later known as The Plaza) to court for not paying its large gas bill.

The company's finances continued to be very much to the satisfaction of the shareholders when maximum dividends were declared at the 1879 AGM. There was also a palpable complacent and self-congratulatory mood amongst the company directors. The chairman remarked that 'the scare of the electric light had not affected the interests of any shareholder', and that 'he never had any fear of the electric light superseding gas for domestic purposes.' Moreover, he boasted that 'the works of the company were never in a more efficient or satisfactory state than at present.' Yet, at the next directors' meeting, the mood was different. The then gasworks manager, James Kemp, was called before the board and 'severely reprimanded and censured for his neglect of the gasworks, and particularly for misleading the directors as to the quantity of coals in stock. Kemp retained his position on that occasion but on 11 November 1879 was summarily dismissed. The directors decided that 'James Kemp be discharged and leave the works and cease to have any connection with the company' and he 'be required to give up to the Company all monies and keys belonging to the Company'. The record in the minutes continued: 'that his wages be paid up to Saturday 22nd day of this month and that notice be given to him to quit the House he now occupied in the Company's Works as manager, on or before the said Saturday the 22nd November 1879.' At the subsequent directors' meeting in June 1879, it was revealed that more of the employees of the gasworks had since been discharged.

Kemp was replaced by 22-year-old William Hardie Jnr, the oldest son of the Secretary of the Newcastle and Gateshead Gas Company. Though young for such an appointment, he was undoubtedly an outstanding candidate and had been awarded a prize for the best paper delivered at the North of England Gas Managers' Association meeting in October 1879.

Another change at the top of the company took place in March 1880. It was initially proposed that Mr W. H. Atkinson, who had been Secretary of the Company since its formation in 1843, become its first managing director, at an annual salary of £500 (the 2022 equivalent of about £235,000) with the company clerk, Mr Davidson, taking over the post of company secretary at a salary of £250 (equivalent to £117,500 in 2022). However, the company received legal advice against such a move. Instead, whilst Mr Atkinson did resign as company secretary, he was then duly appointed as a director and replaced Mr G. Williamson as company chairman, on the same salary that he would have received as managing director. He assumed that responsibility at a time when the company's balance sheet was healthy. Despite considerable maintenance at the gasworks, which had involved repairs to and replacements of furnaces, ovens and retorts, and the renewal of gas mains and service pipes, and extensions of the pipe network, the company had a substantial operating surplus and could again afford to pay its original shareholders the full 10 per cent dividend allowed by law. After the meeting, the company also responded to a request from the local Council to reduce its prices. It did so, but only very slightly. This was the letter sent by the chairman of the Council's Watch Committee in response.

> Dear Sir,
> Referring to our correspondence in April last, on the subject of the price of gas charge in the Borough to private consumers, and to the opinion expressed by me on behalf of the Watch Committee, that the reduction then made was inadequate, and still left the price in this borough higher than that of neighbouring towns, I am directed by the committee again to invite the attention of the directors to this subject, and to urge on them the necessity of making a further large reduction. The Watch Committee cannot but believe that a company possessed of the most improved appliances, in every way so advantageously situated for the manufacture and distribution of gas, and at the same time so efficiently managed as the Gas Company is admitted to be, must be able to produce and supply the article at least as good and as cheap as any company in the locality, and they therefore desire now to put it strongly to the directors to reconsider the question of price, and to endeavour to meet the wishes of the inhabitants of the borough, as now expressed through the committee.

The reply from the gas company's Secretary, on behalf of the directors, thanked the committee for the 'flattering high compliments' but declined to make a further reduction. During the full Council meeting which followed, which was described in detail in the local newspaper, there was evident resentment at the way in which the request had been summarily dismissed, especially 'when they [the gas company] paid 10 per cent and such handsome salaries.' Another member described the gas company's salaries as 'exorbitant' and several speakers insisted that it was time to consider the municipalisation of the gas supply. Alderman Hedley was particularly vociferous in his criticism. He noted that gas was 20 per cent cheaper in Newcastle and he attributed 'the dear gas to the lavish expenditure of the [Tynemouth] company, and boldly suggested that the Corporation might take the bull by the horns and make their own gas. The only objection he saw to such a course was the impending substitution of electricity for gas as a medium of artificial light' (*The Shields Daily News*, 27 November 1880).

Later in the year, the company received complaints about 'the smell arising from the gas' which led to tests on it, on behalf of the Council. They showed that although, when tested, the gas leaving the works was pure, there was evidence that sulphuretted hydrogen (which smells of rotten eggs) had reached the gasholder at the Low Lights, and 'various shops in the town'. The directors of the company conceded that, perhaps because of a problem with the scrubbers, there had been an 'introduction of impure gas for a short time into the holder and that every possible means were being used to correct the mistake, and that a strict order had been issued to the officials to do everything necessary to prevent a recurrence of such like accidents in future.' At the Council meeting, the Mayor rendered this in more down to earth terms: 'It was the result of carelessness on the part of people at the works.'

That, however, was a minor matter compared to the stinging editorial attack on the gas company in the town's local newspaper in February 1881.

The Borough of Tynemouth Gas Company seems determined to wring the uttermost farthing out of the pockets of the helpless consumers of gas. While companies possessing a similar monopoly in other towns are, in view of the gradual and certain approach of the competition of electricity as an illuminating agent, reducing their charges, supplying a better article, and generally setting their houses in order, our local vendors of light are maintaining exorbitant rates for gas, which although it may reach the [minimum] standard fixed by Act of Parliament, cannot be pronounced of superlative excellence. The report of the Newcastle and Gateshead Gas Company states that the directors have decided that a further reduction of 3d per 1000 cubic feet shall take effect from the beginning of the year, making the price of gas in the two boroughs 2s 3d per 1000 cubic feet, less the usual discount of 10 per cent. The price in North Shields, as every householder knows, is 3s per thousand feet with a discount of only 5 per cent. Thus, the consumer at the mouth of the Tyne pays upwards of 30 per cent more than his neighbour up the river. We have heard no pleas advanced for the continuance of the high rate, which would be very difficult to defend upon any other ground than the assumed right to squeeze the highest possible dividend out of the working of a monopoly. Coal of the best quality for gas-making is almost at the company's doors, and the area supplied, though smaller, of course, than Newcastle and Gateshead, is quite large enough for the economical manufacture of gas. We venture to suggest to the company that in extracting at this time the highest possible rate from the gas consumers they are pursuing a short-sighted policy. As we have said, the adoption of the electric light for domestic use is an event of the near future. When this consummation, for which we have special reason to devoutly wish, takes place, the spirit in which the Gas Company will be met by the ratepayers through their mandatories in the Town Council [directors of the company who were also town councillors] will largely depend upon the forbearance which the company now shows to consumers. It is quite certain that the public will not permit any new monopoly to be established, and that the Corporation will either supply the new light or reserve an ample controlling power over its purveyors whoever they may be. There is a growing feeling how the supply of light should not be left to private enterprise and already corporations are turning their attention to electric light. Scarborough Town Council the other day decided to get estimates for lighting certain parts of the town by the electric light. This is an example which the North Shields Corporation would do well to imitate so that the visible darkness of some of our thoroughfares may be exchanged for the bright illumination of electric light. The shareholders of the gas company, if they are alive to their own interests, will insist on the directors moving with the times. The capabilities of gas as an illuminator have never been fully developed, and the valuable residual products of its manufacture will long enable it to meet the competition of electricity with success, if the discoveries of science are fully applied in its consumption. But cheap and good light cannot be prudently withheld from the public much longer (*Shields Daily News*, 16 February 1881).

Ten days after the editorial, the Council was informed that a price reduction would be forthcoming, although much smaller than that demanded by the newspaper, and not nearly enough to bring it in line with Newcastle and Gateshead. The concession did not satisfy local councillors, who complained not only about the price but also the illuminating quality of the gas which was not much more than the statutory minimum.

Despite the mounting criticism, the general atmosphere at the 1881 AGM was still one of complacent defiance. Maximum dividends were declared again, and the small reduction in the price of gas defended as all the company could afford. To cheers, the chairman said that *they* would decide when they could reduce it further and would not be influenced by 'outside pressure (hear, hear)'. He was also satisfied with the quality of the gas supplied to customers. What people outside the company seem to have regarded as the bare minimum (the equivalent of 14 sperm candles), the chairman seems to have perceived as a target.[41] When he turned to the perceived threat from electric lighting, the chairman was positively blasé. So too was the former chairman who insisted that 'for ordinary purposes there was no possibility of it superseding gas.' He also emphasised that Mr Swan, of Newcastle, with the most complete electric light in the area, generated it with a 3½ horse-power *gas* engine. When one shareholder suggested that the streetlights were not lit sufficiently, the Council was blamed for not being prepared to pay for more. It would, he said, 'be well for the Council, instead of trying to fetch the prices down, to keep the flames up (laughter and 'hear-hear').'[42] At the end of the formal business, the chairman and former chairman showed the shareholders the lavish gifts they had, in effect, awarded themselves 'as a token of appreciation for their services to the company'. Mr Atkinson's gift, inside a large oak case, was an ornamental service in heavily gold-plated solid silver consisting of a large two feet high bowl, with handles, mounted on a polished ebony stand, two large flagons and two goblets, decorated with a figured band based on the Elgin marbles. The former chairman's gift consisted of a solid silver dinner, dessert, and afternoon tea service, with cake basket and salver, also inside an oak cabinet. Both sets had been made by, Elkington, the prestigious Birmingham silversmiths (*Shields Daily Gazette* 24 March 1881).

Divisions in the Gas Industry

Despite this self-congratulatory and complacent mood in North Shields, those in the gas industry nationally were very conscious of the need to respond effectively to the challenge represented by electricity. However, the industry's ability to do so was hampered by fundamental divisions which made it difficult to forge a united front. The primary split was between those who produced coal gas and those who designed and sold the gas appliances which made use of it. There was more to this than a simple division of labour. Those responsible for manufacturing gas, including the directors of the Borough of Tynemouth Gas Company, often took advantage of this division in the industry to defend themselves when criticised for deficiencies in their product. They could do that because, at this stage in the development of the industry, they did not sell or hire gas appliances to customers. That was something they left to others and so they could offer a stock response

---

41 In Manchester, gas was supplied at 20-candle power and in Scotland 25-candle power. In London, the corresponding figure was 16.

42 In a subsequent meeting, following a deputation from the Town Council's Watch Committee, the directors did give the works manager authority to improve the purifying process, and construct a new governor house to better regulate the gas supply to customers.

when complaints were made about the quality of the gas they provided, which was to suggest that the problem was not the quality of the gas, but the quality of the burners provided by others. Although sometimes trotted out as a stock response to criticisms, the manufacturers of gas did have a point. Over the years, although there had been significant improvements in gas appliances, consumers often neglected to have them properly maintained or updated. Nevertheless, the relative ease with which responsibility could be evaded by making use of this division in the gas industry was not helpful when it came to fending off the growing threat from the electricity industry.

Amongst those developing and selling gas appliances to the public, competition extended far beyond conventional business rivalry. That is most easily illustrated with the bitter conflict between two major figures in the gas appliance industry: William Sugg and George Bray. Sugg made many contributions to the industry though the most significant was probably the adaptation of the Argand oil burner to gas. It worked

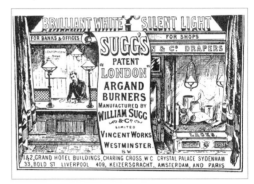

An 1868 advertisement for Sugg's patent London Argand burner (from Trevor William, A History of the British Gas Industry, *p.32).*

by forcing a draught of air at the flame on a circular wick, and was so successful technically and commercially, thanks in part to Sugg's heavy investment in advertising, that it was adopted as the Parliamentary standard burner in 1868.

Bray designed his own precision machinery to improve the performance of gas burners and solved the problem of flickering gas lights by developing a brass burner with a porcelain tip which he introduced into his own design for streetlights. They were windproof, tapered downwards, so they would not cast shadows around the lamp, and were fitted with reflectors to enhance the illumination. The Tynemouth Gas Company set up a Bray streetlight outside its own offices in 1882 and it was judged so impressive that other tradesmen in the town chose to do the same. This was just one of many such innovations which, helped by Bray's extensive marketing, led to his products selling widely inside and outside the UK.

When an International Electric and Gas Exhibition was held in London in early 1882, it presented the gas industry with an ideal opportunity to close ranks and offer a united front, in which it could demonstrate what the industry had to offer in comparison to electricity. However successful the Exhibition may have been in that respect, the organization of the gas section laid bare internal divisions

BRAY'S

PATENT

Flat-Flame Lanterns

Have successfully stood the test of above seven years practical use in Street and other Lighting.

GEO. BRAY & CO.. GAS LIGHTING ENGINEERS. LEEDS.

An advertisement for Bray's flat-flame system which explicitly claims to be as good as lights fitted with Sugg's Argand burner. 'The Flat Flame is the only practicable system of streetlighting and in actual use will yield as much light with common gas ... as any Argand System. This introductory statement has been confirmed by experience throughout the world' (reproduced from Gas World, *1 January 1887).*

which continued to plague the industry for many years afterwards.

At the time, the only organized element of the gas industry was The Gas Institute (a revamp of the BAGM) and it fell to it to arrange the contributions from the gas industry. A three-man sub-committee chaired by George Livesey then appealed to gas undertakings across the country to fund the exhibition.[43] Unfortunately, the physical layout of the gas section of the exhibition proved controversial and led to a bitter conflict between Sugg and Bray, the two major figures in the gas appliance industry. In essence, the problem was that Sugg was given a prime position and Bray was not. Moreover, Bray complained that although stands elsewhere in the hall were 12 feet high, the 8-feet high stand he had been allocated was not tall enough to demonstrate the qualities of his gas lighting. The suspicion that Sugg had been given preferential treatment because of his friendship with one of the organizing committee's three members (who were also members of the same masonic lodge), served only to give Bray more cause for concern.[44] The fact that Sugg was London based and Bray was based in Leeds may also have been another source of friction.

In the months that followed the Exhibition, during which Bray continued to press for an explanation of why he had been side-lined, the divisions in the industry both widened and intensified. At the heart of the problem was that the full members of the Gas Institute were involved in the manufacture of coal gas. They considered themselves professionals and preferred to distance themselves from 'trades people' like Sugg and Bray, who had been allowed to become associate members because of the significance of their role in the industry. The editor of the *Journal of Gas Lighting* (another member of Sugg's Lodge) suggested that the Institute had been 'thrown open too widely' and that 'the price of admission was

---

43 Close to £6,000 was raised. Curiously, although the directors of Tynemouth Gas Company resolved to contribute £25, the accounts of the Institute state that only £5 was received.

44 The Sugg Company, established in 1837, has survived to the present day. See Heritage Lighting Specialists – William Sugg & Co. Lighting

being abused by men who had no moral right to avail themselves of it' (quoted by Hide, pp, 36-7). When Bray persisted in asking for an enquiry into how he had been treated, he was expelled. He challenged his expulsion in the High Court – and won. That meant that the Institute had a legal obligation to reinstate Bray and pay his costs. Rather than resort to that, Livesey and other leading members of the Institute resigned and set up the rival Institute of Gas Engineers, which explicitly excluded 'traders' from membership. Its founding principle was that 'only men actively engaged in the management of gasworks or professionally in their construction were proper men to form an association representing the gas industry.' That rift was still not healed even when the two bodies merged in 1903. Some traders were admitted but only as honorary members, and only if 'they had rendered distinguished service to the progression of gas engineering or have specially promoted the interests of the gas industry.' Bray was admitted to the Institute only on those terms.[45]

Meanwhile, back in North Shields, it was business as usual for the gas company. The demand for gas continued to increase, larger bore pipes were introduced to accommodate it, and in 1883 a gas supply was introduced to Percy Main. At the other end of the Borough, the network now extended beyond Whitley into Monkseaton. All this meant that there was a need for additional storage facilities, and, in September 1883, the manager of the gasworks was given permission to add an additional gasholder to the main site. Subsequently, tenders went out for a 108 feet diameter brick gasholder tank. The following year, 1884, during which the company hosted the half-yearly meeting of the North of England Gas Managers' Association, the gas company appears to have shortened its name from the Borough of Tynemouth Gas Company to the Tynemouth Gas Company. We have been unable to locate any documented decision to change the name, but a reasonable guess is that at a time when there were increasing calls to municipalise the local gas industry, it was concluded that the name of the company should not in any way imply that it was a municipal rather than private company. When the new gasholder was completed, half a million cubic feet had been added to the storage capacity of the Minton Lane gasworks, in addition to the storage facilities that were still in use at the Low Lights and in Hudson Street. Dividends (now being made twice a year) were again at the maximum allowed by law and the balance sheet was healthy despite a further small reduction in the price of gas. However, looking to the future, the chairman announced that the company wanted to

---

45 The Bray Company took out a further patent to improve gas burners as late as 1965, just before the national programme to convert from coal to natural gas got underway. It diversified considerably over the years and became Bray Technologies in 1971 but was dissolved in 2004.

encourage the use of gas for purposes other than lighting and for that reason it had decided to increase the discounts available to those who consumed larger quantities of gas. Given that decision, shareholders would have been pleased to find that some shops in the town were now advertising gas stoves and other gas appliances for sale.

A metal Tynemouth Gas Company name plate reproduced courtesy of Jim Rickard.

The year 1886 began badly for the company. The quality of the gas tested on behalf of the Council, had fallen to the equivalent of 14.6 at the beginning of the year, not much above the minimum level allowed by law. The Council were very unhappy about the state in which roads and pavements were left after gas pipes had been installed or replaced – a complaint about utility companies which continues to this day. The problem for the company was that a programme of pipe replacement, to increase their capacity was essential if they were to satisfy the growing demand for gas. The third element of concern reported at the AGM was that, although the sale of gas had increased by 4.5 per cent (the result of increased consumption rather than more customers), disposing of the gasworks' by-products was proving increasingly difficult. When the 1887 AGM was held, the mood was even more depressed but for a different reason. The company chairman, William H. Atkinson, was 'exceedingly ill'. He died days later, at the age of 64, having been at the helm of the company, first as Secretary and then chairman, for an astonishing 44 years. The former chairman took his place, temporarily, before being replaced by John Moffat.

The company's financial health was not much changed from the previous year, and maximum dividends were declared as usual, although the revenue from coal tar had slumped to just over 20 per cent of what it had been the year before. Once again, during the year, the illuminating power of the company's gas had been challenged. The temporary chairman, in a letter to the local newspaper, claimed that comparing their sperm-candle ratings with those of other companies was flawed because they did not use the same burner for testing as that used in North Shields. His was a fair point but it also served to divert attention from the fact that the illuminating power of the company's gas had fallen to an average of 14.9 compared to 15.2 the year before. The company was also unpopular with the Council at this time because its Medical Officer of Health had been obliged to issue an order to the company 'to abate the nuisance arising from offensive water running to the main sewer from the works'.

The end of the decade marked a watershed in the company's history. Until 1887, under William Atkinson, it had been run very much as his own personal fiefdom. The fact that under his stewardship dividends had always been high meant that his judgements were rarely challenged by the shareholders. Profit was crucially important to shareholders and having a local monopoly virtually guaranteed that dividends would always be the maximum allowed by law. Without competition from other gas providers, or comparable energy sources, prices could be kept high, and concessions made only when they did not undermine the bottom line of the company's balance sheet. Atkinson's control over the company even extended to its offices being in a building which he owned. Following his death in 1887, the directors had to negotiate with his executors to purchase the premises they occupied at 97 Bedford Street.[46]

The company had to cope with another death in 1887. The person in question had a less significant role in the company but the manner of her death ensured it was reported in the local newspaper.

THE DROWNING CASE AT NORTH SHIELDS
GASWORKS INQUEST THIS AFTERNOON

At the Railway Inn, Nile Street, North Shields, this afternoon, an inquest was held on the body of Mary Stead, 65 years of age, who was found drowned in a tank at North Shields Gasworks yesterday. Mr J. R. D. Lynn, coroner for South Northumberland, conducted the inquiry.

William Hardie, manager of the Tynemouth Gasworks, said deceased was his housekeeper. She was a widow. Witness last saw her alive at 25 minutes to four yesterday afternoon. She was then in his parlour. She went out to get tea ready, and he saw her no more until she was brought in dead. That was a quarter of an hour afterwards. Witness and others tried to restore animation, but without effect. A doctor was immediately sent for, and on his arrival pronounced life to be extinct. Occasionally, deceased was in the habit of drawing water from an underground rainwater cistern, which is 4 feet 9 inches in diameter. … She was not at all depressed in spirits that day. There was 22 inches of water in the tank, and deceased would have about 3 feet to reach to get the water.

Martha Wright said she was up at the gasworks yesterday. As she was coming away, she heard someone shouting out 'Oh dear' and ran and told

---

46 William Atkinson was not only a key gas company employee and owner of property. He was also a shipowner. When he died, he left £39,412. In terms of average earnings then and in 2022, that is the equivalent of about £18 million.

Mrs Patterson, the gatekeeper's wife. Witness and Mrs Patterson went back and found deceased with her head down in the tank and her feet about the level of the aperture. She was still shouting, but they could not get her out. They shouted, and help came.

Dorothy Patterson went to Mr Hardie's back door and saw the feet of deceased sticking out of the opening of the tank. She got hold of her and shouted for help, which soon came, and deceased was got out. Witness could not account for deceased getting into the tank. Witness had on previous occasions seen deceased look into the tank to see how much water there was. Deceased had recently complained of giddiness.

The jury returned a verdict to the effect that deceased met her death by drowning in the tank, but as to how she got there, there was not sufficient evidence to show (*Shields Daily News*, 17 February 1887).

It may seem incredible that Mary Stead should have gone outside to get water from an outside open tank to make tea, rather than get it by using the water provided by Tynemouth's private water company. That may have been because, like lots of local people, she did not trust the water provided by the company. Five years after her death, there was still such dissatisfaction with the quantity and quality of its water that a meeting of ratepayers demanded that the Council set up a municipal water company. All that followed at that point was a court injunction to stop the private water company from drawing water from an old mine shaft, but it was allowed to continue to draw water from the Red Burn, not far from the gasworks, which, true to its name, gave the water a distinctive colour. It was not until ten years after Mary Stead's death that the 1897 Tynemouth Corporation Water Act gave the Council the power to acquire the undertakings of the North Shields Waterworks. It was not before time. A 1901 public inquiry subsequently revealed that the private water company had flouted the 1892 court injunction by instructing its employees to use 'an ingenious and secret contrivance, locked and enclosed with brickwork', to intercept the water from the mine shaft and continue to sell it to its customers.[47]

A New Era Under New Management

By the end of the decade, it was clear that under its new chairman, the company was beginning to move in a significantly different direction. It had become 'a

---

47 For an account of the problems relating to the supply of water to the population of North Shields see *Shiels to Shields* (Carnegie, 2016) especially, but not only, pp.119-128, 119-200, 235-237 and 239-242.

trader' in gas appliances as well as a manufacturer and supplier of gas. It also began to advertise its coke much more prominently to potential domestic consumers. Together, these changes brought about a modest improvement in the company's income. At the 1889 AGM, this was attributed to 'an increase in the sales of gas and in the income derived from residual products' and an 'increase in revenue attributed to the use of gas cooking stoves, 80 of which have been lent out [rented] during the last year.' Also, after many years of contention, an attempt was made to resolve the long-running dispute with the Council about the quality of the company's gas. It introduced a new type of burner that provided illumination equivalent to not less than 16 sperm candles.

Much more significant, however, were the changes in labour relations in the gas industry, locally and nationally. Throughout the nineteenth century, manual workers had been exploited. The social, economic, and political structures of the period were rigged so that they were obliged to work in conditions and for wages that would be considered wholly unacceptable today. Although the Combination Act banning trades unions had been repealed in 1824, subsequent restrictions were introduced on how they could operate. Workers could combine to negotiate better terms and conditions, but it was unlawful for them to induce others to breach their contracts, or in any way obstruct either employers or employees during a dispute. That made it difficult to organize strikes without running the risk of falling foul of the law. The divide that this rigged system created in British society was recognized not just by left wing writers like Marx but also Conservatives such as Benjamin Disraeli.

In the case of North Shields, and its local gas industry, that divide in British society can be exemplified by the regular maximum 10 per cent dividend paid to gas company shareholders, whilst many local workers, including some employed by the gasworks, could not afford to have gas installed in the insanitary, overcrowded dwellings in which they were obliged to live. In marked contrast, Mr Atkinson, the long-time Secretary then chairman of the gas company lived not near the gasworks but in the grand Percy Gardens, Tynemouth, overlooking the sea.

For the workers in the gas industry, a modest turning point in terms and conditions of employment came towards the end of the nineteenth century. It was not the first time that gas workers had tried to improve their working conditions in what was accepted as being one of the most difficult and demanding as well as dangerous of jobs. In 1859, London gas stokers called a strike to protest against having to work 12-hour shifts, for seven days a week, with only one day's rest each month. The strike lasted four months but did not achieve its objectives. The strikers were sacked and replaced by unemployed workers desperate to earn any kind of regular wage. In 1872, London gas stokers went on strike at the Chartered Gas Company, which had already sacked 1,400 workers. Despite the 1871 Trade Union Act, five of the strike's leaders were charged with 'aggravated' breach of contract under section 14 of the 1867 Master and Servant Act' and sent to prison for a year. Lord Justice Brett held that even preparing to strike was a conspiracy against employers, and his judgement was regarded as a challenge to the rights of workers to withdraw their labour. His controversial decision led to the 1875 Royal Commission, and its report led, in turn, to the 1877 Employers and Workmen Act, which clarified that the common law doctrine of conspiracy did not apply to a strike by workers in furtherance of a trade dispute.

What happened in the subsequent gas dispute of 1889 is not entirely clear. Historians are still debating many of the details. What is apparent is that after the formation of the National Union of Gas Workers and General Labourers (GWU), and the dispute spreading to the provinces, an eight-hour day was conceded by the owners of the huge Beckton gasworks, and other companies quickly

followed its example. It meant a major reduction of four hours in the working day for those already employed, and the prospect of employment for some of the large pool of unemployed workers at that time. In the words of Will Thorne, the Union's General Secretary, an eight-hour day would 'reduce the inhuman competition that is making men more like beasts than civilized persons.'

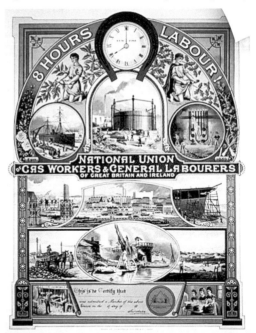

Membership Certificate of the National Union of Gas Workers and General Labourers of Great Britain and Ireland which depicts not only aspects of gas manufacture and other forms of employment but also the crucial breakthrough in working conditions achieved with the eight-hour day. The Union was founded in 1889. It was Will Thorne, its first and only General Secretary, who pressed the union to negotiate an eight-hour working day rather than pursue a wage increase. After 1916, the Union was involved in a series of mergers. Margaret Bondfield, an assistant General Secretary of one of them, went on to become MP for Wallsend (adjacent to North Shields), and the UK's first woman cabinet minister.[48]

---

48 The constituency of Wallsend included the Howdon gasworks which will feature prominently in later chapters.

The GWU also pressed for either an end to Sunday working (something which George Livesey had tried to make unnecessary when he had designed the gasworks in North Shields), or a concession that employees should receive 'double-pay' for working on Sundays, which was eventually agreed. Given how much had been conceded to their workers, the directors and managers of gasworks had hoped that businesses would soon return to running normally. But one big issue remained unresolved and the conflict over it became focused on Livesey's South Metropolitan Gas Company in London. Although, for the period, he had an enlightened attitude towards his employees, he was against unionisation. He had, for example, been advocating a profit-sharing scheme for his workers for 20 years, although never able to win the support of his directors for such a radical scheme. They only agreed to it when Livesey convinced them it would help to break the power of the GWU. The union responded by insisting that at the heart of the profit-sharing scheme was an attempt to undermine the union, and more generally the right of workers to strike. It soon became a major dispute, seen on both sides as an issue of principle. The company replaced members of the union with workers from other areas, happy to work for the better wages and conditions now on offer. Ironically, the very success of the union was now undermining its own bargaining position. Almost everyone with a direct or indirect interest in the dispute was obliged to take sides. The police were deployed to help the replacement workers and supplies of coal get through the picket lines. There were skirmishes, instances of violence and even threats to Livesey's life. The police then intervened directly on the side of the company and the members of the strike committee were thrown out of their offices. If there was an ultimate winner, it appears to have been the company. It agreed to no more than what it had accepted earlier in the dispute: that 'in the event of any vacancies arising the directors will give their former workmen the opportunity of returning to their employment in preference to strangers.' Livesey's 'co-partnership' scheme then developed to the point where workers became shareholders. He also introduced a process of consultation in which workers' representatives were elected to discuss problems and policy with the management, and, even more radically, that three company directors should be elected from the workforce, with the same rights as other directors.

Things were not as confrontational in North Shields during those years, but the Tynemouth Gas Company could not ignore what was happening in London and, like other provincial companies, agreed to an 8-hour working day for their employees. The brief mention of that in the closing lines of the company's annual report made it appear a minor matter, but it was a major change for the company in terms of its labour costs and relationships with its employees. That was made clear, later in the year, when William Hardie, the manager of the North Shields gasworks, gave an address to the Northern Gas Managers' Association. He employed strong language to make it clear that, like Livesey, he was unhappy with the way in which trade unions were developing but shared with Livesey the belief that the future of the industry lay in greater cooperation between 'capital and labour'. This is how his speech was reported in the local newspaper.

During his address, he said the subject of premier importance was undoubtedly the labour question. During the past 12 months there had been a perfect epidemic among workmen, and this upheaval had been simultaneous throughout the civilized world. This wave of labour discontent was apparently one of the results of growing civilization. It was brought about by the workers having formed a higher ideal of living – the luxuries of a previous generation being considered necessaries, and the standard of living having been generally raised. ... . About June last year was formed the Gas Workers Union. ... The right of workmen to combine for their mutual protection for the purpose of improving their position has long been recognized. The new trades unionism is, however, very anxious to add another plank to the trade union platform, and that a very dangerous and unjust one. It affirmed that the time had arrived when a workman would not be allowed 'not to combine' but that he must be forced into a union, no matter how much coercion must be necessary to attain that end. ... Another innovation that the new trades unionists were striving hard to introduce was the forcing of strikes in kindred industries to those in which there was a dispute. ... The threat to stop the coal supply to all London during the strike at the South Metropolitan Gas Company's works was the worst case of this kind. ... The life of the professional agitator could not be indefinitely prolonged. Already he was terribly shaken by arbitration and boards of conciliation, cooperation and profit-sharing; and similar schemes for harmonizing the relations of capital and labour. ... Productive cooperative societies owned by workmen had not yet been carried out to any large extent; but progress was being made. ... Mr George Livesey had, on a large scale, introduced it into the works of the South Metropolitan Company, and had made it a thorough success [49] (*Shields Daily News*, 4 October 1890).

---

49 William Hardie Snr was Secretary of the Association at the time and had previously served as its President.

When the company presented its report to the 1891 AGM, its chairman was able to announce that although the company 'had to contend with the increased price of coal and increased price of labour … financially they were in a good position'. He again announced maximum dividends and added that 'the directors did not think it wise to fall back upon the principle of raising their prices' and could pay the usual dividend 'without having recourse to that expedient.' What he did not dwell on was that they had drawn on the reserves to subsidise the dividends, and that the directors had increased their 'salaries' from £300 to £400 per annum (equivalent in 2022 to £180,000). What the chairman did emphasise was that, over the past ten years, the consumption of gas had increased 50 per cent. 'The great portion of that increase' he explained 'had been derived from the use of gas stoves, for heating and cooking purposes.' To exploit that source of income further, 'the directors have in hand a scheme for altering the present offices, and making a showroom, in which they will exhibit a variety of the latest cooking stoves, gas fires, gas baths, water heaters and lighting appliances' (*Shields Daily Gazette*, 25 March 1891). The showroom was in use by the end of the year. Surprisingly, other than predictable gripes about the directors paying themselves more, the only significant responses to the annual report were calls for an *increase* in the price of gas, to bring it up to the quality of the gas being offered by other companies.

> I'm not sure, sir, if many of your readers will thank me for proposing that the directors of the Tynemouth Gas Company should raise the price of gas. No thank you will, I fear, be the response of most, but when I say that my proposal is not made for the purpose of putting more money into the pockets of the shareholders, but that they may be able to give the public a supply of purer, cleaner gas, perhaps they may be more willing to support one. I don't pretend to be a gas engineer, so that I cannot go into details on the question, but this I do know, that if other companies and corporations require to charge four shillings and sixpence per thousand feet for their gas, it is impossible to sell the same quality of gas for two shillings and threepence, the price charged in Tynemouth. The differences in candle power of gas supplied in different places is enormous, and I question if lower candle power is used in many towns than with us. If anyone will simply procure a new tin kettle and hold it for a short time above a jet of gas he will see what a vast amount of black stuff is given off. Where many jets are used in a room it cannot but be injurious both to health and property. The same result is found in gas engines, too, which are so largely used in different departments of trade. I'm sure the directors of the Gas Company

would gladly talk the matter over with a deputation from the Council, and I'm equally certain that a very large number of gas consumers in the borough would willingly pay another shilling per thousand feet for a brighter and cleaner light (*Shields Daily News*, 31 August 1891).

The company's engineer, William Hardie, responded by explaining that the tin test was based on a misunderstanding and that the soot was intentionally there to be burned in the flame, not deposited on pieces of tin. That led a wit, in a later edition of the newspaper, to submit a 16-verse poem in response (*Shields Daily News*, 7 April 1892).

> The man of ink took up his pen
> On pond'rous themes to write;
> All things to him were heavy then,
> Because there was no light.
>
> And so he sat, and as he mus'd
> His thought came slow along;
> And his poetic soul refus'd
> To burst out into song.
>
> Then up he sprang, and up he said,
> 'Can I be made of brass?
> Now is the darkness in my head,
> Or in the Tynemouth gas?'
>
> His sanity -? (sic) He did begin
> At once to prove the same;
> So he took up a piece of tin
> And held it in the flame.
>
> The tin – he felt that he would fall
> 'Twas blacker than his boot;
> The gas – it wasn't gas at all,
> 'Twas nothing else but soot.
>
> Like Goethe, for 'Light more light', he sighed
> His theme now filled his head;
> 'Men cannot see through soot', he said
> 'So give us gas instead.'
>
> Chuckling, he straight took up his pen,
> And made the matter plain;
> With tin, and soot, and gas, and then
> Said 'Don't do so again.'

Thus with his colours to his mast.
He felt his task was done;
'With proof like this I have them fast,
Their gas is fairly gone.'

The man of gas now forward came,
Indignant, yet serene,
And ask, 'Sir, are you making game,
Or are you in a dream?'

'For you must know that gas is gas,
It is not soot at all,
This is as plain as grass is grass –
So you've been talking tall.'

'Tis plain as bacon comes from hog,
On this I must insist;
For if you are not in a fog,
The you are in a mist.

Gas comes from coal, and that is black,
How then can soot be white?
You thought that you were on my track,
And that you'd struck a bright.

Now hydrocarbons are to burn,
And not to place on tin;
So give your wit another turn,
Your argument is thin,

And these must burn now with the flame,
Till incandescent bright,
They change their nature and their name,
They are not black but white.

My gas I'll guard you from all attack,
Then moderate your views;
If soot you touch you must be black,
So mind your P's and Q's.

(*Shields Daily News*, 7 April 1892)

The company's 1892 AGM was unusually lively although the attendance was small. There was no support for a price increase to boost gas quality but the fact that the chairman felt obliged to address the point is significant. His argument was that the cost of increasing gas quality would be prohibitive, especially at a time when the company had been obliged to replace two 1872 boilers with expensive

Galloway steel boilers fitted with Meldrum dust furnaces, which would use the refuse from coke to reduce running costs. However, the chairman's subsequent remarks suggested that his reluctance to improve gas quality was really because the directors' priority was to keep production costs down and deliver maximum dividends each year. He noted that unlike half of other gas companies over the past year, they had been able to maintain their dividend level. Nor, unlike many other companies, had they raised their prices. That was, in part, he maintained because they 'had not adopted many of the new-fashioned ideas in making new and different kinds of gas or employed any of the new inventions for simplifying the stoking of the retorts'. The chairman also emphasised that the volume of gas sold by the company was now 171 per cent more than it had been when he first became a director in 1871. Much of that increase was due to the growing use of gas heaters and cookers; and he noted that in addition to those they had sold, the company now rented out over 200 gas stoves. He hoped that these additional uses of gas would be boosted by a gas exhibition which was to be held in the fashionable Albion Assembly Rooms the following week, 'with an experienced lady [from the Nottingham School of Cookery] giving daily demonstrations on the use of gas as a cooking agent.'

Although offering an upbeat report to shareholders, the directors did not escape criticism. One shareholder disliked the cosy convention of re-appointing retiring directors each year and forced an election, but his nominee was defeated, and the board's membership remained unchanged. Another shareholder wanted to reverse the decision to increase the directors' fees by 33 per cent, which had been agreed at the last AGM. He maintained that it 'had caused a great deal of dissatisfaction amongst the shareholders.' However, that motion too was defeated.

The trading conditions for the remainder of the year were difficult. At the 1893 AGM the chairman explained that the company had been faced with a sharp rise in the price of coal, followed by a strike in the coal industry which had increased it still further. At the same time, the market value of coal tar and sulphate of ammonia had fallen. In addition, to maintain the quality of the company's gas, it had been necessary to install two new scrubbers. Despite these factors, the chairman boasted that the gasworks produced almost 10 million cubic feet more gas than the previous year, at an average of 16.25 sperm candles, and the company had been able to declare maximum dividends without resorting, as most of the countries gas companies had done, to raising prices. The fact that, despite the difficult trading conditions, the company again declared the maximum dividends allowed by law was not missed by local people. One of them wrote to a local newspaper, mocking the tone of the annual report and the claim at the

AGM that the company's main concern had been to provide a good service to the public in difficult times. In a tongue-in-cheek letter he made it clear that he had no doubt that the company would have raised its prices if that had been necessary to maintain its maximum allowable dividends.

> What a lot of nice, kind-hearted gentlemen the directors and shareholders are, to be sure. You wouldn't believe it hardly, what sort of trials and tribulations that unhappy combination of strikes and depressions have had for them during the past year, and how magnanimous and self-sacrificing they have been through it all. I am afraid that the general public are not half grateful enough for the good things bestowed. Just imagine, in all these trying times they refused to increase the price of gas. It was such a grand opportunity to do it, too, when people were feeling the keen pinch of poverty so, and hundreds of men walking about in enforced idleness. The temptation came strong upon them, for they were actually pressed to raise their taxes, as other companies had done. But they resisted it right nobly. Of course they knew they must have the full dividend of 10 per cent – naturally they looked for that as they looked for darkness after daylight – and they got it too. But I wouldn't suggest that they might have increased the rates if there had been no other source of making up the required profits. Not I. FRIAR JOHN (*Shields Daily Gazette*, 30 March 1893).

In 1893, the company announced its intention to sell its site between Hudson and Northumberland Streets at the east end of the town. The area of 1600 square yards, with a 112-feet frontage on to Hudson Street, went on the market in May 1893. Within its 'massive boundary walls' was a 3-roomed house, a large stable, and a yard with sheds. The site was auctioned off and bought by a local builder. The sale contributed to the increased profits which were announced in 1894. Instead of raiding reserves to maintain dividends, the company was able to carry a balance forward, thanks in large part to the reduced price of coal. Again, there had been an increase in the consumption of gas, which the chairman was keen to point out contrasted with most other gas companies in the country. However, he warned the shareholders that, after 22 years, the no longer new gasworks at Minton Lane needed further investment: to increase the efficiency of the gas purification process; introduce an elevator to lift coke from the trucks on to the railway sidings; install a new sulphate of ammonia plant and extend the carbonising plant. These changes were duly made and reported to the shareholders at the 1895 AGM.

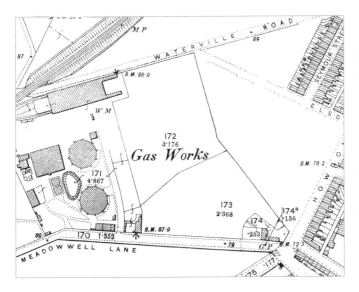

Section of the 1894 Ordnance Survey map of North Shields showing the Minton Lane gasworks courtesy of the Godfrey Edition, Tyneside Sheet 2, North Shields and Chirton (www.alangodfreymaps. co.uk). Note that Howdon Road had now been constructed and there are rows of terraced houses in the vicinity. Note too that Minton Lane is still known as Meadow Well Lane at this stage. We have been unable to determine precisely when or why the name was changed.

Once again, the directors had stood their ground when served another request from the Borough Council to reduce their prices. That helped them to declare another good year's trading with the usual maximum dividends. Although there were signs that the long-anticipated competition from electricity for lighting was imminent (especially when across the river, in South Shields, a scheme was underway to install electric lighting on a section of the main street), William Hardie, the engineer of the Tynemouth company, was not unduly concerned. That was in part as he explained in a lecture at the Albion Assembly Rooms because lighting via electricity was still considerably more expensive than gas lighting. The other reason he was not unduly concerned was that the Welsbach gas mantle was now readily available in North Shields and represented a major advance on the kind of gas burners previously available. Older readers may remember those delicate and easily damaged textile cups, which produced a surprisingly bright

An original North Shields Gas Company gasholder can be seen in this 1900 image of flooding at the Low Lights, adjacent to Carr's Pottery. Note the holder at the original site was still in place even though the later gasholder constructed at the Hudson Street site had been advertised for scrap in 1893.

incandescent light. Their introduction, along with reliable pre-payment meters, allowed the gas industry not only to compete with electricity for lighting for several decades further but also increase the domestic demand for gas.

Overall, 1895 may have been a good year for the company but it ended badly, with the death of its 67-year-old chairman, John Moffat, who owned a drapery business in the town. Mr Williamson, a former chairman, took his place.

Tragedy

The year 1896 began with a major tragedy at the Minton Lane gasworks. On 20 January, what should have been an unpleasant but otherwise routine task of removing and replacing a layer of iron oxide from the floor of the 30 feet wide purifying box of the ammonia house, ended with six men dead.[50] At the inquest on 4 February 1896, a representative of the Alkali Works Inspectorate explained that during the process to purify coal gas it was necessary to distil the ammonia given off. During the process, sulphuric acid, and sulphuretted hydrogen (H_2S) were given off, which were condensed with iron oxide. It was when the oxide had absorbed so much that it became foul that it had to be removed and replaced. It was essential, when this was done, to turn off the valve which allowed the gas to enter the box. In his evidence, William Hardie, the company's engineer, explained that the purifier was cleaned about every two weeks, so it was a routine matter with which those involved had considerable experience. The accident occurred after most of the spent oxide had already been removed from the box over the previous few days. For a reason never established, on this occasion, the valve was not fully closed and when John Main entered the box, he was immediately overcome by the H_2S gas. Charles English, who had been standing on the wall of the tank, was also overcome, and a witness saw him fall into the box head-first. William Vickers, the works foreman, David Taws and Christopher Cumpson, then jumped into the box but succeeded only in pulling English to the side of it before being overcome themselves. Only Cumpson managed to get out alive. At the inquest, William Ray described how, on hearing a commotion, he and William McGuire ran over from the retort house and saw men lying prostrate in the box. Before entering it, he took the precaution of stuffing his mouth with cotton waste (a technique he knew could help to prevent the inhalation of gas). He advised McGuire to do the same but reported that he had replied 'it's alright' before he too succumbed to

---

50 The dead were (in alphabetical order): William Brown (who died later from the after-effects of his attempt at a rescue), Charles English, a labourer, married but with no family; Joseph Main, an unmarried labourer; William McGuire, a fireman, married with a family; David Taws, a labourer, married but with no family; and William Vickers, a married man with a family. The two injured men were J. Patterson and Joseph Forster. Subsequently, Royal Humane Society medals were awarded to William Ray and James Cummings, and certificates to John Johnson, John Patterson, Joseph Forster, Henry Harrison, Thomas Cook, Joseph Vickers, Christopher Cumpson and William Brown.

the fumes. Ray managed to get the foreman Vickers to the edge of the box, and others helped pull him out, but he died soon afterwards. Even with the cotton waste in his mouth, Ray felt giddy and had to leave the box, inhale deeply, and replace the cotton waste before returning to the rescue attempt. Eventually, with the help of others on the edge of the box, he got his workmates out. Despite two doctors administering artificial respiration, five men died on site. Of another three men overcome during the rescue, one died a few days later and two others were expected to suffer lasting ill effects from their exposure to the H_2S. The inquest jury concluded that the cause of death of the men was 'asphyxia as a result of inhaling sulphuretted hydrogen.' They also concluded that two of the men died in the execution of their duty whilst the other men lost their lives in attempting to rescue their workmates. The cause of the accident, the jury concluded, was that the valve to the box had accidentally been left open a little.

Although the company was to claim in its 1896 annual report that it had been exonerated from any blame, that was not the case. During the inquest William Hardie, the experienced and highly regarded company engineer, admitted that he was unaware that respirators were required equipment in chemical works for such emergencies. The jury recommended not only that the provisions of the Act be carried out but that steps should be constructed in the pit so that people could enter and leave it more easily. In commenting on the accident, the editor of the trade journal *Gas World* remarked that he understood that such steps were already more or less standard in gasworks and that 'where they are not the lesson of North Shields will, it is hoped, be sufficient.'

In a small town, in which the local population had a developed sense of identity, the funeral was an occasion for an outpouring of grief. On 23 January, five hearses, and 17 carriages carrying the close relatives and friends of those who died, made their way to Christ Church.[51] Because McGuire had been attached to the naval reserve, the band of the Wellesley Training Ship, 50 men from the naval reserve and several of the crew from the Medusa, a naval vessel moored in the Tyne, attended the

Memorial in Preston Cemetery to those killed in the 20 January 1896 accident (photo courtesy of Mike and Jim Scott). One side of the impressive memorial is inscribed with the following words overleaf.

---

51 At this stage William Brown was still alive.

service along with representatives of the company and numerous members of the public. Thousands more people lined the route to show their respects as the funeral cortège made its way from the church to Preston Cemetery.

ERECTED
BY THE EMPLOYEES OF THE
TYNEMOUTH GAS CO.
TO COMMEMORATE THE DEATH
OF THEIR FELLOW WORKMEN
CHARLES ENGLISH
AND
JOHN MAIN
WHO WHILST FOLLOWING
THEIR EMPLOYMENT WERE
ASPHYXIATED BY AN ESCAPE OF
SULPHURETTED HYDROGEN GAS
AT THE TYNEMOUTH GASWORKS
ON THE 20th OF JANUARY 1896
ALSO
WILLIAM VICKERS (FOREMAN)
WILLIAM VENUS M^cGUIRE
DAVID TAWS
WHO LOST THEIR LIVES IN A NOBLE
ATTEMPT TO RESCUE THE ABOVE
ALSO
WILLIAM BROWN
ONE OF THE RESCUE PARTY
WHO SUCCUMBED TO HIS INJURIES
AT A LATER PERIOD.

The Tynemouth Gas Company paid for the funerals and provided some initial temporary help for the families, until a relief fund was set up. Its own contribution to the fund was 100 guineas, equivalent to about £40,000 in 2022: not much when divided amongst six families, especially in a year when everything had gone well for the company financially, and dividends were again paid at the maximum rate. To put the 100 guineas for six families in perspective, the companies' two auditors were each paid 20 guineas for their services. Fortunately, the bereaved did not have to rely solely on the company and several local events raised an additional £500 for the relief fund. One of them was a concert and dance at the Albion Assembly Rooms leased at the time by Arthur Jefferson (the father of the then six-year-old boy later to become known to the world as Stan Laurel).

Chapter 6

The New Gasworks at Minton Lane (Phase 2)

The Threat of Municipalisation

Over the years, criticisms of Tynemouth's gas company had often been accompanied by calls for the gas supply to be brought under municipal control. Those demanding the municipalisation of the water supply were even more vociferous. The local, privately-owned, water company had declined an opportunity to merge with the Newcastle and Gateshead Water Company in 1869. Subsequently, it struggled to meet the growing demand for water and was obliged to start buying additional supplies from the Newcastle company at the then going market rate. As its financial situation deteriorated, so too did the quality of the water it provided from its own resources. Much of it was pumped from a disused colliery shaft in Shiremoor and polluted before it reached the surface. From there it drained through fields 'heavily manured with town refuse'. The water then made its way to the Red Burn, where it was further polluted by the red precipitate which gave the burn its name. Sold to consumers without any filtering, the precipitates in the water were sometimes so substantial that they blocked water pipes. Things came to a head in 1896. A Bill was introduced into Parliament and in 1897 the Tynemouth Corporation Water Act gave the Council the power to acquire the North Shields Waterworks.

It was not a coincidence that, in the same 18 November 1896 local newspaper, listed side by side with the sixteen clauses of the Tynemouth Corporation Water Bill, were eight clauses of a new Tynemouth Gas Bill. The latter was represented as being mainly about raising more capital. However, it was also designed to consolidate the company's monopoly position and make it more difficult for the Council to municipalise the gas company in the way that it was doing with the local water company.

At a special meeting on 11 January 1897, the company chairman reminded the shareholders that the residential areas of the Borough were expanding very quickly and that places like Cullercoats, Whitley and Monkseaton, which had been small villages a few years ago, now had significant populations. To meet the anticipated demand for gas, the company engineer insisted major changes were necessary.

> I am of the opinion that it is impossible to continue adding to our present works each year only as much as the year's increase demands, because you cannot put up retort houses, gasholders etc piece-meal, and we could not, even were it possible, take proper advantage of all the recent improvements for cheapening production, such as regenerator furnaces, stoking machinery, elevators and conveyors, and the like, by making small additions to the present plant. It is therefore desirable, in my opinion, that we should duplicate our plant by erecting new works complete with all the recent improvements on our ground adjoining our present works.

The chairman continued:

> Such new works would require us to have a total producing power of at least a million and a half cubic feet per day, and with the necessary railway sidings and other modern plant and appliances, distributing plant, and a liberal but necessary allowance for pre-payment meters it would, on Mr Hardie's estimate cost over £120,000 … spread over 12 to 14 years.

On the same day that the gas company's shareholders agreed unanimously to the proposal to submit a new Bill to Parliament, the Borough Council held a meeting of ratepayers and property owners to seek authorisation to oppose the Bill, unless clauses were introduced to safeguard the interests of ratepayers. It is noteworthy that the issues which most concerned the Council do not appear to have figured significantly in the gas company's meeting even though they would have been known, given that Horatio A. Adamson was both Tynemouth Borough's Town Clerk and the solicitor to the gas company. The now familiar concepts of 'conflict of interest' and 'declaration of an interest' do not appear to have been taken seriously in local government, or at least in the Borough of Tynemouth, at that time. As it happens, Adamson's dual role did not last much longer. He became ill shortly after the meeting and his role with the gas company went to another solicitor.

The issues that most concerned the Council were, first, the all-embracing clause 5 of the Bill which would allow the gas company to 'enter into agreement with any other county district or parish council, local, sanitary, or other authority, body, company, persons or persons, either within or beyond the Company's limits of supply, for the supply of gas in bulk or otherwise, to such councils, authorities, bodies and persons.' One councillor pointed out that if this were to be agreed, along with the projected increase in the capitalisation of the gas company, its stock would be greater than the rateable value of the whole Borough. He insisted that if they did not challenge the Bill, they would be helping 'to create a huge monopoly which would be a great barrier to their progress if they sought to take over the gas supply as well as the water supply.' Secondly, the Council was concerned that there was nothing in the Bill which would oblige the gas company to match the cheaper prices and better-quality gas now being offered by other companies in the north-east of England. Nor did the Bill acknowledge that the Council already had a provisional order that would allow it to replace gas streetlighting with electric lighting. The Council further sought that a clause be introduced into the Gas Bill to oblige the company to reinstate streets properly after they had been dug up to lay or maintain gas mains. One councillor noted that Bedford Street had recently been re-paved from top to bottom but that, within a few days of the work being completed, the gas company had ripped it up and left it 'in a fearful condition', despite the company having received a notice from the Council 'to attend to their pipes, if necessary' before the re-paving started. To applause, another speaker is reported to have said, 'Speaking as a businessman, to businessmen, before the Council approaches the directors, it would be better to strengthen their hands with power to oppose the Bill. They must go with a bayonet in their hands.' The motion to oppose the Bill was carried unanimously (*The Shields Daily News*, 12 January 1897).

Sufficient concessions were made by the gas company for the Council to withdraw its opposition to the Bill. As well as reductions in price and improvements in quality, it was agreed that if the Council deemed it appropriate it could replace up to 50 gas streetlamps each year with electric lights. Also missing from the Bill was any mention of the company's wish to extend its scope beyond its existing boundaries. It is noteworthy that when the Bill was later considered in Parliament, it was reported that 'the object of the Bill is to *consolidate* the existing shares and stocks of the company ... and authorise the company to raise additional capital for the extension and improvement of their *existing* gasworks' (our italics).

That was later followed by an explicit statement that 'This Bill does not authorise the construction of any *new* works' (our italics). This terminology seems to have been deliberately disingenuous. It was at odds both with the company chairman's claim in January (that the Bill was necessary because the company needed to 'duplicate our plant by erecting new works complete with all the recent improvements on our ground adjoining our present works') and with how these developments were described by the company when completed in 1903.[52]

The preparedness of the gas company to make these several significant concessions suggests that its Bill may have always been, in part, a negotiating ploy. By seeming to give way to the Council's demands, it reduced the likelihood that the Council would take any action to municipalise the gas supply.

Although the gas company may have survived the threat of municipalisation, it was soon subject to a different kind of threat from Tynemouth Council. After decades of fraught relations with the town's private water and gas companies, the Council had taken a precautionary measure to ensure it did not end up in the same subservient position with respect to electricity. It had acquired a provisional order which gave it the authority to generate and supply electricity to the town – at a time it chose to do so. It was obliged to confront the issue in 1898 when an application from the British Electric Tram Company was made to run two services, using an overhead electricity supply, from the ferry landing to Saville Street, and another from the Grand Parade Tynemouth, through Cullercoats into Whitley. At the initial inquiry into the proposal, the Council opposed it, because the company wanted to purchase the Council's option to provide the town's electricity supply. Instead, the Council, insisted that its support for the new tram system was conditional on the company purchasing electricity from a Council plant – even though no such plant had even been designed still less built at that stage! Indeed, the members of the Council who considered the issue seemed unable to make up their minds. A sub-committee was set up in August to consider submitting a Bill to Parliament for 'a scheme of tramways in the Borough to be worked by electrical *or other power*' (our italics). Eventually, in May 1899, the Council applied to the Local Government Board for permission to borrow the capital needed to build a power station 'by Tanners Bank'. Tenders went out in August and in the closing days of December it was reported that the plant should be in operation 'in the early part of next year'.[53]

---

52 The passing of the new legislation coincided with the resignation, because of failing health, of W. B. Davidson, the company secretary who had been with it for 43 years and who had also been the Borough of Tynemouth's first Town Clerk. He died in February 1900. On his resignation from the company he was replaced by J. J. Carr.

53 Trams had been introduced in North Shields in 1880 but were horse-drawn. From 1881, trams powered by steam, were run with varying degrees of success by a succession of companies. The last of them, the North Shields and Tynemouth District Tramways Ltd., ran them until taken over by the British Electric Traction Company in 1899. It changed the name of the company to The Tynemouth and District Electric Traction Co. Ltd. and built a new electric tramway from the New Quay in North Shields to Whitley. It opened in 1901, after Tynemouth Corporation had enhanced the local electricity supply. The line was further extended to the Whitley Bay Links in 1904.

At the gas company's 1899 AGM, the chairman referred to the impending competition from electricity, but insisted there was room for both. Thanks to the diversification of the company, away from its earlier reliance on lighting, he was able to claim that the company was in a stronger position than ever. Maximum dividends had been paid again and additional income channelled into the reserves. Such financial success seems to have been based, in part, on the maxim that 'if you look after the pennies, the pounds will look after themselves.' Consistent with that, the company had taken a 12-year-old boy to court in March because, whilst in the gasworks yard to buy coke, 'he had stolen a quantity of metal, valued at 3d, from a scrap heap'. For this petty crime, the boy was fined 2s 6d, ten times the value of the scrap he had taken.

Although two years earlier the company's engineer had claimed that significant improvements were not possible without duplicating the gasworks, some parts were overhauled and led to 'much better results … first in the retort house by getting more gas per ton of coal, and second by reducing waste and leakage from defective mains, services, and meters' (over a thousand had been repaired during the previous year). In addition, new stores and workshops had been constructed on site, equipped with 'excellent machinery for doing repairs to the distributing and manufacturing plant promptly, cheaply and efficiently.' The company also now had Board of Trade certified equipment for testing gas meters, including the 397 penny-in-the-slot meters that had been installed in the locality. But much more was planned for the two acres of additional land that had been acquired.

At its 1900 AGM, the chairman congratulated the company on its success in tracing 'gas unaccounted for'. He then explained to the shareholders how, although the gas yield was up by 6.4 per cent, the revenue received for gas was up by 8.9 per cent.

Now every gas company suffers from a malady known as 'gas unaccounted for' and as all gas after it is made passes through and is registered by a large meter at the works, the difference between the quantity so registered, and the quantity paid for by the consumer, less of course what is used on the works etc, is the 'gas unaccounted for', and one of the amusements of every gas manager is to try and lay hold of this straying and very volatile quantity. We have so far succeeded, in that we have reduced the percentage of loss from 9.2 per cent, which it averaged the 10 years previous to 1898, to 8.3 per cent in that year, and this year it is again reduced, to 6.7 per cent. This percentage of loss will bear very favourable comparison with other gas companies. We are an old gas company, and many of our mains and services have been in for a long time. … First, we have renewed many hundreds of faulty services we have tested, and, where necessary, regulated burners in the streetlamps, so that they will only burn for the stipulated five [cubic] feet per hour. We have had a large proportion of the private meters brought in and tested, and where found incorrect and out of order, repaired and adjusted. Many of these meters have been in use for periods ranging from 10 to 20 years and were found to be worn out and registering heavily against the company. … We have during the same period renewed many of the large mains. The result of all this is, that now we are able to face a very considerable increase in the price of coals without undue alarm, and should the high prices now ruling not be maintained too long, we may yet hope that no serious advance in the price of gas may be necessary.

During the same chairman's report, shareholders were told that extensions at Minton Lane were underway. The land had been enclosed by 'a suitable wall' and tenders gone out for an overhead railway. The plans for the retort house, purifying

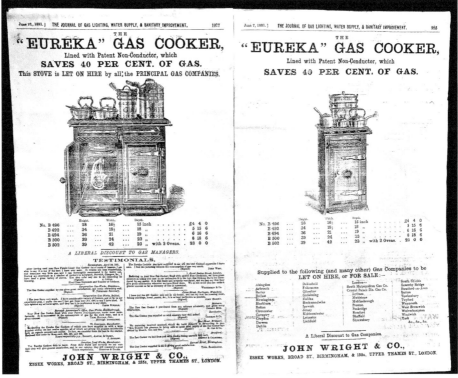

Advertisement for Eureka gas cookers targeted at gas companies in The Journal of Gas Lighting, Water Supply and Sanitary Improvement *21 June 1881, on display at the National Gas Museum in Leicester:* www.nationalgasmuseum.org.uk

and boiler houses were well advanced and it was anticipated that they would be ready in the latter part of 1900. The expenditure was subsequently raised by the release of up to £30,000 of new ordinary stock which, based on average earnings then and in 2022, is the equivalent of about £12 million.

> Great attention has been given by our engineers to ensure that only the most approved and economical methods are adopted … The directors are satisfied that the new works will be model ones, both in efficiency and economy.

The initial years of the twentieth century went well for the company. There was a steadily growing demand for gas from existing and new customers. The number renting the popular Eureka cooking stoves increased by 20 per cent between 1901 and 1902 and the number of consumers using automatic pre-payment meters increased over the same period by almost 90 per cent. Even the markets for residuals, which had often been a problem for the company in the past, was satisfactory.

The Growing Competition from the Electricity Industry

On 3 April 1901, Tynemouth Borough's own municipal electricity works on Tanner's Bank was opened, in the same Low Lights area of the town where both the North Shields and Borough of Tynemouth gasworks were first located. The power station opening ceremony was conducted by the Mayoress, Mrs Dalglish, who asserted that 'electricity was a great improvement on the gas system' (but failed to mention that both were generated from coal).[54] From the outset, the plant had enough capacity to light 15,000 lamps and all the power needed for the electric trams running in the Borough.

The original pre-payment meters provided by gas companies took 1d coins. This later Smith's meter took 6d or 1s coins. Note the padlock to try to prevent people from breaking into it. Image courtesy of Lynn Farleigh.

The safety of the system was emphasised at the opening ceremony. The switchboards governing the power for the trams were fitted with automatic 'cut-out' switches so that should a cable break, the current would immediately cut out

---

54 She was presented with a gold brooch, set with diamonds and rubies, with the cluster of diamonds representing an electric light. This unique brooch appeared on an episode of the BBC TV programme *The Antiques Road Show* in 2019 and was valued at between £1,500 and £2,000.

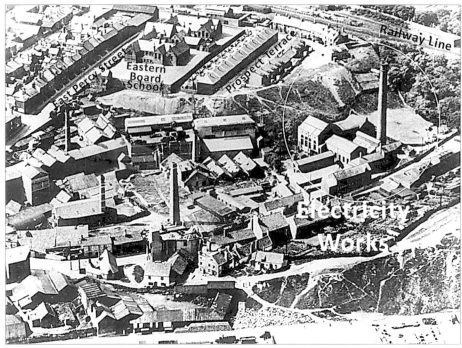

Aerial image of the Tynemouth Borough Council's Electricity Plant on Tanners Bank, in the industrial Low Lights area of North Shields. Also shown is the Eastern Board School, built in 1875, complementing the Western Board School built near to the Minton Lane gasworks in 1872. The source of the image is unknown but was probably taken by the well-known local photographer Roland Park.

and there would be no danger to those in the vicinity. However, that did not stop other kinds of accidents occurring.

ELECTRIC CAR IN COLLISION

On Saturday night, while one of the electric trams was proceeding along Tynemouth Road, it came into collision with Mr Charles Petrie's potato-chip van and seriously damaged it. The van overturned and fish and chips and all the paraphernalia used by Mr Petrie in his business were scattered about the roadway in hopeless confusion. The driver and two little girls who were in the vicinity had a narrow escape from injury (*The Shields Daily News*, 17 June 1901).

Just months later, it was the directors of the gas company who had cause to be embarrassed. In December, there was an explosion which 'blew up a portion of the roadway and pavement' whilst gas company workmen were looking for an escape of gas in the cellar of a confectioner on West Percy Street. Fortunately, no one was injured (*The Shields Daily News,* 28 December 1901). That was not the only unfavourable publicity the company received that year. Earlier, employees of the gas company, after finishing a Friday night shift, became involved in a brawl, which had begun as a dispute whilst they were still at work. In addition to the injuries sustained using fists, one of the men was badly injured by a blow to the head with a bottle. Another received knife wounds to his nose, above his eye and on his neck, which were sufficient to keep him from work for two weeks even 'under the most favourable circumstances'. In summing up, the spokesman for the magistrates concluded that:

> They had an impression that there was a very large amount of disorder going on in the gas yard, and if it was caused by excessive drinking on the part of the men, and he believed it was, they hoped that the company would take steps to prevent men from going out for a drink.[55]

Even though the magistrates further concluded the use of the bottle and knife could have had fatal consequences, only two fines, of 5s each, were issued. This would suggest that the magistrates regarded the pilfering of a small bit of scrap metal from the gas company, to be almost as serious as the crime of actual bodily

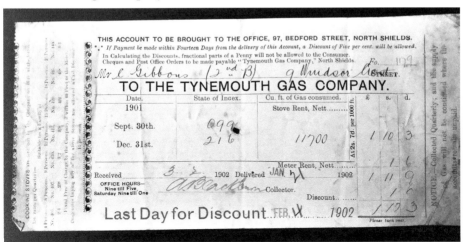

Tynemouth Gas Company bill.

---

55 What the magistrates do not appear to have considered is that the intensity of the heat in gasworks was such that many of men had no other option but to drink frequently and copiously to prevent themselves becoming seriously dehydrated. However, at that time in North Shields, the quality of the drinking water was questionable. It was because of its poor quality that the service came under municipal control in 1897 and it was not until 1908 that the newly constructed Fontburn Reservoir was opened and marked a major improvement in water quality. One consequence of the poor quality of drinking water is that it encouraged many people to drink beer because it was safer than water (see Lawrence, 2016 pp.121-127).

harm. Not long before they had levied a fine of half of that amount against a 12-year-old boy who had stolen a small piece of worthless metal.

Shortly after this public criticism, the company's image suffered a further blow in September 1901. Although at the AGM, the chairman had been optimistic that an increase in the price of gas could be avoided, it was raised by as much as 15 per cent.

Nevertheless, despite such potential setbacks, the company continued to flourish, with no indication that the competition from electricity was making any significant difference. At its 1902 AGM the maximum dividend allowed by law was paid to shareholders as usual. It was reported that the number of 'ordinary' (i.e. not business) customers was up by 5 per cent; the number of pre-payment meters by 89 per cent (to 4,109); and the number of rented cookers by 20 per cent (to 1,294). To meet the increased demand for gas, production was up by 10 per cent (to 369 million cubic feet). As a further indication of the company's ambitious plans, the chairman explained that when the current developments at Minton Lane were complete, they would be able to produce 1.25 million cubic feet of gas per day and still have the capacity to double that if necessary. A new retort house had already been completed, along with high-level railway and stove store, and boundary wall. Tenders were out for automatic stoking machinery, coal elevators, coke conveyors, boilers, condensers, engines, exhausters, and scrubbers. Further tenders went out later in the month for engine and boiler houses, engine foundations, boiler seatings, and a chimney shaft and flue. They were to be financed by £16,000 of additional capital (the equivalent of about £6 million in 2022).

The extent to which the company's directors were preoccupied with making profits for themselves and their shareholders became further apparent in May 1902. Queen Victoria had died on 22 January 1901, after being on the throne since 1837. She was succeeded by her son, Edward VII. His formal Coronation ceremony was scheduled for 26 June 1902, and Tynemouth Council hoped to mark the occasion with, amongst, other things, unusually bright local illuminations. To that end, the gas company was asked if it would be prepared to supply the Council with free gas for the two days of the celebrations. The company declined to do so on the spurious grounds that as mere directors they could not take a decision on behalf of their shareholders (something which they often did) yet chose not to call a special meeting to sound shareholders out on the proposal. All they did was make a small donation toward the occasion. However, the company did choose to make a gesture when the Boer Wars came to an end in June 1902. The town marked the occasion with a huge parade and numerous civic events and the Mayor requested householders to illuminate their homes. The gas company played its part. The local newspaper reported: 'The outside of the Tynemouth Gas Company's Offices in Bedford Street was a complete blaze of light, and the effect was most interesting' (*Shields Daily News*, 3 June 1902).

In the event, the Coronation celebrations planned for later in the month had to be postponed. The King developed appendicitis and his doctors concluded that only emergency surgery could save his life. The celebrations that had been planned in North Shields for the Coronation then became a celebration for his survival after what, at the time, was pioneering surgery. The celebration also represented a contest between the local electricity and gas companies, and between private enterprise which had dominated the nineteenth century and the municipal-based form of socialism increasingly favoured in the twentieth. The local newspaper adopted a relatively neutral stance but, though devoting more words to the display by the gas company, suggested that the finest display was that put on by the Council. Unfortunately, no images of the displays have survived.

In response to the Mayor's request, a very large number of inhabitants of the Borough of Tynemouth illuminated their residences and places of business last night, and the general effect was most attractive. The Corporation set the example by lighting up the Town Hall. The front of the building was ablaze with red, white and blue electric bulbs; there were two large illuminated discs bearing upon their faces counterfeit presentments of the King and Queen; while at the eastern end of the building appeared the sentiment 'Long May He Reign', with the letters E R underneath, the whole being formed by electric lights. Some thousands of people were assembled in Saville Street awaiting the illuminating of the building, and when the lights flashed out there was quite a demonstration of cheering. The next finest show in the town was at the Tynemouth Gas Company's offices, the front of which was practically one mass of flame. The showroom windows on the ground floor were illuminated by about 80 new pattern incandescent gas burners, each giving a light of over one hundred candles, or between eight and nine thousand candles altogether. The burners were tastefully arranged, and the elegant globes were mostly of pretty colour, causing a delightfully brilliant effect. Externally, the whole building, even along the eaves of the roof, besides every window, was outlined by numberless gas burners, each containing several holes, forming the jets into representations of roses, tulips and other flowers. In addition to all these numberless lights, a large star was fixed in the centre of the building, and on either hand the letters E R shone brightly. Above all was mounted an excellent representation of the Union Jack, which appeared to be waving proudly over the thousands of admiring eyes in the street below (*Shields Daily News*, 1 July 1902).

When the postponed Coronation was held in August, the local newspaper reported that the gas company's premises were lit up in the same way, for two nights. There was no comparable report to suggest that the Council had repeated their electrically powered display on the Town Hall.

Even at that early stage in the life of the municipal electricity company, there were indications that it was going to have to compete with more than the local gas company. The privately-owned Newcastle Electric Supply Company was already encroaching on its territory. When the North-Eastern Railway Company embarked on an ambitious plan to electrify its network, beginning with the line from Newcastle to Tynemouth, it had agreed to have its power supplied by the Newcastle company. A further reminder of the Tynemouth company's vulnerable position came in 1903 when, although the Earsdon Urban Council were in negotiations with the Tynemouth Gas Company to provide gas lighting for New York and Murton, they were planning to have the other parts of the district lit by electricity supplied not by the municipal Tynemouth company but the private Newcastle Electricity Supply Company. The threat from the Newcastle company was to become more direct in the following years.

The private Tynemouth Gas Company was in a stronger position to withstand competition from the municipal electricity company, than the latter was to withstand competition from the private Newcastle electricity company. It enjoyed a local monopoly and by the time of the 1903 AGM, the extensions at the gasworks were close to completion. To mark the occasion, the company published a souvenir booklet for its shareholders, in which descriptions of the changes were accompanied by a collection of photographs. The company's assistant engineer also described the changes in great technical detail (including the separate cost, detailed measurements, and function of every component) in an article in the *Journal of Gas Lighting*.

Very early in his article, the company's assistant engineer drew attention to the fine boundary wall which has survived to the present day and is now all that is left of the gasworks. Made of brick, with a panelled effect, it is 9' 6" (2.9m) above ground and 3' 3" (1m) below ground.

Coal was brought to the works by rail, something easily achieved because the original site had been

A small section of the Minton Lane gasworks perimeter wall at the junction with Howdon Road. The huge retort house is the most obvious of the structures that can been seen behind it.

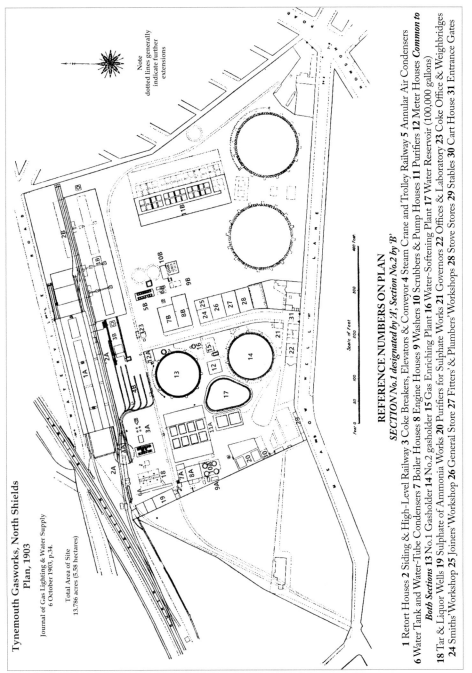

Tynemouth Gasworks, North Shields
Plan, 1903

Journal of Gas Lighting & Water Supply
6 October 1903, p.34.

Total Area of Site
13.786 acres (5.58 hectares)

REFERENCE NUMBERS ON PLAN

SECTION No.1 designated by 'A'; Section No.2 by 'B'

1 Retort Houses 2 Siding & High-Level Railway 3 Coke Breakers, Elevators & Conveyor 4 Steam Crane and Trolley Railway 5 Annular Air Condensers 6 Water Tank and Water-Tube Condensers 7 Boiler Houses 8 Engine Houses 9 Washers 10 Scrubbers & Pump Houses 11 Purifiers 12 Meter Houses *Common to Both Sections* 13 No.1 Gasholder 14 No.2 gasholder 15 Gas Enriching Plant 16 Water-Softening Plant 17 Water Reservoir (100,000 gallons) 18 Tar & Liquor Wells 19 Sulphate of Ammonia Works 20 Purifiers for Sulphate Works 21 Governors 22 Offices & Laboratory 23 Coke Office & Weighbridges 24 Smiths'Workshop 25 Joiners'Workshop 26 General Store 27 Fitters' & Plumbers' Workshops 28 Stove Stores 29 Stables 30 Cart House 31 Entrance Gates

Scale of Feet

Feet 0   50   100   200   300   400 Feet

Note dotted lines generally indicate further extensions

Plan of the envisaged Minton Lane developments. Although the plan does not make it clear, neither of the two large gasholders had been built at this stage, which is why they are not numbered. The one to the left was constructed in 1905 but the projected large gasholder to the right was never built. The two numbered gasholders in the table below (13 and 14) are the original gasholders. Note that in 1903 the road alongside the gasworks is still labelled Meadow Well Lane. Source: Journal of Gas Lighting and Water Supply, 6 October 1903, courtesy of the Warrington Gas Archives.

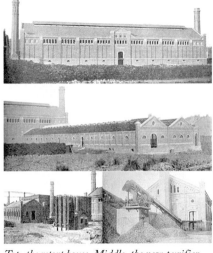

Top, the retort house. Middle, the new purifier house. Bottom left, the scrubbers, condensers, engine, and boiler house. Bottom right, the new coke conveyor, and breakers. Source: Journal of Gas Lighting and Water Supply, *6 October 1903, courtesy of the Warrington Gas Archives.*

located alongside the North-Eastern Railway line. Once on site, 10-ton waggons containing coal ran along a 17' high railway. They were moved as required by a compressed air driven capstan, controlled by a single operator using foot pressure. Once in position, the contents were discharged into the store by opening the bottom boards of the waggons. The new retort house shown at the top of image 42 was 294' long and 75' wide and had 12 settings of eight retorts (i.e. 96 with room for double that number). Because it was so close to houses, it had two 100 feet high chimneys.

Although the account of the extended site in the trade journal is much too detailed and technical to summarise here, the local newspaper did include a much-simplified description for its lay readers.

There are large openings in the walls of the [retort] house through which the coal runs, regulated by steel sliding doors, and it is then raised by means of steel buckets, on the dredger principle, into large steel hoppers which are fixed overhead at each end of the house, the retorts being charged at both ends. The charging machines, one of which is placed at each side of the house, are each operated by one man, and receiving coal from the overhead hoppers can travel along the house from retort to retort, charging them with surprising rapidity. The doors are then fastened upon the retorts, and in about six hours all the gas that can be got out of the coal has been extracted.

The drawing machine then comes into operation. The doors are removed from the retorts and a long rake is thrust in and draws out the incandescent coke. One man manipulates this machine also, and he being six or seven feet away from the hot mass suffers very little of the discomfort which the unfortunate individual who has to do this sort of thing by hand.

As the white-hot coke drops from the retort mouth it falls upon a conveyor. This consists of endless chains with steel bars across at intervals, and the contrivance is in motion constantly along a sort of channel way. The bars carry the coke away, sprays of water cooling it, and the coke is

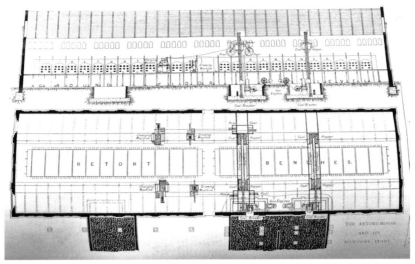

Plan of the interior of the new Minton Lane retort house. Source: Journal of Gas Lighting and Water Supply, *6 October 1903, courtesy of the Warrington Gas Archives.*

eventually tipped outside of the retort house ready for consignment or general use. In connection with this tip, there is a breaking machine, which crushes the coke into lumps suitable for household consumption. [The coke conveyor belt and breaker are shown in the bottom right-hand corner of the image above]. The coke required for the regenerated furnaces, which are fired on one side of the house only, falls upon a movable shoot attached to the drawing machine as it is drawn from the retorts, and thus passes into the furnaces without cooling, the furnace being below the retorts. The whole of the coke machinery is driven by gas engines but the charger and drawing machine are driven by compressed air. All the coke 'breeze' of dust is used up on the premises for heating boilers etc, a special forced draught making its consumption quite complete.

The gas passes through the ordinary treatment after its manufacture, but the various kinds of purifying apparatus are most conveniently arranged [see the middle and bottom left images opposite]. There are all kinds of workshops attached where any kind of repair work can be done, and, taken altogether the complete installation is one of the neatest most compact and thoroughly modern in the country (*Shields Daily New,* 7 March 1903).

The company chairman further explained at the 1903 AGM that:

The new works … are a complete and independent gasworks in every particular, with the exception that the gas made is passed into the old holders, and the whole of our lighting area is now being supplied entirely from this new portion. It has been working at its capacity for about three months. … The number of men required to accomplish the same work is reduced to less than half that required under the old system, but, more than this, the men are working under very different conditions. In the old house the stokers had a very arduous and trying class of work to perform, and, unfortunately, for some time to come during the winter months will still have it to do until we are able to alter the old house to the automatic system also. … In the new carbonising house, the men are protected from the intense heat of the retorts and furnaces almost entirely, and the mechanical stokers do the whole of the hard work, the man in charge simply manipulating a series of levers which set in motion the air motors.

The chairman went on to broach the controversial subject of the quality of the gas being produced. He asserted that now that gas was increasingly being used for cooking, and that incandescent mantles were so much more effective than traditional burners, there was no longer a need to produce gas to the 16-candle level. Moreover, if the quality could be reduced to 14-candle power, cheaper coal could be used, and the price of gas reduced. A Parliamentary Bill, including that reduction, was published early in 1904, along with proposals to extend gas mains to Earsdon; seek authority to raise capital by a further £15,000; and borrow a further £50,000 (comparable, in total, to about £48 million today). At a special meeting in February, the chairman explained that more capital was needed because of the rapid growth in the population of the area supplied, and the increased demand for gas because of the growing popularity of penny-in-the-slot gas meters. If current trends continued, he pointed out, the demand for gas would double in a decade. The current priority was a new and larger gasholder because, with the new facilities in operation, there was now insufficient capacity for even a single day's output. The Bill was subsequently passed. It came at a propitious time because the gasworks manager and engineer, (now Councillor) William Hardie, had by November been with the company for 25 years. At a special event he was presented with a gold watch, courtesy of the employees of the company. In his acceptance speech, Hardie said he was proud that gas was now half the price it had been when he took over the post, and 'it had been brought about without the workmen being detrimentally affected.' He added that hours of work had been reduced (from a 12 to an 8-hour day); working conditions greatly improved, and wages had increased over the period by 25 per cent (*The Shields Daily News*, 28 November 1904).

During his remarks at the 1903 AGM, the chairman drew attention to the growing popularity of pre-payment meters. However, they were not without disadvantages. They needed to be situated in convenient places within dwellings so that coins could be inserted into them, much like a child would insert coins into a money box. Perhaps inevitably, some of those short of money seem to have thought of them in precisely that way. Frequent reports of thefts from gas meters began to be reported in the local press. For example, in August 1903, a woman broke into her own meter and was subsequently fined five shillings and ordered to pay 10 shillings costs. At the same hearing, two boys aged 12 and 13 were charged with breaking into and stealing from their parents' meters. Each was sentenced to three strokes of the birch.

At the 1905 AGM, the chairman reported 'a year of continued progress and prosperity in every department'. Business was booming to such an extent that the company needed larger premises for its increased office staff and had secured the use of buildings in Little Bedford Street, parallel to its main offices on Bedford Street. The growing number of customers who lived beyond North Shields and Tynemouth also warranted the opening of a second showroom (and offices) in Whitley. The following year, a new showroom was opened in North Shields adjacent to the company's offices in Bedford Street. It featured appliances for producing large quantities of hot water. They included *John Wright's High-Pressure Boiler* which 'will send hot water at 150° [F] to any part of the house, night or day. By this arrangement hot water baths can be had continuously'; the *Wilson Heater* for 'hot water for shaving at the lavatory basin'; and *Fletcher and Russell's Multitubular Boiler* 'capable of heating 30 gallons of tea water' (*The Shields Daily News*, 6 November 1906). At the gasworks site on Minton Lane, work had started on the planned new gasholder to hold 1.5 million cubic feet. More than a hundred years later, that was the gas holder that was part dismantled in 2009 and then eventually removed entirely by NGN in 2017.

The chairman's report in 1906 was equally buoyant except for a new threat posed not by competition from the electricity generated by the local Tynemouth Council's municipal electricity works, but electricity generated by the much bigger and technically innovative private Newcastle Electric Supply Company. The Newcastle company had submitted a Bill to Parliament to allow it to supply power to a wider area, including the Borough of Tynemouth, Whitley Bay, Monkseaton, Earsdon and Seghill. It also sought the power to enter into working agreements with other local electricity power companies. Tynemouth Council perceived both elements of the Bill as threats. After having for many years been dissatisfied with the service the local community was receiving from the private monopolies supplying gas and water, Tynemouth Council had tried to avoid the same happening with electricity by setting up its own municipal company. Now it was in danger of being undermined by another private monopoly and worse, one from outside the district. Readers who currently reside in and around North Shields, who since 1974 have been governed at a distance by the much larger and more disparate North Tyneside Council, may need to be reminded that in the nineteenth century when the North Shields economy was booming, and many of its most successful business people were also elected members of the local council, there was a strong sense of identity as well as community pride amongst them and indeed the population of North Shields as a whole. The editor of the *Shields Daily News* saw it in similar terms. In a leader he wrote:

TUESDAY, FEBRUARY 6, 1906
TYNEMOUTH ELECTRIC SUPPLY
A DANGEROUS ATTACK

The public interests of this town are seriously threatened by a powerful private monopoly. The Newcastle Electric Supply Company are now promoting a Bill in Parliament, one of the objects of which is to bring the County Borough of Tynemouth within the area of their operations and give them power to compete for custom amongst the ratepayers' own electrical undertaking. Putting it another way, the ratepayers are shareholders in a concern in which £90,000 has been invested (the equivalent of at least £35 million in 2022) and which, with the consent of Parliament, they established for the purpose of supplying themselves with electricity, and now the Newcastle Company, whose primary object, be it remembered, is private gain, and not public benefit, and who for their own undertaking enjoy a monopoly over a very wide district, are seeking powers to enter North Shields, select there those customers whose business will yield them satisfactory profits, and leave, to be supplied by the Corporation, those whose custom they think not worth having. We observe that the Council are taking steps to oppose the Bill, and we think rightly so. We trust that the opposition will be conducted strenuously and determinedly to a successful issue, for we feel assured that the permanent and real interests of the Borough will be sacrificed if the company achieve their objective.

The editorial went on to challenge, in various ways, the claims that the price of electricity would come down if the scale of operations were bigger. It pointed out, for example, that in just its fourth year of operation, the Tynemouth plant was pricing over a million units of energy at just over half the cost of a similar output from the Newcastle company in its 11th year. It also made the obvious point that as the Tynemouth company was not allowed to supply areas beyond its boundaries, it would be an extraordinary injustice if a private company had official approval to do just that, especially when it already had a monopoly in its own area.

> The success of the Company's Bill, therefore, threatens a calamity of no little magnitude to the Borough of Tynemouth, just beginning to recoup itself for years of heavy expenditure in this and other departments of municipal administration.

A week later, the newspaper's editorial added the following observation, which reflected the long-running, often bitter, and sometimes violent, conflict in past centuries between Newcastle and North Shields and, indeed, all the other towns on the river. With the connivance of the Crown, Newcastle had in the past claimed a legal monopoly of trade on the Tyne. This new threat from Newcastle was a reminder of that enmity.

> We have never had much to thank Newcastle for, save in the matter of litigation, and this new attempt to interfere with our Borough in its efforts to control its own affairs is one more instance of the arrogance and selfishness of a city which would like to constitute us one of its suburbs, and let us live only in 'the suburbs of its good pleasure' (*The Shields Daily News*, 12 February 1906).

Similar sentiments were expressed by the Mayor of Tynemouth.

> This is neither more nor less than an attack on the vital interests of this Borough, and it is the duty of our Corporation to oppose the Newcastle Bill to the utmost of its power.

But it was an unequal struggle. The Newcastle company was in a different league to Tynemouth Council's local municipal electricity company. It was not just bigger. It was a nationally significant and genuinely innovative company. For example, as early as 1900, it had become the first UK company to use three-phase electrical current, which it generated at its Neptune Power Bank Power Station. It was also the first UK company to supply electricity for industrial purposes as well as lighting. From then the Newcastle company had grown at a remarkable rate, building more power stations and taking over so many neighbouring companies that by 1912 it had evolved into the largest integrated power system in Europe.

First reports in May 1906 suggested that Tynemouth Borough Council had achieved a remarkable victory over the aspirations of the Newcastle company.

> We, at noon today, received a telegram from the Town Clerk of Tynemouth stating the deputation from the Tynemouth Council now in London have succeeded. The Newcastle Electric Supply Company … we are informed are to have no *locus standi* to supply within the Borough (*The Shields Daily News*, 4 May 1906).

However, it soon became clear that there had been a fudge, and the form of words employed by the Town Clerk to describe what had happened was mere face-saving obfuscation!

> It was resolved that in the event of an offer being made by the Newcastle Electric Supply Company Ltd., for a supply in bulk which the deputation having charge of the Bill, on the advice of their experts, think would be more advantageous to the Corporation than continuing to produce their own electricity, that the deputation would be authorised, should it be deemed expedient, to accept the same (*The Shields Daily News*, 17 May 1906).

The editor of the local newspaper put it more bluntly.

> The Electricity Committee decided that it would be preferable to come to terms with the Newcastle Company, and not to continue to produce their own electricity.

The face-saving element of the capitulation was that the Council would continue to be the nominal supplier to its own local citizens, although what it would be selling to them was electricity generated by the private Newcastle company. It was an arrangement which would soon lay them open to criticism not just because the investment in Tynemouth Council's own municipal generating plant had been squandered, but because the local municipal electricity company charged its customers more for the power it received than it was paying the Newcastle company to provide it.

The immediate practical consequence of the agreement was that the Council's electrical engineer was:

instructed to prepare a report for presentation at the special committee showing what plant will be lying idle during eight months of the year, and also showing what will be the full cost of the administrative charges under the proposed altered system of working, and what reduction of charges, if any, and staff, he proposes. It was further decided that the electrical engineer be authorised to advertise for sale the new plant which was ordered before the arrangement was made with the Newcastle Electric Supply Company (*The Shields Daily News*, 17 May 1906).

By 1907, the growing popularity of electricity was beginning to impact on the local gas company. At its AGM, the chairman noted that compared to previous years there had been only a small increase in the gas consumed and revenue was down. Two of the company's largest consumers, The North-Eastern Railway Company and the Albert Edward Dock, had switched from gas to electric lighting. Despite that, dividends remained at the maximum level allowed by law. The chairman was also able to report that the 'large' new gas holder, with a capacity for 1.5 million cubic feet had been completed. Although designed by the company's own engineer, Councillor William Hardie, who also acted as clerk of works for the project, much of the construction had been contracted out to companies outside the Borough. The concrete tank, for example, had been supplied by the Nowell company of Stockton and the steel holder by the Whessoe Foundry company of Darlington.[56]

The company were keen for the public to see their modern plant, and in August 1907 it was the turn of the members of the North Shields Literary Society. They were shown around by Cllr. Hardie, the company engineer who in 1909 would become the town's Mayor; his assistant A. C. Hovey, and Mr George Duncan, the 30-year-old company chemist (who will feature prominently in subsequent chapters). The tour focused particularly on the contrast between the old plant and the new, and especially the retort houses where the old methods of filling and cleaning the retorts by hand had been superseded by what the local newspaper described as 'ingenious and scientific machines.'

The huge annular condensers were next pointed out, and the manner in which the coal tar and ammoniacal liquor is removed was very carefully

---

56 The Whessoe Foundry was formed in 1890 but had roots going back to 1790. For many years it concentrated on manufacturing equipment for the gas and oil industries. It went on to supply reactor vessels for most UK nuclear power stations. It is currently owned by Samsung and concentrates on cryogenic and low temperature storage. Although the company's headquarters remain in Darlington, construction is carried out in several places around the world.

explained. The utilisation of these waste products is particularly interesting – how from the coal tar valuable compounds such as aniline dyes, phenols etc are obtained while, by redistilling the ammoniacal liquor, ammonium sulphate is obtained. The engine rooms were also visited, where gas exhausters and air compressing machinery for supplying motive power were to be seen. Further apparatus for the purification of the gas was viewed, that for the naphthalene by means of oil being especially noteworthy. The enriching apparatus, large meter, the gasholders, the offices, chemical laboratory, and the photometrical appliances used, were all visited in turn, and many interesting facts about their working were obtained during the visit which lasted over two hours and was thoroughly enjoyed by all present (*The Shields Daily News*, 22 August 1907).

At the 1908 AGM, the company chairman, Joseph Williamson, reminded the shareholders that by May he would have been a director for 21 years. He explained to his audience that at the time he was appointed, the Welsbach incandescent mantle had just been invented but was too expensive and not sufficiently reliable to be in general use. Since then, not only had the price come down and reliability improved, but the inverted, shadowless mantle and burner had become available. That had given gas lighting a renewed popularity. He also noted that at the beginning of his time on the board, cooking by gas was virtually unknown, now the company hired out over 7,000 cookers. Within the last eight years, efficient gas fires had also become available, conveniently at the same time as pre-payment meters. Compared to the days when the company was reliant on lighting, and streetlights were not used in the summer months, the use of gas was now much more uniform throughout the year. When he was first a director, the quantity of coal carbonised was 18,800 tons giving a gas yield of 174 million cubic feet. In 1907, 42,000 tons of coal were used, with an output of 457 million cubic feet. The sale of coke had increased over the period by 260 per cent and there had also been an increase in the sales of other by-products, particularly because of the improvements made to the gasworks in 1903. As a result, whereas at the beginning of his term in office the income from the sale of by-products was equivalent to 56 per cent of the expenditure on coal, it had reached the equivalent of 80 per cent in 1907. The 1903 improvements to the gasworks had also, he emphasised, reduced manufacturing costs at the same time as improving the working conditions for the company's employees, justifying the decision to double the capacity of the retort house by the winter months. The shareholders appear to have been delighted at the report, not least because their dividends were again the maximum allowed by law.

A change was also announced to the management of the gasworks. The assistant engineer, Arthur Hovey, was leaving to take up the post of chief engineer with a gas company in Milan (*The Shields Daily News*, 25 February 1908).

In contrast, supplying electricity to the town was not going smoothly. Neither the Council nor consumers seemed happy with the new arrangement with the Newcastle company. At a Council meeting in June 1908, the Town Clerk reported that a claim was being made against the Newcastle company for its failure to supply current in accordance with the terms agreed in 1906. The Council's electrical engineer also expressed his belief that the Newcastle company's meters 'were fast' and the Council was being over-charged. Consumers were complaining that the municipal company was charging them twice as much as it paid the Newcastle company for the electricity and yet, despite that, was losing money. Additional problems arose in 1909 and, in each instance, the Council was obliged to make concessions. In contrast, the only significant event of the year for the gas company was that, now that the Minton Lane works was operating so well, the old gasholder at the Lowlights was dismantled, and the site put up for sale. In December 1912, it was announced that the land, 'at the foot of the Brewhouses Bank' had been purchased by Irvin and Son Ltd. Subsequently, part of it was exchanged for a plot owned by the local Council. That proved mutually beneficial and allowed the Council to widen a section of road that would not have otherwise been possible.

The gas company made further steady progress in 1910 but 1911 proved more difficult, as the chairman explained during the 1912 AGM. A rail strike threatened the supply of coal to the gasworks and so larger reserves had to be kept on site than was usual. Later in the year, in response to the threat of a nationwide strike of miners, the company built up even larger reserves. A third issue had been demanded, on the part of gas workers generally, for a significant increase in wages. The chairman reported that this had been resolved in North Shields with 'a kindly and friendly spirit prevailing on both sides' and hoped that 'the wage question is settled for some time to come.' Despite the increased outlay on coal, all the other indicators for the company showed an improvement and the dividends, as usual, were the maximum allowed by law. During the meeting, it also emerged that although coke 'commands a large scale locally', sufficient was being produced for some to be 'shipped abroad.' In addition, 431 tons of sulphate of ammonia had been sold during the year, 'largely used abroad for agricultural purposes.' The coal tar produced was used mainly in making roads but also 'sprayed on country roads to mitigate the dust nuisance.' This is how the chairman explained this new use to the shareholders.

A specially prepared tar free from water is necessary for this purpose. To meet the demand for this class of tar, a special up-to-date plant has been erected on the works, to deal with large quantities of tar. Practically the whole of the water can thus be eliminated. The prepared tar can then be pumped into barrels on the works or delivered direct into tanks on rail. I believe we are the pioneers in this new departure in the north of England (*The Shields Daily News*, 26 February 1912).

Over the preceding year, the company had produced just short of 500,000 gallons of such tar. Overall, the sale of residuals was sufficient to offset the manufacturing cost of gas and keep the price down for consumers. What also became apparent during the ensuing months is that just as the company was exporting its products beyond the local district, so too it was sometimes using coal that had not been mined locally or could even be delivered to the works by train. So, for example, in March 1912 a shipload of coal arrived at the Albert Edward Dock in North Shields, from the mines of Methil on the Firth of Forth and then had to be 'carted' to the gasworks, an operation which took a considerable number of days.[57]

The chairman's report to the 1913 AGM, after reporting another good year of trading, referred to the nationwide six weeks' miners' strike which began in March 1912. Once again, precautionary action had been taken before the strike was underway. By the time it began, the company had filled every available space in the works with 5,000 tons of coal, which proved to be enough for the duration of the strike, and so, unlike in many other towns, there was no interruption in gas supplies to customers. The 'residuals' business side of the gasworks had also done well. The demand for coke had increased as the availability of coal had decreased, and the demand for dehydrated tar was so great that the company was considering doubling its capacity to produce it.

What received only scant mention during the meeting was the Bill which had been introduced into Parliament towards the end of 1912, which sought permission to extend the company's network to Earsdon, Seaton Delaval and Hartley. It also proposed the introduction of a co-partnership scheme with the workforce. Although no details were given, it is reasonable to assume it would have resembled the scheme introduced in George Livesey's South Metropolitan Gas Company, which gave the company's workmen a share in the profits, in addition to their wages. With growing industrial unrest nationally, it would

---

57 In this still early period for motor vehicles 'carted' probably would have meant by 'horse and cart'.

seem the company saw co-partnership as a way of institutionalizing the relatively amicable way that demands for better wages had been settled locally in the past. Tynemouth Council expressed reservations about both these (and other) parts of the Bill. It was concerned that there was no limit to the amount of new stock which might be issued under the co-partnership system. As always, the councillors were apprehensive at the growing sphere of influence and power of a private monopoly, especially given the Council's own short-lived attempt to provide competition through its municipal electricity undertaking. The Council also had reservations about the lack of detail in the proposed co-partnership scheme. It wanted guarantees that partnership bonuses would be related to the price of gas (the higher the price the lower the bonus) as in the London scheme. In the event, the Parliamentary committee declined to approve the principle of co-partnership, unless and until an actual proposal was put forward and agreed by the Board of Trade. In this and several other respects, what was eventually passed was a significantly watered-down Bill, and the Borough Council members had reason to feel vindicated by their opposition to some of its clauses.

Despite this minor setback for the gas company, its overall position was strong, and the future looked bright. However, the relatively halcyon days, when it was free to develop as it chose, and virtually guaranteed maximum dividends to its shareholders, were soon to come to an end in circumstances from which the company would never fully recover.

1914-18 The Great War and its Aftermath

The year 1914 began with business as usual. In May, the company took over the main hall in the Northumberland Square Presbyterian Church for the week to exhibit its products. On show, were gas cookers, gas fires and water heaters. One hot water circulator pump featured heavily because it had a patented thermostatic valve, which reduced the gas use to the minimum necessary to maintain the selected temperature. The new Thermox gas fire also featured, which it was claimed was more efficient than earlier models and 'completely abolishes the necessity of placing a dish of water in front, being so hygienically constructed that there are no obnoxious fumes'! In addition, each afternoon and evening, there were lectures on 'high class and household cookery', using the company's gas cookers, by Mrs H. C. Grey LNCC MCA who it was boasted had a 'first-class diploma from the Nottingham School of Cookery' (*The Shields Daily News*, 8 May 1914).

However normally the year may have begun, by the end of June the whole of Europe was plunged into what, because of its scale and horror, came to be known variously as *The Great War,* the *First World War* and *The War to End War.*[58] On the 28th of June in that fateful year of 1914, a Bosnian Serb nationalist assassinated the Archduke Franz Ferdinand, the heir to the Austro-Hungarian Empire. At a time when foreign travel was much more limited than today, such an event would have seemed immaterial to most British people. However, because of a series of interlocking treaties, Europe was effectively divided into two power blocs, with Austria-Hungary, Germany, and Italy in one, and the UK, France, and Russia in the other. It was because Russia backed the Serbs, that when Austrian-Hungarian forces shelled the Serbian capital of Belgrade, it brought many other countries into the conflict. By August, the UK was at war. Initially, it involved only its professional army which fought alongside French troops to try to thwart the advance of German forces into France. However, the war came closer to home on 16 December 1914 when three German cruisers, no more than 400m from the shore, shelled the coastal town of Hartlepool, destroying the gasworks and hitting many public buildings and about 600 homes. The ships went on to attack Scarborough and Whitby. There were 137 deaths and an estimated additional 600 casualties. The attacks created concern in all north-east coastal towns and led the North Shields gas company to post this notice in the local newspaper the following day. The warning was reissued several times during 1915.

IMPORTANT NOTE
TO ALL
GAS CONSUMERS

THE TYNEMOUTH GAS COMPANY

may receive instructions at any time of day or night
from the General Commanding Tyne Defences
to turn off the supply of all gas at once.
It is hereby requested that if at any time
the supply of gas be turned off that every
consumer shall at once turn off the gas supply
to their homes and/or premises by means
of the main cock fixed near the meter, also
all cocks on gas fittings, fires, cooker, and
other gas apparatus being immediately
made secure. If the gas is turned off during
the evening of any day it will not be turned
on again before 8 a.m. the following morning.

---

58 Tragically, the latter term was to prove entirely inappropriate and just 21 years after the armistice which ended the First World War, the same countries were plunged into the horrific Second World War.

> The supply of gas was turned off in the
> whole of the Tynemouth Company's area on
> Wednesday morning in accordance with
> instructions received from the General.

At the Company's AGM in March 1915, the impact of the war was the first item on the agenda. The chairman told the shareholders that 45 of the company's employees had volunteered for military service and expressed his hope that they would all return home safely after a short war. He continued:

> What immediately concerns us as a profit-earning company is the loss of revenue caused by the serious drop in the price of residuals. This is mainly caused by the lack of buyers on the Continent, who, in ordinary times, use large quantities of our coke. … The restrictions have been placed upon the lighting of the streets in the borough and the outside areas of supply. A large number of lamps remain unlighted, and the outside illumination of shops and public buildings has been much reduced. Public houses are closed two hours earlier, and, speaking generally, consumers of gas are going to bed earlier, and are consequently using less light and heat. Despite these problems, largely because of the 9 per cent increase in the cost of gas, the revenue from gas sales was still slightly more than in the previous year.

Shortly afterwards the company announced a further increase of 10 per cent in the price of gas.

Perhaps because of the need to halt the decline in business, the company began to run frequent lectures and demonstrations, at different venues, including its own Bedford Street premises, on cooking with gas. Younger readers may not know, or need to be reminded, that during this period a large proportion of homes had a ready alternative to using gas cookers. Houses were equipped with what were known locally as 'black-leaded stoves', a term for the substance used to polish them. They combined both open coal fires and the means to boil water and cook (either directly over the fire or in the attached oven) with heat generated from the same coal fire.[59] Between May 1915 and the AGM in March 1916, 44 events were held to encourage people to use more gas, and close to 5,000 people attended them. Here are just two of the numerous advertisements that were

---

59 Danny Lawrence: 'My mother cooked (very successfully) on such a black-leaded stove until 1955 when I was 14 years old. Only then, after we moved following her serious illness, did we buy a shiny new, white enamelled gas cooker with four burners, eye-level grill, and oven, and have an Ascot gas heater installed which gave us running hot water for the first time.'

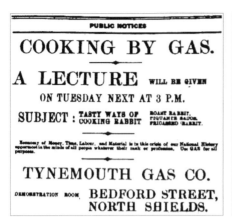

Tynemouth Gas Company advertisement in the Shields Daily News 29 January 1916 on tasty ways to cook rabbit by gas. Courtesy of the British Newspaper Archive.

Tynemouth Gas Company advertisement in the Shields Daily News 19 February 1916 on how, in view of THE SERVANT PROBLEM, to cook three popular puddings, by gas. Courtesy of the British Newspaper Archive.

placed in the local newspaper during the year. They both appeared prominently on the front page.

Streetlighting was curtailed during the war. Plans to do so in coastal towns like North Shields had been prepared by Winston Churchill in 1913, in his role as first Lord of the Admiralty, and were implemented in 1914. Similar restrictions were extended to the rest of England in 1916. The lighting of shops and other places of business were also significantly reduced. Overall, the gas output from Minton Lane was down by 20 million cubic feet, and that figure would have been greater had there not been a partially compensating increase in the use of gas in munitions factories, and for gas cookers, fires, and water heaters. Despite the difficult, wartime conditions, the company was still able to declare maximum dividends at the 1916 AGM. Its financial position had been helped by an increase in the price of gas, a reduction in the price of coal, and greater efficiency in the retort house. Other items in the annual report related specifically to the circumstances created by the war. The workforce was paid a war bonus as well as higher wages. Eighty workers had volunteered or been conscripted, and many departments were operating with fewer staff, though some of the vacancies had been filled by women. As well as increased labour costs, the company was paying substantially more in insurance premiums.

Large premiums have had to be paid to cover the insurance of the works, the distribution plant, as well as the offices at North Shields and Whitley, with the stocks of all these places, against bombardment and air raids.

The insurance has had to be carried out on a liberal scale, in order that the interests of the shareholders may be protected against any probable loss through damage caused by our ruthless enemies.

In addition to the naval bombardment of some coastal towns, there were 20 air raids in the area around North Shields. For example, on 15 June 1915, a Zeppelin L10, passed over the gasworks in North Shields before dropping a bomb on the adjacent town of Wallsend, and then several more on Hebburn Colliery and Palmer's shipyard (immediately across the river to North Shields), which led to 17 men being killed and 72 injured. Shortly after the company's 1916 AGM, 22 people were killed and 128 injured after a bombing raid in and around Sunderland, less than 10 miles away 'as the crow flies'. Five Zeppelins were involved in another raid close to the gasworks on 8 August. Because of the danger to the gas supply during these attacks, the North Shields gasworks was put under military control throughout the war and on 12 occasions was ordered to completely shut down the gas supply to customers. The Ministry of Munitions also insisted there were no extensions to the existing network during the war. Making matters worse for the company is that in an incident unrelated to the war, a fire destroyed the Whitley Bay showroom and offices in August 1916.

Despite all these problems, a further increase in the price of gas, along with more use of coke locally, meant that the company's shareholders still received the maximum dividend on their investments. At the 1918 AGM, the chairman was also able to report that innovations at the works were continuing despite the difficult conditions.

This company was the first in the north to recognize practically the value of broke coke for domestic purposes. It is about 20 years since the first coke-breaker was erected at the works. I remember well the huge pieces of coke that were sent out for household use and how one had to go into the cellar and break these pieces up either with a big hammer or the chopping axe. That way is gone, and everyone now, whether for home use or other purposes, has the coke delivered in nice pieces and free from dust. This old coke-breaking machine has been in constant use ever since it was erected, and it is now absolutely worn out, and although we also have another machine at work, it is necessary to erect one in place of this old one.

Loading coke by hand is a slow and costly method. The new machine will be fed directly from the retort house ovens along the coke conveyor to the coke-breaker, where it will be broken into pieces of suitable size.

The broken coke will then pass over a grid where the dust is removed into a large hopper. The motor-waggons or carts go under this hopper and by working a lever the coke falls directly into them: this will save a great deal of manual labour and much time. When the work is completed, coal will not be touched by hand from leaving the colliery until it is tipped in the form of coke at the customer's door.

The chairman had one final thing to tell shareholders.

We have started to erect on the works, and expect shortly to have in use, a crude benzol recovery plant. It is being put down at the request of the Ministry of Munitions solely for reasons connected with the war. It is a costly piece of plant, particularly at present when prices are so high, and the directors expect little profit to be made by its introduction. Still, it was a patriotic thing to do (*The Shields Daily News*, 6 March 1917).[60]

At the start of 1918, the Tynemouth Gas Company was poised to put another Bill before Parliament which would allow it to increase the price of gas beyond the level allowed by existing provisions. At a special meeting called on 23 January, the chairman described it as 'a war measure' … 'forced upon them by the conditions – high prices of material, high price of labour, and other heavy charges.' The threshold needed to be raised, he argued, as 'a reasonable precaution to enable them to meet the very modest dividend which their [ordinary] shareholders got of 5 per cent' (as compared to the company's preferential shareholders who received 10 per cent).[61] In other words, the directors regarded a 5 per cent dividend as an absolute minimum, whatever the knock-on consequences for consumers. The only dissent from shareholders present at the AGM was that they should ask not for the right to raise the threshold by 25 per cent but by 40 per cent! Consistent with its ambition to raise the threshold price of gas, the company had already notified the Borough Council of its intention to almost double the specially negotiated charge for streetlighting and increase the charge for the maintenance of the lights. As a result, the Council asked its electrical engineer to report on whether it would be

---

60 Benzol (benzole) which consists mainly of benzene and toluene, was blended with petrol and used as a motor fuel. The plant also produced materials for explosives.

61 Holders of ordinary shares (sometimes known as common shares) are in a less favourable position than preferential shareholders. The latter can expect to be paid a fixed dividend each year, before ordinary shareholders receive any dividend. In the event of the company being wound up preferential shareholders are paid first and ordinary shareholders last. If there is nothing left after preferential shareholders are paid, then ordinary shareholders receive nothing.

advantageous to install cables for electric streetlighting instead. News of the price increase in gas led one local resident to write to the local newspaper in protest and suggest (as had been done so often in the past) that the price hike was a consequence of the private company being in a monopoly position.

> … For 60 years the company have received their maximum dividend, now, when, like most other undertakings, their income is shrinking, they are hurrying to hand over the burden to their unfortunate customers, whom, owing to the company's monopoly, cannot leave them or deal next door (*The Shields Daily News*, 23 January 1917).

Before the 1918 AGM, the company lost its long-standing and highly regarded gasworks manager, Cllr. William Hardie J.P. He had been in what was described as 'failing health for a few years' but died suddenly on the way home after a session on the bench of the local magistrates court. His obituary in the local paper had this to say about him.

> During his long residence in the borough, he has won universal respect, and he was recognized as one of the most disinterested workers in the public service, a man of lofty character, and lovable disposition.
>
> Mr Hardie was born in 1857, entered the service of the Tynemouth Gas Company as manager and engineer as long ago as 1879, at the early age of 22. He was the son of the late Mr W. Hardie, who for 40 years was Secretary of the Newcastle and Gateshead Company. On completing his education at the Royal Grammar School, Newcastle, having decided to adopt the profession of a gas engineer, he entered the College of Physical Science, and subsequently passed through the engineering shop of a well-known firm. During his 39 years association with the Tynemouth Gas Company, he has carried out great developments at the works, introduced the most scientific methods of gas making, and raised the establishment to a very high standard of efficiency. Throughout his long career he has maintained the highest confidence of his directors. Occupying a high position in his profession, he was a past President of the North of England Gas Managers' Association, a member of the Institute of Gas Engineers, and an associate member of the Institute of Civil Engineers.
>
> Mr Hardie entered public life in 1904, when he was returned as representative of the Trinity Ward in the Tynemouth Borough Council. He was elected mayor in 1908 and two years later was elected to the chairmanship

of the Finance Committee, a post he occupied with conspicuous ability in the last eight years. He also rendered valuable service as a magistrate, and as a member of the Education Committee. He was a Liberal in politics, and a Presbyterian, formerly attending the Northumberland Square Church but, after his removal to Cullercoats, he worshipped at the Tynemouth Congregational Church (*The Shields Daily News*, 2 February 1918).

At the 1918 AGM, on 25 February, despite the warnings introduced into the Bill to be presented before Parliament to justify a rise in the maximum price of gas, the revenue from gas and rentals and the sale of residuals was significantly higher than in the previous year, and dividends were paid, once again, at the maximum level. Perhaps because of that, but ostensibly because of the death of William Hardie, the Bill was 'withdrawn'. Hardie was replaced by Frederick C. Willis (FCW) who had been the assistant engineer to the company for the previous ten years.

William Hardie reprinted from his obituary in the Gas World, *9 February 1918, Courtesy of the Warrington Gas Archives.*

Post-War Changes

By the autumn of 1918, the German military appear to have accepted that they could not win the war. After their last attempt at an offensive had failed, there were desertions from the army, and such disenchantment amongst civilians that many groups tried to set up alternative forms of local government based loosely on the kind of thinking which had triggered the October 1917 revolution in Russia. When the German navy mutinied rather than follow the order to launch a massive attack on the Royal Navy to try to undermine the armistice negotiations, it was evident that the end had come. Kaiser Wilhelm abdicated, and an armistice was signed on 9 November, to come into effect at the 11th hour of the 11th day of November, the 11th month.

However, although the conflict may have ended, the repercussions of the war featured prominently in the company's AGMs for years to come. At the 1919 AGM, in reviewing the previous four years, the chairman reminded the shareholders that 123 of the company's employees had served in the armed forces. Four had been decorated but, tragically, 16 had lost their lives. Whilst they had been away, the company had supplemented their service pay and kept their jobs open. At the time of the AGM, 62 of those who had been demobbed had returned to work. Also complicating the post-war affairs of the company was that it no longer needed the special machinery the Ministry of Munitions had required it to install to produce chemicals for the manufacture of explosives. In total, it had produced 172 tons of TNT and 467 tons of picric acid, sufficient for almost 2 million 18-pound shells.[62] At the end of 1918, the company was officially thanked for its efforts and, in response, took advantage of that token of appreciation to make a case to the Board of Trade for a lifting of the cap on the price of gas. Given that in the previous year the company had not needed to raise the price of gas to the threshold and yet was still able to pay shareholders the maximum dividends, it seems that the company saw the letter of gratitude from the Ministry of Munitions as too good an opportunity to miss. The application was successful. Permission was granted to raise the price of gas by up to a third.

At the same 1919 AGM, the chairman expressed his concern about the general deterioration in labour relations and growing industrial unrest.

> It was to be expected that the termination of the war, with all the strains and weariness involved, would cause a measure of unrest. It was not even to be desired that we should go back to conditions prevailing before the war. On all sides it has been recognized that the reconstruction of our industrial life on a peace basis must be carried through in a way which will give the workers the opportunity to live under healthier and happier conditions than have hitherto prevailed. Unfortunately, in the position which has arisen there is much to cause the gravest anxiety. Let us all hope that wise counsels will prevail, and that no precipitous action will be taken by any body of our workers which will bring hardship and suffering and will only result in causing a state of severe industrial depression throughout the country. In common with other industrial undertakings, this company has had to face a very great increase in its wages bill, while the cost of our raw material 'coal' has increased by leaps and bounds (*The Shields Daily News*, 5 March 1919).

The chairman's concerns were based not so much on local conditions as on the widespread unrest around Europe. Workers were not prepared to put up with the low wages and often terrible living and working conditions they had endured

---

62 The explosive yield from TNT became the standard against which the destructiveness of other explosives were measured.

before the war. The Tzar had been deposed in Russia and a revolution had taken place in 1917, ostensibly in the interests of the country's working classes. Even before the capitulation of Germany, workers' movements were growing in strength and, following the harsh terms of the Treaty of Versailles, both communism and national socialism became popular ideologies. Although at odds with one another, both were opposed to capitalism based on liberal democracy.

In the UK, although such alternative ideologies had relatively little support, Lloyd George had promised during the 1918 general election campaign that if his Coalition government won a majority there would be comprehensive reforms to tackle poor education, housing, and health, to make the UK 'a land fit for heroes'. So, what the chairman of the gas company had implied at the 1919 AGM, was that circumstances might change in such a way that the shareholders could no longer count on a maximum dividend as if it were their birth-right. He was certainly correct in anticipating a period of industrial unrest, which was greatly aggravated by the major economic slump which followed the end of the war. The industries hit the hardest were the old staples of coal, steel, shipbuilding, and textile manufacturing. The response of many employers was to lay off workers, cut wages, and increase working hours. That in turn led to a wave of strikes. In response to the strike of coal miners in October 1920, which had major implications for the coal gas industry, the government introduced a series of emergency measures to conserve coal stocks. They were the Coal Emergency; Gas and Coal Emergency; and Lighting, Heating, and Power Emergency Orders. It was the second of these which most immediately affected the Tynemouth Gas Company and its customers. The Gas and Coal Emergency Order empowered undertakings to produce gas only during specified 'essential' hours. As a result, the Tynemouth company placed this appeal in the local newspaper.

> The supply of gas to local consumers has already been restricted and modified by the Tynemouth Gas Company, under the Gas and Coal (Emergency) Order, 1920. The Company appeals through our advertisement columns to consumers to exercise economy in the use of gas in every possible way. The company stated a few weeks ago to one of our representatives that a normal supply of gas could be maintained for one month from the cessation of the mines' operations. With a lower and modified supply, it is hoped to extend that period, and with the economical assistance of the public, the Company will do their best to keep up the supply (*The Shields Daily News*, 18 October 1920).

Despite the limitations placed on the company by that Emergency Order, Councillor Rowe, at a December meeting of the Electricity Committee, complained at the quality of the gas currently being supplied to households. He described it as 'abominable' and remarked that 'if one was trying to burn two burners at the same time, one couldn't get a light from either by which one could see to read a newspaper.' He added, 'and in the streets, whether it was in the 'aristocratic' part of the town or the poor neighbourhoods, wherever gas was in use the same thing applied. The light was absolutely poor.' He went on to assert 'without any hesitation that the Borough of Tynemouth was the worst lighted town in the United Kingdom.'

Though the situation was obviously difficult for the company, it did not prevent it from celebrating Mr J. B. Williamson' 25th anniversary as its chairman. At the end of 1920, he was presented with an engraved silver rose bowl and a pair of silver flower vases.[63] However, when he stood to make his annual report at the AGM, in 1921, it was to describe a markedly different situation from that which the company had enjoyed for most of the previous quarter century he had been at the helm. In those years, the company had been in control of its own destiny; been able to take advantage of its monopoly position to expand its scale and sphere of influence, and rarely failed to deliver to shareholders less than the maximum dividend allowed by law. The picture he portrayed in 1921, was one of a company now buffeted by changing circumstances, and instructions from politicians and government officials to which it had no other option but to comply. Although the company had still declared a respectable profit, it had not paid the maximum allowed dividend. Labour costs had risen by 26 per cent and coal prices by 32 per cent. For a period, the government had banned the export of coke. Although the ban was lifted in December 1920, since then the company had discovered that the market for it had collapsed and that 'orders were practically unobtainable at any price'. The amount that could be asked for tar had fallen 30 per cent in just a few months, and that for sulphate of ammonia by 50 per cent. All these adverse trading conditions came at a time when there was a need for more capital expenditure. It had been necessary to build a new purifying plant, replace some stoking machinery, introduce a new 8-inch steel trunk mains pipe to Whitley, and

---

63 Joseph Burrell Williamson was, like other members of the Board of Directors, a leading figure in the town. Born in North Shields, he was the owner of Williamson and Hogg, a local chemical and pharmaceutical company on Union Street, and a well-known and impressive chemist's shop on Bedford Street, just a few yards from the offices of the Gas Company. The shop is remembered fondly by numerous older people in North Shields because, in addition to the usual pharmaceutical and related personal products, it roasted and ground coffee beans on the premises and the aroma from that was enjoyed by all those in the vicinity.

an extension of the mains to Percy Main. Work was also underway to improve the capacity of the plant by as much as one-third.

In the discussion that followed, one shareholder emphasised that the company revenue was now insufficient to cover the manufacturing cost of gas and that the company had, in effect, been subsidising it through the sale of residuals. Others complained that the price of gas needed to rise still further because a 3.75 per cent was 'a very small dividend'. Another complained that it was government interference on the sale of coke that had resulted in them not receiving the usual maximum dividend. Alderman Hogg maintained that whilst they had all agreed that 'the ordinary canons of finance should be put to one side for the sake of winning the war, they had every right to protest when the war had been over two years or more and industry was being strangled by government interference, and hordes of officials who ought to have been set about their business as soon as ever the war was over' (*The Shields Daily News*, 8 March 1921).

Such remarks suggest that many of the directors and shareholders of the company, along with similarly well-off people in the country, were no longer in sympathy with the sentiments of the Prime Minister, David Lloyd George, who in a speech as the war was ending in 1918 had called for the wartime spirit of comradeship to be kept on 'as long as we can.'

What is our task? To make Britain a fit country for heroes to live in. … The Great War has been like a gigantic star-shell, flashing all over the land, illuminating the country and showing up the dark, deep places. We have seen places that we have never noticed before, and we mean to put those things right. Those in charge of recruiting came to the conclusion that if the people of this country lived under proper conditions, were properly fed and housed, had lived under healthy conditions – had lived their lives in their full vigour – you could have had a million more men available and fit to put into the army. Put it at its lowest – trade, commerce and industry all suffer through it. A vigorous community of strong, healthy men and women is more valuable even from the commercial and industrial point of view than a community which is below par in consequence of bad conditions. Treat it if you like not as a human proposition but as a business proposition. It is good business to see that the men, the women, and the children of this country are brought up and sustained under conditions that will give strength and vigour to their frames, more penetration and endurance to their intelligence, and more spirit and heart than ever to face the problems of life which will always be problems that will require fighting, right from the cradle to the tomb (the Prime Minister, David Lloyd George, Wolverhampton, 24 November 1918).

During the Great War, the critically important coal industry (along with the railways) had been controlled by the government. After the cessation of hostilities, state control of the mining industry continued until April 1921, when it was returned to its private owners. They refused to honour the wage levels paid by the government from 1917-21 and insisted on a significant reduction of wages. The miners refused to accept the cut and a three-month long strike began. Although the striking miners did not enjoy the *full* support of other unions, transport and railway workers refused to handle imported coal, and industrial unrest became more widespread when wage reductions were forced on merchant seamen, and there was also a month long, well supported strike amongst dockers.[64]

When coal deliveries were threatened, the Tynemouth Gas Company took out large advertisements in the local press, urging the public to economise as much as possible in their use of gas and consider using coke as a substitute for coal. The following day, it issued a formal notification to the public that, under the Emergency Powers Act, they were now required to reduce gas pressure.

TYNEMOUTH GAS COMPANY
CONSUMERS ARE AGAIN URGENTLY REQUESTED TO
Exercise Strictest Economy in the Use of Gas

As owing to the continued prolongation of the Coal Dispute, available stocks of Coal are now critically low. Wherever possible

REDUCE THE NUMBER OF LIGHTS.
REDUCE GAS COOKING.
REDUCE THE USE OF GAS FIRES.
REDUCE THE USE OF WATER HEATERS.
REDUCE GAS FOR INDUSTRIAL PURPOSES.

THE PRESSURE OF GAS shall require to be
STILL FURTHER REDUCED forthwith.

(The Shields Daily News, 2 April 1921)

---

64 The scale of the industrial conflict on 24 April 1921 resulted in the 1921 Census being delayed until 19 June 1921.

Similar notices appeared at regular intervals throughout April with an additional notification that with the authority of the Board of Trade, the price of gas was to be increased by almost 75 per cent. Following the announcement of this huge increase, towards the end of the month, the public were informed in another series of notices that 'the Company is reluctantly compelled under the Emergency Powers Act, 1920, to comply with and REDUCE THE PRESSURE OF GAS FORTHWITH' (*The Shields Daily News*, 20 April 1920). The situation had deteriorated further by the first week in May and led to this additional notice.

TYNEMOUTH GAS
Supplies Likely to be Cut off at
Short Notice
An important notice to consumers was
issued this morning by the Tynemouth Gas
Company. The company state that owing to
the continuation of the coal dispute they
will be unable to continue the supply of gas
for more than a few days, and that unless
further supplies of coal are received by Tuesday
next the supply of gas is liable to be
shut off without further notice.
(*The Shields Daily News*, 5 May 1921)

By the end of May, further limits on the supply of gas to consumers were required. Gas was released only at mealtimes, for a total of 6.5 hours each day. 'At all other times **THE PRESSURE OF GAS WILL BE REDUCED** to a point below that which will permit its effective use in all gas apparatus, and consumers are requested in the interests of safety to see that their **GAS TAPS ARE TURNED OFF** between the periods named, otherwise there is a danger of their burners going out' (*The Shields Daily News*, 31 May 1921.) [65]

In the event, that did not happen. The miners were obliged to return to work on terms even less favourable than those they had been offered at the outset of the dispute, and the company's normal supply of gas to customers was restored on 16 July. Mr Willis, the manager of the Minton Land gasworks later explained how the company had managed to keep the gas flowing, albeit to a limited extent, without fresh supplies of coal. Before the strike began, work had started on a new

---

65 The only good news for the company during this period was that their engineer and manager, F. C. Willis, had received the honour of being elected President of the Northern Gas Managers' Association for the coming year.

plant capable of deriving gas from both coke and oil, rather than coal alone. It was completed in time to allow it to be coupled up to the coal gas plant six weeks into the strike. By then, they were down to using 30 tons of coal a day rather than the usual 130 tons but, thanks to their new plant and a 6,000-ton stockpile of coke, they were able to use 500 tons of it, along with 50,000 tons of crude petroleum, to supplement the reduced output of gas from coal.

This new development, and the restoration of coal supplies, did not signal a full return to normality for the company. It was now operating without its long-serving chairman who had stepped down at the AGM because of declining health.[66] He was replaced by Thomas Young, the owner of the Shields Engineering and Dry Docks Company.[67] Inevitably, after paying homage to his predecessor, he began his review of 1921 by reminding the shareholders that it had been a difficult trading year. He referred to the 'most disastrous coal dispute and stoppage … that had ever happened before', the abnormally hot summer, trade depression and marked fall in the demand for the company's residuals. Before the war, the return from residuals was 82 per cent of the cost of coal. It had then fallen to 68 per cent and because of the increased cost of coal and fall in demand for residuals, the ratio was now 50 per cent. Gas sales were also down by 5 per cent. Despite that, by increasing the price they charged for gas, the company had still managed to make an operating profit in 1921. But, as he explained to shareholders, the dividend still had to be less than that paid in previous years. That was a requirement of the Board of Trade's agreement to allow the company to raise the price of gas beyond the previous limit with the stipulation that, in any period that gas was sold at more than the previous maximum, dividends could not exceed 75 per cent of the previous maximum. So, within those limits, the dividend to shareholders was again as high as was permitted by law.

The chairman went on to explain another change which was being forced on the company by the Board of Trade. The Gas Regulation Act of 1920 now required the company to switch from charging by the cubic capacity of the gas sold, to charging for its calorific value. That, he maintained, was a revolutionary change because it required companies to charge by quantity multiplied by quality, measured in thermal units. Given the complaints over the years at the varying quality of the gas the company had supplied to customers, the change was plainly important. In future, the company's gas would be tested by official gas examiners appointed by local authorities. He added that the change reflected the growing

---

66 He died on 3 July from complications after breaking a leg whilst on holiday.

67 The company was established in 1899 and specialized in the repair of trawlers, drifters, lightships, and other small vessels. It merged with the North Shields Smith's Dock Company in 1955.

use of gas for cooking and heating, and the increased use of incandescent mantles which depended for their illuminating power on the quality of the gas supplied to them. The new chairman ended on a cautious but optimistic note.

> Regarding the future, I will not attempt to prophesy, but I can only assure you that the management are exercising the most careful economy, and with cheaper coals and a smaller wage bill, we have considerable hopes that most of our troubles are now behind us and we are looking forward to brighter times for our industry (*The Shields Daily News*, 14 March 1922).

He was correct, at least as far as shareholders' dividends were concerned. By 1923 they were back to the maximum allowed by law, 'compared to the miserable dividend of 3.75 per cent in the previous three years.' There had been a 7-fold increase in profits compared to the previous year, despite a 6 per cent fall in the amount of gas sold and a reduction of 30 per cent in the revenue from residuals. The profit was the result of a 30 per cent reduction in the expenditure on coal and oil, and a 23 per cent fall in the wages bill. Although this had enabled a small cut in the price customers were charged for gas, a further reduction was postponed because it was anticipated that the price of coal would soon begin to rise again.

At the AGM, the chairman indicated that he was hoping for an increase in gas consumption from new housing developments, for example in the Balkwell area to the north-west of the town. As part of that scheme, the gas company had agreed to lay a new main and run services from the mains to the meters, as well as supply and fix gas fittings in the houses. Arrangement had also been made with the Council to install 1,500 more gas streetlamps.

When the decision about streetlighting was presented to the Council's Electricity Committee, some councillors questioned why they were not installing electric rather than gas streetlighting, especially given the recent increases in the price of gas. Cllr. Lonie raised a laugh with his quip that, 'Electricity was very rarely mentioned in the Electricity Committee: it was always 'gas, gas, gas'!' Cllr. Miller remarked that he found it difficult to understand why 'they were all endeavouring to introduce electric light into their own homes, yet every time a report was brought up on the question of lighting the town in the same way, it was shelved without any adequate reason'. He was supported by Cllr. Coats who urged, 'Let us start here and now.' However, the advocates of electric streetlighting were reminded by other members of the Committee that at an earlier stage the council's electricity engineer had drawn up a plan for electric streetlighting, but they had concluded that the cost of cabling alone was much too expensive. Cllr.

Thirkle added that 'they were all anxious to have the town lighted by electricity, but they had the ratepayers to consider.' Ald. Sir Henry Gregg agreed: 'It was a question of cost, purely and simply' (*The Shields Daily News*, 23 February 1922). Local cynics, of course, not without good reason, would have wondered how many local councillors were also shareholders in the gas company. Over the years that had certainly been the case, and at the time of this discussion several councillors and aldermen were directors of the gas company, in addition to those councillors who were shareholders. What was finally agreed after a heated debate was that consideration would be given to introducing electric streetlamps to streets which already contained electric cables.

Following the meeting, Cllr. Lonie continued to press for a more extensive use of electricity, for example in schools. His demands elicited an interesting response from the editor of the national *Gas Journal*. He rejected Lonie's claim that electricity was healthier for children. On the contrary, the editorial suggested that by creating convection currents, provided there was 'a means of air ingress in the upper part of the room', gas lighting improved ventilation. In contrast, it suggested, electricity encouraged the air to stagnate. He also claimed that the almost invisible filaments in electric bulbs produced an unhelpful glare which was not present with the larger lit area of an incandescent gas mantle. Finally, he made the point that it was more expensive to introduce electric lighting, especially when gas lighting was already installed. The editor's response ended with the following jibe.

> We fancy that at the bottom of the whole business is the fact that the electricity undertaking is a municipal concern: the gas supply is in the hands of private enterprise (*The Shields Daily News*, 15 October 1923).

The *Gas Journal* editor refrained from adding, as he could have done, that Cllr Lonie was a Labour councillor, with a preference for municipal rather than private ownership.

In June, the company applied to the Board of Trade for extensive new powers, including the right to increase profits for shareholders and fees for directors but also 'grant pensions, allowances or other payments to employees of the company or the widows, families or dependants of such employees and to subscribe or make donations to funds raised for national emergencies.' Those powers were granted in November.

After several difficult years, the company chairman was able to report better financial results to the 1924 AGM. Gas consumption was up, the income from residuals had improved, the workforce had agreed to a nationally negotiated wage *cut,* and a small reduction had been made in the price of gas. He also maintained that when comparing the merits of gas and electricity, shareholders should be aware that coal gas production contributed more to the country than many people realised. The local newspaper summarised his observations in the following way.

> Gas played a very important part in the life of the community, especially in view of its very valuable by-products, which were of enormous value in many ways. For instance, coke was available for many other industries, and for domestic purposes. Tar produced materials for dressing the surface of roads, dyestuffs, creosote for pickling timber, benzole spirit for motors, and many other things. From ammoniacal liquor was produced sulphate of ammonia, a nitrogenous fertiliser second to none in the world. All these services by the gas industry were apt to be forgotten by the people who wax eloquent as to electricity and its future. … Gas producers had no desire to deny the many and great uses for electricity. … but there is plenty of scope for them both (*The Shields Daily News*, 10 March 1924).

That there seemed to be room for both was exemplified by developments in Whitley Bay later in the year. At the same time that the sea front was illuminated with electricity for the first time, the gas company opened new offices and a showroom, with living accommodation above, 'in fashionable white stone, of quite oriental design, which adds to the attractiveness of the neighbourhood. A few more buildings of this character would certainly make a favourable impression on anyone visiting the town' (*The Shields Daily News*, 9 July 1924).

That favourable mention in the local press was soon overtaken by news of a tragedy at the gasworks. A worker, tasked with cleaning a pipe, died in hospital after falling into four feet of 'scaldingly hot water' when one of the two planks on which he was standing gave way. Reading the reports of the accident makes it plain that workers were expected and prepared to take risks that would not be tolerated today.

The 1925 AGM began with a warning that there was an urgent need to replace 'old and worn-out plant', including the two oldest gasholders over the next few years. This coincided with a period when profits were down and the income from residuals was falling. The chairman described the outlook for coke as disquieting and noted that the value of tar was only about a third of what it had been 18 months earlier. As a result, the annual accounts showed a considerable overspend on capital expenditure, covered by issuing mortgage deeds at an interest rate of five per cent. The gradual reduction in the charge for gas over the previous few years had ended, and an increase was now under consideration. Nevertheless, despite these less than optimistic forecasts, dividends remained at the maximum level.

The 'delicate' nature of labour relations also received a mention at the AGM. Given that the cost of living was about 80 per cent higher than it had been pre-war, there was an inevitable demand for an improvement in wages yet, in the difficult economic circumstances following the end of the war, employers were pressing their workers to accept wage cuts. The gas industry, because of its dependence on coal, was particularly concerned by the increasingly fraught situation in coal mining. Many of the richer seams had been depleted during the war years and that led to a fall in post-war output, despite longer working hours. To ensure shareholders continued to receive dividends, miners' wages were cut by over one-third over seven years – despite the huge rise in the cost of living at the same time. In response to the deteriorating industrial relations in the mining industry, the Conservative government led by Stanley Baldwin set up a Royal Commission. Its recommendations only made matters worse. It proposed that the government's subsidy of miners' wages should end and there should be a further reduction of 13.5 per cent in wages. In addition, the owners insisted there should be a further lengthening of the working day. The Miners' Federation flatly rejected such terms: 'Not a penny off the pay, not a minute on the day.' This time, the miners seemed to have wider support and the Trades Union Congress (TUC) called a general strike 'in defence of miners' wages and hours.' The country was split between those who supported the recommendations and those who could see the miners' point of view – which included King George V who is reported to have said 'Try living on their wages before you judge them.' The government was well prepared when the strike began at one minute to midnight on 3 May 1926 and, after just a few days, with volunteers offering to act as strike-breakers, troops breaking up picket lines, and the recently formed BBC under Lord Reith abandoning all pretence of impartiality and coming out firmly on the side of the government, the *general* strike was called off on 12 May. Despite that, the miners continued to strike but, by the end of the year, because of sheer economic necessity, the large majority of them returned to work.

The impact of this miners' strike, coming so soon after the previous one, had serious consequences for the gas industry but, at the AGM in 1927, the chairman insisted that locally it had coped well, and he was once again able to declare maximum dividends. He boasted that not once during the seven months without supplies of coal from UK mines had they 'failed to keep up the required pressure of gas supplies in their mains, and never sent out gas at a less calorific value than that prescribed by law.' That was in large part because it had installed a second carburetted water gas plant on the site of the old retort house which produced gas from the company's own stock of coke. The process involved blowing a mixture of air and steam over the heated coke to produce semi-water gas. In this form, it has a low calorific value and burns with a *non*-luminous flame. However, by treating it with vaporised oil in a carburettor and then passing it over a super-heater, it was converted into the more valuable water gas. The process also had the advantage that it could be made in a comparatively small space, without much labour and the process started up more quickly than the standard process to carbonise coal. In all, during this period, Minton Lane used over 3,000 tons of coke and almost 250,000 gallons of oil to supplement its stock of coal. As a result, gas sales were two per cent more than in the previous year and the company had over 1,000 new customers, the largest increase in 18 years. The chairman added: 'While many householders had now adopted the electric light, it was gratifying that a supply of gas for a gas cooker, wash boiler or gas fire was, almost without exception, asked for in the case of all new houses recently erected, and in certain cases gas was still being adopted for lighting.' What he did not mention is that since 1926, the company was supplying gas to what was the largest gas furnace in the United Kingdom – at the nearby Smith's Dock shipyard. Sales of coke and tar were also up and, although sulphate of ammonia 'did badly', the overall revenue from residuals was up about 5 per cent on the previous year. The chairman concluded his remarks on this optimistic note.

> So far as this [coming] year is concerned, there is every prospect of steady expansion and, in order to cope with the growing demands of the cooking and heating loads, it will be necessary to re-lay several lines of trunk main in various parts of the district, as well as install additional boosting and compressing plant at the works (*The Shields Daily News*, 7 March 1927).

Takeover

Given this claim of a successful performance in such a difficult year and the marked optimism for the future which the chairman had expressed at the AGM, local people must have been astonished to read in *The Shields Daily News* in September that 'on reliable authority' a provisional agreement had been entered into between the directors of the Tynemouth Gas Company and Newcastle and Gateshead Gas Company, which if agreed by shareholders would lead to their amalgamation.

This was not the only expansionist move made by the Newcastle-based company during this period.[68] In December 1924, the Board of Trade had agreed to the Newcastle company acquiring the Walker and Wallsend Union Gas

---

68 In this and subsequent chapters, the Newcastle and Gateshead Gas Company will sometimes be referred to as 'the Newcastle company'.

Aerial view of the Tynemouth Gas Company Minton Lane gasworks on 1 October 1927, at the time it was taken over by the Newcastle and Gateshead Gas Company. The image was taken by Aerofilms during flight AFL192710. Courtesy of Historic England, EPW019846. EPW019846 – Aerial Photo | Historic England.

Company, and also the Chester-le-Street Gas Company. The 13 square miles covered by these two smaller companies meant that the private Newcastle company now had a monopoly to supply gas to the residents of an area of 173 square miles.

Unlike the Tynemouth company, which was satisfied with the methods it had adopted to survive the prolonged coal strike, the Newcastle company opted for a radically different solution to prevent it being affected in the same way again. It entered into a long-term agreement with the Consett Iron Company to take a bulk supply of the gas generated from the huge array of coke ovens which were to open in 1928, on the site of what had been Crowley's Ironworks, once the largest in Europe. The company Secretary described this contract as 'of permanent benefit to both parties' (Jackson, p.31). It may well have been to him and to the *directors and shareholders* of the Newcastle company but, during a period of high unemployment in what the government had officially labelled 'a depressed area', it was not obviously of benefit to those *employees* of the Newcastle Company involved in the manufacture of coal gas. It was certainly not of benefit to the employees of the Tynemouth company in Minton Lane.

Although couched in terms of an amalgamation, the disparate size of the Newcastle and Tynemouth companies, meant that such terminology would have fooled no one. The Tynemouth company supplied gas to the residents of an area of 28 square miles, just 16 per cent of the area over which the Newcastle company now enjoyed a monopoly. There is no question that what the directors of the Tynemouth company proposed to shareholders was a takeover. That it was not an amalgamation as the chairman preferred to call it, is readily evident from the fact that he and the vice chairman (Roland Lishman, who seconded the motion) became members of the Newcastle Board but in personal rather than their *ex officio* capacities. Nor was provision made for anyone else from the Tynemouth company to replace them as Newcastle directors on their retirement or death. The takeover was obviously attractive in hard, economic terms for the bigger company but, as will become clear, was also of significant financial value to the directors and shareholders of the Tynemouth company. When the Newcastle and Gateshead company made its submission to the Board of Trade to extend the area of its private monopoly, it sought permission 'for the transfer to the Newcastle Company of the undertaking of the Tynemouth Gas Company', including:

> … all rights, easements, powers, authorities and privileges whatsoever of the Tynemouth Company and all property whatsoever including cash balances, reserves and other funds, investments, interests, obligation and things in action belonging to the Tynemouth Company, but subject to all contracts, debts, liabilities, obligations and incumbrances of the Tynemouth Company. To provide for the dissolution of the Tynemouth Company and the winding up of their affairs. …

In compensation for the loss of all their assets, the shareholders of the Tynemouth company were to receive an equivalent number of shares in the Newcastle company. In addition, the Newcastle company undertook:

> To provide for the retirement from office of directors and officers of the Tynemouth Company and for the payment to such directors and officers as the Order may prescribe in compensation for loss of office and to the payment of by the Newcastle Company pensions to persons now or formerly employed by the Tynemouth Company.

But, whilst the directors and officers would obviously benefit substantially from the takeover, the future of the Tynemouth gasworks and its employees was not guaranteed.

> To authorise the Newcastle Company to hold and use for the purposes of *their* undertaking the lands hereinafter mentioned and on the said land to maintain alter improve extend renew and use or *discontinue* the existing gas and other works on those lands to erect maintain alter and use or *discontinue*

new or additional gasworks machinery and other apparatus and to store gas and convert and manufacture the residual products of gas (our italics).

The Newcastle company acquired not only the land occupied by the Minton Lane gasworks but also a second piece of land of over two acres 'bounded on or towards the north-east by the existing gasworks on or towards the south-east and east by Meadow Well Lane and on or towards the north-west'.

Given that the company was in the middle of takeover negotiations, it is a little surprising that it chose 15 September 1927 to announce a cut in the price of gas, when just six months before it had been defending a price rise. The reduction was made just a week before a meeting of shareholders to decide on the recommended takeover. One inevitably wonders if the reduction was designed to encourage local people to believe that they would benefit from the change in ownership. Interestingly, a *Shields Daily News* editorial on the day before the shareholders meeting noted 'There is, I believe, a feeling that an amalgamation of the two concerns will be to the advantage of consumers in the Borough of Tynemouth'. It conceded that the Newcastle company had tended to sell its gas more cheaply than the Tynemouth company. However, it pointed out to its readers that, under the terms of the takeover, the Newcastle company would have the right to charge a different rate for the gas sold in the area currently supplied by the Tynemouth company.

The crucial meeting to decide the future of the company was held on 27 September 1927. For many of those present, there was much more at stake than pecuniary and commercial considerations. For centuries, life on the Tyne had been dominated by Newcastle, with the help of royal charters designed to hold back the economic development of the river's other towns such as North Shields. Only with the advent of market economics had North Shields become free to develop in its own way and at its own pace. It had since been remarkably successful. Consequently, the takeover of the company by a Newcastle company would have had symbolic as well as commercial significance for some shareholders and many of the North Shields company's customers. The town had already had to yield to purely economic pressures when its municipal electricity undertaking had, after just a few years, gone from being a producer of electricity to no more than a distribution facility for a Newcastle-based private monopoly. Now it was about to lose its independent gas company to another Newcastle-based private monopoly.[69]

---

69 For a full discussion of this often-bitter relationship between North Shields and Newcastle, see Lawrence, Danny *Shiels to Shields. The Life Story of a North Tyneside Town* (Carnegie, 2016).

Aware of that history, and the pride in subsequent local achievements, the chairman began by referring to what he chose to call 'sentimentality.'

> It is quite likely that there are a fair number of shareholders of this company who hold a sentimental feeling as to this matter of losing our identity, and of being absorbed by the Newcastle and Gateshead Gas Company. I confess that I myself, when this question first came before me, had considerable feelings of sentiment in that direction, but after a good deal of consideration and thought, I came to the conclusion that, in these strenuous days, and with the high cost of living, together with many other factors, the attribute of sentiment today lay more in the pocket than in the heart.

That was undoubtedly the essence of the matter. A first approach made by the Newcastle and Gateshead company in 1923 had been dismissed. The Newcastle company had now made the directors and shareholders offers they could not refuse. Those holding the Tynemouth Company's *ordinary* stock were to receive £125 of Newcastle's *preference* stock for each £100 they held in the Tynemouth company. Those holding Tynemouth's *preference* stock were to be allocated comparable stock in the bigger Newcastle company, and it was anticipated that its value would be 11 per cent more than for their existing Tynemouth stock. The directors and officers would, in addition, be compensated financially for their loss of office and the Newcastle company would take on the company's mortgages.

The chairman did suggest that other considerations had played a part in the decision to recommend what he insisted on calling the 'amalgamation', but these were unconvincing. He claimed that for some years the company had made little or no progress with increased gas sales: something not supported by the evidence. He claimed they were suffering from the 'intensive competition in the matter of another illuminant' whereas the truth was that by diversifying they had found burgeoning new markets and even come close to holding their ground in terms of gas lighting. He chose to pass quickly over the fact that the Newcastle company would charge Tynemouth customers more than Newcastle customers and instead concentrated on assuring the shareholders that the company had written guarantees that 'no workman or official will be worse off in wages or security of employment.'[70]

The Board of Trade agreed to the *purchase* of the Tynemouth Gas Company by a special order on 23 March 1928. For the company's directors it was a wholly

---

70 Tynemouth Corporation objected to the takeover because of this differential charge. As a result, the terms were eased a little but there would still be higher prices in Tynemouth, in perpetuity.

satisfactory arrangement. For the company's employees, it was the start of a new chapter characterised by uncertainty and apprehension. That was acknowledged at the final meeting of the directors in 1928. The chairman referred to a report 'that had got about that Newcastle proposed to close down the Tynemouth gasworks.' In his carefully worded reply, he did not actually deny that. All he could offer was that 'it was a very unlikely event within the next few years' (*Newcastle Journal*, 8 March 1928). The editor of the *Shields Daily News* made his views on a possible closure very plain. 'The closing down of the North Shields Gasworks would be nothing short of a calamity to the Borough. The loss which it would mean in rateable value and employment would probably more than counterbalance any saving to local gas consumers that the transfer of the undertaking is expected to bring about (*The Shields Daily News*, 5 March 1928).[71]

The loss of the locally controlled gasworks was symptomatic of wider changes in the local North Shields economy. After centuries of suppression by Newcastle, the town had enjoyed a huge expansion in economic activity, made possible by the emergence of market economics, but motivated by more than economic self-interest. In much of what emerged in North Shields, it is possible to discern a sense of local identity and vitality allied with civic pride. Many of the town's business leaders were elected members of the local council and there was a great deal of cross-cutting membership between these and other local bodies such as the then thriving churches and voluntary groups. Those prominent leaders, to use a cricketing analogy, were not just batting for themselves but for the town of North Shields. Their own businesses and in some cases personal fortunes were, and were recognized as being, inextricably linked with the fortunes of the town. During the 1920s and 1930s, because of the deep depression and other difficulties which followed the First World War, companies which had once prospered, struggled to survive. Others, like the locally owned Preston Colliery, which encountered difficulties with its coal seams, could not weather the economic storm and were forced to close completely, and put large numbers of people out of work. However, what can be discerned in the handing over of the Tynemouth Gas Company to the Newcastle and Gateshead Gas Company is something different. The Tynemouth company was doing well at the time. It had been remarkably successful in coping with difficult trading conditions. Though the creation of larger gas companies may have made for greater efficiency in the industry as a whole, what the handing over of local assets to the Newcastle company meant for North Shields was that

---

71 The Newcastle and Gateshead Company's relentless expansion continued when in 1937 it acquired the South Shields gas undertaking and then, in 1940, the Morpeth Gas Light Company Ltd.

a small group of people had chosen to put their personal self-interest before community interest with respect to what was probably the town's biggest company. They could not have been unaware of the potential impact of the takeover on the Tynemouth gasworks and its workforce. They made no attempt to seek sufficient representation on the board of the Newcastle company to even give them the opportunity to try to exercise influence over what would happen subsequently at Minton Lane. To put it bluntly, they took their money and turned their backs on the local people whose custom over many years had so consistently provided them with the maximum dividends allowed by law.[72]

The acquisition of the Tynemouth Gas Company by the Newcastle company *could* be represented as *just* a change of ownership. Yet takeovers are rarely just that. Following a takeover, key decisions are made by people who may have no sense of identity with the formerly independent company, or the community of which it is part. The corporate and legal responsibilities of the directors and officials of the parent company are to run it efficiently and at a profit, if necessary, irrespective of what the consequences may be for the formerly independent units they now own and control. That is how it was with the takeover of the Tynemouth Gas Company. Its glory days were over. From 1927, what happened at Minton Lane was decided by people who, with a couple of exceptions, lived outside the Borough of Tynemouth. The North Shields gasworks was just one manufacturing station amongst a growing number within the Newcastle company. Moreover, the Newcastle company was now making use of large supplies of coal gas produced by an entirely different company. The takeover could not but have negative consequences for the once proud, independent Tynemouth company and its employees. The directors and shareholders may have continued to receive their dividends, almost as if nothing had happened, but the situation proved to be markedly different for the former employees of the Tynemouth Gas Company, and what went on within the walls of the Minton Lane gasworks.

---

72 For a full discussion of the development and character of the local North Shields economy see Lawrence, Danny. *Shiels to Shields. The life Story of a North Tyneside Town* (Carnegie, 2016), especially chapters 2, 5 and 7.

Chapter 7

Under New Ownership

IN APRIL 1928, accompanying the change in ownership, there were changes in the management of what had been the Tynemouth company's gasworks. Frederick Willis (FCW), the company's engineer and manager, became an assistant engineer to the Newcastle company. His replacement as manager at North Shields was George John Duncan, the Tynemouth company's chemist, who until then had also been the works superintendent, with a 24/7 on-the-spot responsibility for it. Fortuitously, Duncan had been living on site with his family since 1918 so his appointment did not involve his family in a further move. This change of manager met with the approval of Thomas Taylor, an administrator at the gasworks who kept a detailed journal, albeit sporadically, between 1927 and 1934. On 2 August 1927, shortly before the takeover was announced, Taylor wrote of FCW, the then works manager, 'I have never met a man who likes to stand on his dignity and assume his position as much as Freddy. He can't help it, poor soul. I often try to see his good points, but it takes a magnifying glass to find 'em'. His opinion of the company chairman was even worse. He described him as 'our much-despised chairman, a parasite.' In contrast, he clearly held the new manager in high regard and, always, respectfully, referred to him as Mr Duncan or Mr D.

Taylor was born in 1898, started work with the company in its Bedford Street offices in 1914, and was 29 at the time of the takeover.[73] Although we know nothing about his education, his journal reveals a good command of English. He read widely and critically, had an impressive knowledge of classical music and, amongst his accomplishments, was a capable pianist and organist. He was a discerning theatre goer and serious film critic. Fascinated by current affairs, he also used his journal to record detailed facts and figures relating to his work, and

---

73 The several volumes of Taylor's journal are lodged with the Tyne and Wear Archives. He lived in modest circumstances in North Shields with his elderly step-grandparents but was well-connected locally. He was a freemason and, independently of that connection, socialized with the Earl and Lady Tankerville of Chillingham Castle. He appears to have created his journal by making hand-written notes which he later typed up in spare moments at the gasworks office. None of Taylor's handwritten notes appear to have survived.

he maintained a commentary on developments at the Minton Lane gasworks. As a 'participant observer', his entries provide a valuable additional dimension to the kind of information available from other sources.[74] In addition, his observations are useful because they illustrate how top-down reorganizations imposed by takeovers (or recommended by management consultants) can falter. What such top-down changes cannot take into account, and what Taylor's journal reveals so well, are the existing personal loyalties, jealousies and enmities, as well as established but informal and undocumented ways of working, which can undermine changes imposed from above.

Taylor first heard of the possibility of a takeover on 23 August 1927, when Mr Duncan confided to him that there was a strong likelihood that the Newcastle and Gateshead Gas Company would mount a takeover *in the next 12 months* [our italics]. It seems that not even the superintendent and future manager of the site knew that the takeover was imminent. Taylor's journal response to Mr Duncan's prediction was 'what else can you expect of Tynemouth with its dithering directorate, its senile secretary and its incapable engineer.'

When Taylor returned to work after his annual summer holiday in 1927, 'there was endless talk among staff members about the takeover.'

> Wilder and wilder rumours in circulation over the change of company. Mr Duncan very much upset and has had an interview with Ald. Hogg (a senior director) who had requested him to state his case in writing and promised every possible help in seeing that the staff will be provided for before the amalgamation is a signed fact. F.C.W. tells Mr Duncan that there is every probability that he himself will be automatically 'resigned' when the change takes place. Well, it will not be an unmixed blessing in getting rid of him; and I do hope that Mr Duncan is promoted to works manager. ... He has been on these works all his life, and to be thrown out of employment now after so many years of useful service would be nothing short of a calamity (2 September 1927).

Mr Duncan was away on his family holiday when the staff were summoned to the Bedford Street offices at short notice to be told that a takeover deal had

---

74 The participant observation method usually involves a trained anthropologist or sociologist spending a lengthy period as part of the group or organization they are studying. The researcher plays two roles, that of subjective participant and objective observer. Although Taylor was not a trained disinterested observer, his journal contains many valuable insights and much documented information not available from any other source.

been agreed with the Newcastle and Gateshead Gas Company. According to the chairman of the Tynemouth company, at the special meeting called in late September to give shareholder approval to the deal, 'deputations from the staff, and the workmen have been interviewed, and the contemplated change explained to them, and they have expressed their satisfaction in the matter.' That is not how Taylor described the meeting. He had gone to work as usual on 7 September but at 11.45 received a phone call from F.C.W. requiring him to attend a meeting at the Bedford Street offices, about a 30-minute walk away, at 12.30. It was not, in any sense, a consultation. The terms of the takeover agreement had already been signed by the two companies before the meeting began. Taylor and his colleagues were there only to be told what the directors had agreed.

> Actually, what we had been told was a load of eyewash, and it was only a matter of conscience-easing that we had been called and told about a scheme already settled and done with. Not only had the whole stock of the old company been turned over to Newcastle, but every employee sold in a like manner. A civilization very proud of itself and its achievements had abolished actual slave-buying and selling long ago – but the selling and buying goes on under the guise of commercialism just the same. … We are bereft of redress and as powerless as all slaves whether in the cotton fields or the offices of a highly commercialised company. It is all trade and profit and the human being is not considered. … Now we must WAIT AND SEE. … We have no guarantees from Tynemouth and must accept with grace the ball of fortune which may roll with us or against us. … It seems that F.C.W. goes over with us worse luck – and we were all hoping we would be getting rid of the bounder.

On the first occasion Taylor had the opportunity to discuss the amalgamation on Mr Duncan's return from holiday, the latter anticipated that they would only be safe for a time and, after that, there could be wholesale changes. Nevertheless, when Taylor resumed his journal after a lengthy break in 1930, he was not only still employed but had a more interesting, varied and important job than under the old regime. The descriptions of his work make it clear that he was Mr Duncan's 'right-hand-man'. Interestingly, though it was by then two years since the takeover, he continued to think of the Newcastle company in 'us and them' terms and, as a former soldier in the Great War, sometime used military expressions to describe the relationship between the formerly independent companies.

All quiet on the gasworks front, the normal trench-trench routine, and a few strafes from the enemy who is in strong positions at Elswick and Grainger Street. There is the usual morning 'exchange' with both positions; then the activities subside, and we are able to get on with work more closely associated with our own undertaking (19 February 1930).

Several days later, after describing a heavy routine day at work he added:

Each day brings the same routine and very little variation unless Elswick and Grainger Street want some special work – and then we swear, for whenever these benighted departments ask for statistics, it is usually something big and time-taking. And they always ask when we have our hands full. Being imperious in their demands, they insist on immediate attention, and worry us stiff until their demands are satisfied.

It is not clear what role F.C.W. had in relation to the North Shields gasworks that he used to manage. Although he had become an assistant engineer with the Newcastle company, his occasional appearances at the North Shields' gasworks after the takeover suggest either than he had retained a supervisory role over it, or that as someone with first-hand knowledge he was despatched to the scene on behalf of the parent company whenever it was deemed necessary. These occasional appearances did not go down well with Taylor nor, according to him, the rest of the staff.

F.C.W. paid us a visit right on five o'clock – still the same kind of man and we do not recognize him at these works. He is definitely a back-number – and it serves him right. It is entirely his own fault. Had we had an energetic manager at the works, and an energetic Secretary at Bedford Street, we should not have been under the Newcastle regime today. F.C.W. was more interested in the sale of ashes [coke] at a shilling per ton than he was interested in the declining workings of the Retort House. We became a Works for the sale of ashes and not gas manufacture. He spent pounds to save shillings – hence the demise of the Tynemouth Gas Co. He always treated his staff, irrespective of position, with contempt and insult, and none of us are likely to forget that HE is the man who has kept us back in respect of salaries. F.C.W. took jolly good care that he got his thousand a year – but it was at our expense, and I was always surprised that the old Tynemouth Directors were not more wide awake. But they were all moribund old gentlemen puffed up with the sense of their own importance and hibernated peacefully whilst the electricity folks made steady progress in the district (12 March 1930).

The quantity of gas produced from coal at Minton Lane fell from 588.1 million cu. ft. in 1929 to 539.7 million in 1930, and that from oil from 93.2 million to 71.2 million. In terms of therms, which reflected the quality as well as the quantity of gas, the output from coal fell from 3.1 million to 2.9 million and that from oil from 291,000 to 214,000. There had also been corresponding falls in the production of tar and sulphate of ammonia. However, it is not clear how much credence should be given to Taylor's beautifully presented tables because, a few days later he mentioned that recent orders have 'reduced our *paper-stock* of coke to under a hundred tons' [our italics]. 'Actually, we have nearer 500 tons in the yard' (9 January 1931). Later in January, he admitted in his journal that he was trying to conceal the poor performance of the retort house by massaging the figures he was sending to head office.

> The gas made for the week was 10,881,000 cu. ft. and the average thermal yield 67.14 – a 'paper-figure' quote only, for the actual results came out at about 65 therms per ton, and we had to 'adjust' some 19 tons of coal to reach the figure stated. Headquarters expect us to return 67 therms and more each week, and as long as the powers that be see satisfactory figures on paper their minds (such as they are) are at rest. But this 'veneer' does not take away from the point that the results from the retort house for the week have been decidedly unsatisfactory (29 January 1931).

Taylor was also in a position to compare how Minton Lane was performing in relation to other plants in the company. Assuming that their figures had not been massaged too, it was doing less well. In 1930, the average figure for the company was over 70 therms per ton of coal. In Elswick it was reportedly as high as 74 therms. However, Taylor considered that Minton Lane's output ought to be regarded as satisfactory 'considering the poor condition of some of the beds in the retort house' and that the once 'state-of-the-art' plant was, by 1930, 'old and out-of-date'. But Taylor also believed that the foreman of the retort house was complacent and speculated on how he would feel when the 'first coke oven gas' (COG) arrived on site, which had been manufactured by a third party and only purchased by the Newcastle company. That process began in September 1930 when COG gas from Consett was fed into some of the North Shields gasholders, via the nearby Howdon gasworks through a specially installed 24-inch diameter pipe to Minton Lane. Taylor recognized this as a critically important development and he considered it ironic that F.C.W., who he held responsible for the declining performance of Minton Lane as a manufacturer of gas, was on site to witness the gas begin to arrive from Howdon.

The Howdon Gasworks

Taylor's subsequent many negative references to competition from the Howdon gasworks requires explanation. He regarded it as a 'Johnny-come lately' because it had not opened until 1908, almost 90 years after the first North Shields gasworks was established and nearly 40 years after the opening of the Minton Lane works. The residential area of Howdon, which lay just to the west of North Shields, did not enjoy any gas streetlighting until 1855, when it was supplied by the Willington Quay gasworks which lay a short distance further to the west of Howdon, between it and Wallsend.

In 1866, the Willington Quay Company combined with the Walker and St. Anthony's Gaslight Company to establish the Walker and Wallsend Union Gas Company. It was the threat from this new company, in 1867, to supply gas to the Chirton area of North Shields, which spurred the Tynemouth company to establish the new gasworks at Minton Lane. Although the Walker company did not pursue its initial plan to engage in direct competition with the Tynemouth company, it did provide gas as far as Howdon, which was adjacent to the western boundary of the Borough of Tynemouth. Had it not been for the Walker and Wallsend company, Howdon would have been an obvious next target area for the Tynemouth Gas Company to supply.

Thirty years later, by the end of 1899, the Walker and Wallsend Union *Gas* Company, supported by some heavyweight local industrialists, received Parliamentary approval to transform itself into an *energy* company, by providing electricity as well as gas to its customers. It was the first company in the UK to do so. It achieved this pioneering role by working in conjunction with the Newcastle Electric Supply Company.[75] The official opening of the joint venture took place at the newly constructed Neptune Bank Power Station on 19 June 1901. It is indicative of the high status of all forms of engineering on Tyneside in that era that the opening was carried out by no less a person than Lord Kelvin,

---

75 The same company that would take effective control over the municipally owned Tynemouth Electricity Company a few years later in 1906.

thc internationally renowned mathematical physicist and engineer.[76] Although the Newcastle company bought out the Walker and Wallsend company's share in the joint venture as early as 1903, the gas company itself continued to prosper in its original form. It was the first gas company in the area to introduce a co-partnership scheme for its workers. Moreover, to ensure the scheme was not perceived as an anti-union measure (which was an issue when co-partnership was introduced into Livesey's South Metropolitan Gas Company), the 1908 scheme specifically emphasised that it 'in no way interferes with the right of any workman being a member of a trade union.'[77]

The Walker and Wallsend company's proposal to build an entirely new gasworks at Howdon received Parliamentary approval in 1905. The new gasworks opened in May 1908, on a 12.5-acre site, situated conveniently between the Willington Quay and Howdon Railway stations, and just a short distance from the River Tyne. The old gas plant at Willington Quay was then dismantled. During the opening, the chairman of the Walker and Wallsend company noted that the gas yield at its inception had been 18 million cubic feet. In 1907, it was 307 million cu. ft.[78]

It was in February 1924 that the directors of the Walker and Wallsend company were approached and agreed to the takeover of their company by the Newcastle and Gateshead Gas Company. The pre-emptive move, which had not involved any consultation with the elected members of Wallsend Council, was deplored by local councillors but, despite a committee of seven of them being appointed 'with power to act if necessary', the takeover was sanctioned by the Board of Trade later in the year. Consequently, by the time the Newcastle company took over the Minton Lane gasworks in North Shields in 1927, the Howdon works had for three years already been incorporated into the Newcastle company's planning. That, and the fact that Howdon was a wholly new plant when opened in 1905, rather than an extended plant as was the case in Minton Lane in 1903, gave it a competitive advantage over the North Shields gasworks.

---

76 Lord Kelvin (William Thomson) was a mathematical physicist and engineer who for 53 years was Professor of Natural Philosophy at the University of Glasgow. He played a key role in developing our understanding of electricity and the formulation of the first and second laws of thermodynamics. His work in determining the value of Absolute Zero led to the Standard International Unit of Temperature, the degree Kelvin, being named in his honour. He was the President of the Royal Society from 1890-1895, and in 1892 became the first British scientist to be elevated to the House of Lords. Kelvin was probably best known to the public for his work on the transatlantic telegraph project which led to him being knighted by Queen Victoria in 1866. He would also have been well known to those in the shipbuilding companies of the area for his important work on the mariner's compass.

77 The Tynemouth Gas Company did not introduce a co-partnership scheme until 1912.

78 It had the capacity to produce 450 million cubic feet a year.

Despite that, and although 'the make' of gas at Minton Lane may have been declining, it was still manufacturing more than the Howdon plant in 1930: 11 million cu. ft. each week compared to 7 million cu. ft. at Howdon. However, Taylor was convinced that the policy of the Newcastle company's engineer was to reduce the gas produced at North Shields to allow the Howdon works to be kept fully occupied. It was that same policy which led to a significant reduction in the workforce at Minton Lane. In April 1930, it was down from about 200 to 111. By April 1931 it had fallen further to 92 and, by then, about 45 per cent of the gas leaving Minton Lane had been pumped to it via Howdon. On 19 February 1931, Taylor recorded that 'things do not get better in the retort house, despite all the effort and exhortations of our Chief.' A week later, he added that Frank Tarratt (F.P.T.), the Newcastle company's chief engineer, had told Mr Duncan that we must reduce the number of beds in use in the retort house from 12 to ten. Given that the retort house was equipped with 24 retort beds, that further reduction led Taylor to remark:

> It is quite clear there is a possibility that the North Shields gasworks will close down. F.P.T. admitted there was that feeling in 'certain quarters' and he is not doing anything to save us. … At any rate, G.D. [Mr Duncan] will make a fight of it – and it will be a fight for our very existence.

Taylor did not leave Mr Duncan to fight alone. The next day he had a meeting with a former director of the Tynemouth Gas Company and current shareholder in the Newcastle company.

> Later in the morning I went down to Union Street where I discussed with J.R. the possibility of the North Shields gasworks closing down. Not only is J.R. a late director of the old Tynemouth Gas Company but he is also an important shareholder [in the Newcastle company]. There is a shareholders' meeting at head office tomorrow afternoon and as J.R. has always evinced considerable interest in the question of our carrying on, I thought he could possibly raise the point in a discreet manner, but our friend did not think it advisable to do so at a public meeting. At the same time, he said that if at any time we had any real evidence to go on he would take up the fight with relish. He gave me a copy of a letter which Mr Cowan had addressed to Mr Young [the last chairman of the Tynemouth company] and it is interesting to note that as early as September 5th 1927, the famous F.C.W. was busy looking after his own interests while he pretended to us that he knew nothing about the proposed amalgamation.

I am of the opinion that the Newcastle company can do very much as it pleases with the ordinary staff and can easily fly in the face of Mr Cowan's 'definite undertaking that no workmen or official in your company will be worse off either in wage or security of employment as the result of the proposed amalgamation should it be carried through.' Had there been no amalgamation of the old Tynemouth company with that of Newcastle, the North Shields gasworks would still have been making 100% gas instead of the present 60% – the remaining 40% coming from Consett. This [the arrangement with Consett] was a scheme already drawn up and settled, and being put into operation when the proposed amalgamation was being discussed with the Tynemouth Board. It is no use shouting fire before we see the flames but there is smoke on the horizon. It is up to us to find out our position as members of the old Tynemouth staff before we are thrown overboard when it is too late for redress.

Taylor was well informed. In 1927, the Newcastle and Gateshead Gas Company had entered into an agreement to purchase a bulk supply of gas from the Consett Iron Company's Coking Plant at Derwenthaugh, about 15 miles from North Shields, across the River Tyne in County Durham. It began production in 1928. Coal was used to manufacture coke which, because it generates intense heat but little smoke, was ideal for smelting iron and steel. During the manufacture of the coke, large quantities of coal gas were produced. As the Consett Iron Company had no intention of competing with existing gas companies, it was happy to sell them the coal gas which, for them, was no more than a by-product of their coking process. Plainly, with such an arrangement in place, the Newcastle company had no need to increase its own manufacturing capacity. However, it was of significant benefit to the Newcastle company to be able to sell the Derwenthaugh gas to the customers in the additional 28-square mile area gained by the acquisition of the Tynemouth Gas Company, especially given that the terms of the takeover allowed it to charge Tynemouth customers more than its Newcastle customers (Jackson, 1945 p.31).

On 30 March 1931, F.C.W. and another visitor from head

Derwenthaugh Coke Works on the River Derwent (a tributary of the River Tyne) opened in 1928. They were owned and operated by the Consett Iron Company near to what is now the huge Gateshead shopping precinct, the Metro-Centre. This image is circulating on the internet, but we have been unable to trace its origins to acknowledge the source.

office came to the North Shields gasworks, unexpectedly, to inspect the retort house and hold a discussion with Mr Duncan. Such was the apprehension that such visits caused, that Mr Duncan played an April Fools' Day trick on Taylor and others two days later when he suggested to them that he had learned that someone from head office was about to make another unexpected call. The vexed issue of how much gas would be manufactured in North Shields as distinct from pumped to Minton Lane from Consett, via the Howdon gasworks, cropped up again in April.

> The Chief Engineer's policy has been for North Shields to keep down 'the make' so as to allow Howdon to keep working in full style. Our costs have suffered and labour is now down to an irreducible minimum (10 April 1931).

Taylor's verdict on the relationship between the Howdon and North Shields gasworks was accurate. While manufacturing capacity was being run down at Minton Lane, in Howdon a 3 million cu. ft. gasholder was under construction, along with other improvements. Despite that policy, Taylor felt that there had been a slight improvement in the performance of North Shields and that they were slowly recovering some of the ground lost since the summer of 1930. The thermal yield was even 66.85 without any massaging! The most pressing problems were the large stocks of ammoniacal liquor and coke.

The Declining Fortunes of the North Shields Gasworks

Although by 1931 there seemed to be an acknowledgement within the Newcastle company that the future of lighting lay with electrical power, it had by no means given up trying to persuade the public to use gas lighting. This is a typical advertisement being carried at the time.

In the meantime, the municipal electricity undertaking, distributing power generated by the private Newcastle Electric company, was still trying to persuade the local population to switch from gas to electricity. As its chief engineer

Gas Lighting advertisement to illustrate that electricity had yet to eclipse gas as the only form of domestic lighting. Source: The Shields Daily News, *2 February 1931, courtesy of the* British Newspaper Archive.

conceded in his 1931 annual report to Tynemouth Council, that was far from easy, and the relative merits of both fuels were still the subject of public discussion. For example, the Liberal Literary and Debating Society on 18 February 1931 discussed the question, 'Is Gas or Electricity the more beneficial to the household?' The vote at the end of the debate resulted in a draw (*The Shields Daily News*, 18 February 1931).[79] This local debate was part of the competition at a national level which the chairman of the Newcastle Gas Company described as the 'gas versus electricity war' in his remarks at the 1931 AGM. He complained that recent government measures had 'certainly nurtured and almost pampered the electricity supply industry' at the expense of gas companies. The local newspaper reported that he then continued in the following vein.

> Mr Cowan said electricity and gas had their respective uses, but neither should be artificially thrust on the public. He was not decrying electricity; indeed the company used it for certain specific purposes. 'But we protest most strongly against governments and Ministers of State advertising and, by guaranteeing loans, subsidising electricity at the expense of gas' (*The Shields Daily News*, 24 February 1931).

That gas versus electricity was still a charged issue locally was made further apparent in July. With unemployment in North Shields at over 30 per cent, and poverty widespread, there was a belief among some comfortably off people that it was their duty to hold cookery demonstrations to share what they assumed was their superior knowledge of housekeeping with those struggling to make ends meet.

> In a great many households various observers had seen that there was a distinct lack of cooking ability with the result that the meals served up were poor in quality, and in the buying of foodstuffs there was a great deal of extravagance or waste which would not be tolerated in households on a much higher social scale (*The Shields Daily News*, 15 January 1932).

The reality was probably that the demonstrations were unnecessary because those living at or below the poverty line had long been expert at making economies to make their unemployment benefits or reduced wages 'go further'. But our

---

79 It is indicative of the norms relating to gender roles at that time that the newspaper account included the following observation: 'An experiment was tried by the Tynemouth branch, who had *two ladies* as proposer and seconder' – who spoke in favour of electricity' [our italics].

point here relates not so much to the patronising assumptions underlying the demonstrations, but Tynemouth Council's official response, which reflected a reluctance to give the impression that it was in any way sponsoring Newcastle's private gas company. When it was first suggested to the Tynemouth Health Committee that they should provide support for the demonstrations, the members agreed, reluctantly, with the proviso that 'the Medical Officer is satisfied that the demonstrations will not be used as propaganda for gas'!

However, whatever the merits of gas compared to electricity, it appeared to be potentially more dangerous. There were numerous reminders of that in the local newspaper. During this period of high and long-term unemployment, suicides were frequent, with often several in North Shields in the same week. Gas poisoning by 'putting your head in the gas oven' was not just a preferred method but a commonly used expression.[80] Death and injuries resulting from accidents with gas were also not uncommon, including gas explosions. For example, in April 1931 a gas oven in North Shields exploded and a child had a narrow escape. In June, an explosion followed when someone tried to track down a gas leak with a lit candle. Later in June there was a freak accident in which a gas streetlamp was knocked over by a motor vehicle and the head of the lamp fell through the window of an elderly lady's house and released gas into her bedroom. It was not until the following morning that the incident was discovered by neighbours and the lady, who had slept through it, brought out to safety. That incident was followed in July with the report of two further gas oven explosions in the town. The *Shields Daily News* on 10 April 1931, alongside a photograph under a headline **Gas Explosion Causes Wreckage**, and the photograph of a small scullery torn apart by the explosion, carried the caption: 'The picture above shows all that remains of the gas oven which blew up at the house of Mrs E. Rogers, 23 Shakespeare Street, North Shields yesterday. One of the children had a narrow escape from being killed. The photograph shows the wrecked room and oven.' Just three weeks later, on the 30 July 1931, the same newspaper under a **Gas Explosion** headline and photo of the disconsolate five members of a household (including two young children) carried the caption: 'A gas oven explosion which might have had serious results occurred at 4 Jackson Street, North Shields, last night. The picture above shows the little boy, William Gibson, who had a narrow escape, and Mrs Alan Weir, who also received a shock from the explosion.'

---

80 Inhalation of domestic coal gas was the most common method of suicide in the UK in the mid-twentieth century.

It is unfortunate that Taylor made no entries in his journal in July 1931. If he had, he would not only have commented on these events but also on what had happened to the former Tynemouth Gas Company's prestigious offices on Bedford Street. What is evident from an advertisement in the local newspaper is that, by July 1931, number 97 had been sub-divided, and parts were available for let. The gas company continued to occupy part of the building but 97a was let to Barry Noble, a fruit and vegetable shop, and 97b became an employment exchange exclusively for women. The gas showroom continued to occupy number 98.

Whatever the problems and circumstances in North Shields at this time, according to the British Commercial Gas Association, which existed to promote the interests of the gas industry, it was continuing to do well nationally. To proclaim that

> TO LET.
> GAS OFFICE CHAMBERS
> BEDFORD STREET.
>
> ———
>
> EXCELLENT
> SUITES OF ROOMS
>
> SUITABLE FOR CAFE, SHOW ROOMS OR OFFICES,
> WITH IMMEDIATE POSSESSION.
>
> Apply RICHARD A. JACKSON,
> AUCTIONEER AND VALUER, NORTH SHIELDS.

Advertisement offering parts of Tynemouth Gas Company's Offices in Bedford Street for sale or rent, Shields Daily News, 20 July 1931.

message it paid for a several column-inch, bold advert in local newspapers in February 1932, with the title **Amazing Progress of Gas**. It noted that total gas production in the British Isles in 1929 was 322 million cu. ft., more than double what it had been in 1902, and that between 1929 and 1931 it had increased still further to 332 million cu. ft. That was emphasised in a large typeface in the adjacent column with the words, **ten thousand million cubic feet increase in two years** (*The Shields Daily News*, 29 February 1932). New uses were also still being found for coal gas. At the British Industries Fair in Birmingham in February 1933, there were demonstrations of a coach and local bus, powered by coal gas. Moreover, even when it came to street illumination, electrical lighting was still not an automatic choice. The local Council in Whitley, supplied with gas from the Tynemouth and now Newcastle company, after careful deliberation, *replaced* its existing electric lighting with gas on Whitley Road in 1933, with 'new standards peaked by copper light-holders, which are very smart, each with five burners' (*The Shields Daily News*, 12 May 1933). Several days later, the local paper, under a headline **BEST LIGHTED TOWN Ambitious Plans at Whitley – Scheme for Whole Area**' described how a plan had been drawn up in which the area under Whitley Council's control had been divided into 12 districts and in each case the existing gas lights would be 'replaced by stronger lights also of gas'. With the aim of improving Whitley's popularity as a holiday resort, it had also been decided to fit new gas lighting on the Promenade and in the main part of the town.

Another item which appeared in the local newspaper in September 1933 emphasised that gas lighting was markedly more convenient from what it had been in the past, and that now it 'can be switched on and off from the door, or any other convenient point, as conveniently as electric light.' However, it then went on to give a tip which, to those of us living in the twenty-first century, hardly seems consistent with the notion of 'convenient modern illumination'!

> To strengthen a gas mantle and make it last longer, run a thread through the loop at the top, then dip the mantle in vinegar. When it has been thoroughly soaked, hang it up to dry. After it has been placed on the burner, light the gas before placing on the globe. This treatment will improve the light, and also make the mantle last much longer (*The Shields News*, 29 September 1933).

Advertisements by the British Commercial Gas Association and the local gas company might have helped minimise the loss in sales during the mild winter of 1932-3, but the Newcastle company would still have been disappointed to have had to announce a 1 per cent fall in sales over the year at its 1933 AGM. Also unwelcome were continuing reminders in the press that gas as a fuel was inherently dangerous. One such example is that, on 30 January 1933, a recently qualified gas plumber, George Brigham, went to a house in North Shields to investigate a suspected leak. As he opened the cupboard where the gas meter was installed, there was an explosion 'as deafening as a gunshot'. Brigham was flung back against the kitchen door, and 'a mass of flames belched out into the passage' causing some burning to his face (*The Shields News*, 31 January 1933).[81]

When the Newcastle company took over the Tynemouth company in 1927, there had been concern that it insisted on charging Tynemouth customers more than Newcastle customers. Many complained that the price difference was unjustified because all the necessary pipework was already in place at the time of the takeover and the Newcastle company had not been involved in any additional costs. Despite the differential, there were occasional modest reductions in the price charged for gas in the area which had previously been supplied by the Tynemouth company. A fourth such reduction was made in October 1933. Although it was of only 2d a Therm, the equivalent of 1d per 1,000 cubic feet, at a time when unemployment was high and so many people were struggling to make ends meet, any reduction would have been welcomed. That there had been a small reduction

---

81 We will learn more of George Brigham later in the book.

in the price, however, was no consolation to those who insisted that the provision of gas streetlighting had not improved since the takeover. A letter to the local newspaper, signed 'Ratepayer' complained that although he or she:

> … had no desire to go into the merits of lighting by gas or electricity, I just wonder if any town in England has such a spasmodic street lighting system as the County Borough of Tynemouth. After coming from Whitley [a different urban authority] into Cullercoats [within the Borough of Tynemouth] is like coming into "No-Mans Land". (Yet) from the new lighting of Queen Alexandra Road one would think some famous airmen were expected. The light is in the air and the ground effect is bad.

On 12 December 1933, there was a near calamity at the Minton Lane gasworks. Taylor recorded that an urgent message was sent to Mr Duncan to warn him that:

> … the exhauster engine had stopped and that the gas was blowing back through the retort house settings. There might have been a nasty explosion but, thankfully, Mr Duncan is a man who can keep his head and he got things going before the red for danger line had been reached. Headquarters will now hold an enquiry. They will want to place the blame on someone, and so justify an exalted existence – and existence so well salaried!

The following day, Taylor noted that after 'yesterday's mishap', in which the exhaust plant had been out of action for about an hour, gas production had been significantly reduced. As he had anticipated, it resulted in a visit by F.C.W. (now nicknamed Fra Diavolo)[82] and a three-hour cross examination of Mr D 'until our Chief felt that he was attending a court martial'. It appears that although F.C.W. no longer had a day-to-day management job at the Minton Lane gasworks, in his role as assistant engineer with the parent company he was still capable of behaving in the same way he was reputed to have done when he was works manager.

Events such as these did nothing but deepen Taylor's general pessimism. He was not optimistic for the country, the gas industry, or the Minton Lane gasworks. His journal includes numerous references to the relationship between the World War One allies and the resurgent military in Germany under its new

---

82 Presumably derived from the bandit in the comic opera of that name, or perhaps the Laurel and Hardy version *Fra Diavolo* which had been released in May 1933, rather than the *real* Fra Diavolo, which was the nickname of the guerrilla leader who led a popular insurrection against the French occupation of Naples.

Fascist leaders. He noted on 14 October 1933, for example, that Germany had cut off all ties with the League of Nations and the Disarmament Conference, and that the Reichstag, the German equivalent of the United Kingdom's Parliament, had been dissolved. He saw these and other developments as an indication that we were heading for another world war. Taylor was similarly pessimistic for the future of the gas industry. On New Year's Day 1934, he referred to the launch of the nationwide electricity grid and commented:

> Switch out the old, switch in the new. At midnight, as 1933 faded out, two operators, one in London and the other in Didsbury, Manchester, pulled over a switch and 1934 came in – electrified by the grid. We of the gas industry tremble (1 January 1934).

Taylor was aware that the Newcastle Supply Company, which provided electrical power to the Borough of Tynemouth, already had the most integrated power system in Europe. However, until then, supplies of electricity in the rest of the country had been fragmented. But, in 1926, following the Electricity Supply Act, the Central Electricity Board was set up to create a national grid. It began operating in 1933, initially with a series of regional grids, but with a plan to switch to a nationwide grid by 1938. As well as being apprehensive about how the fragmented gas industry could cope with this new-style competition, Taylor was also apprehensive about the implications of the relatively poor output figures from Minton Lane. In December he noted that 'results are poor' and he added, again, that 'we had to make adjustments with our coal carbonised figures before we reached an average of 69.61. therms for the week' (7 December 1933).

Taylor's interest in national and international events is a reminder that whatever was happening to the gas industry in North Shields was against a background of an increasingly worsening situation, nationally and locally. It was not just the inexorable drift towards another major European war which concerned him, but the terrible conditions in which ordinary people were living, made worse by the depression in world trade. Taylor and others at Minton Lane had already been obliged to accept wage cuts – but at least they were still employed. For those without work, the situation was almost invariably dire. Unemployment was particularly high in areas like the north-east, heavily dependent on the old staple industries. In North Shields, during the period the Tynemouth Gas Company was taken over, and the Minton Lane gasworks began to operate as part of the Newcastle and Gateshead company, the circumstances were far from propitious for those trying to persuade the public to buy or hire more gas appliances and use more gas. Ministry of Labour statistics for North Shields show that at the start of 1927, 22 per cent of those covered by unemployment insurance were unemployed. By October 1928, the figure had grown to 28 per cent. After two better quarters, the figure rose to a staggering peak of 46 per cent in October 1932. It fluctuated around the 40 per cent mark until 1936 when it began to fall – but was still at 28 per cent in April 1939 just months before the outbreak of the 1939-45 Second World War. These figures, we must emphasise, understate the actual scale of unemployment. Many unemployed workers with homes in North Shields were excluded from these statistics because, they had gone elsewhere in search of work. Moreover, many of those in work were under-employed or obliged to accept wage cuts, as part of the ill-judged attempt to ameliorate the country's economic problems which only served to drive it further into depression.

At a time when there was usually only one breadwinner in a family, these high rates of unemployment meant that a much larger number of people were subsisting at or below the poverty level. When unemployment insurance benefit ran out, the unemployed and their families were subjected to the humiliation of the hated 'household means test'. Introduced in November 1931, benefit was paid only after a meticulous investigation of a household's 'means', conducted to ensure that its members had no undisclosed earnings, savings, or other resources to draw on. Yet the unemployment benefit, even when paid, was deemed insufficient to remain healthy according to the panel of nine doctors appointed by the British Medical Association (BMA) to determine the minimum level that a family could live on healthily, if all its resources were used for that purpose. Other studies during the inter-war years showed that many wives and mothers suffered malnutrition because they considered it their duty to give priority to their menfolk and children. A Pilgrim Trust Report on unemployment indicated that, in many instances, women were literally starving themselves to do that. Other responses to unemployment included people moving from small into even smaller accommodation to cut costs, including their bills for heating and lighting. Studies carried out during the depression concluded that the impact of long-term unemployment on individual families was often very great. For example, one Medical Officer of Health reported finding a high incidence of abnormal psychological conditions amongst unemployed men, characterised by disabling fears, anxiety, related sympathetic physical conditions as well as functional disorders. There is also ample evidence that the deprivation caused by long-term unemployment included loss of life. The newspapers of the time included numerous reports of suicides, most commonly by people putting their head in their gas oven, or by lying down alongside a tube attached to a gas connection.

Throughout this time, the Newcastle company continued to make good profits and pay maximum dividends. Although the company balance sheet indicated it had no obvious need to make significant cuts in the workforce, it had been shedding staff from Minton Lane since shortly after the takeover. That included getting rid of 'old Carr from the time office', just two months before his due retirement at 65. He left without a pension and no hope of further employment. Taylor's bitter feelings towards his distant superiors were expressed in a striking way the following day. After recording that he had been to the cinema to watch Laurel and Hardy in *Twice Two* – essentially a farce based on the theme of marital discord – he added, 'We have these comedians in our headquarters at Elswick! – I refer to F.P.T. and his henchmen' (11 December 1933).[83]

Taylor does not explain in what way 'the comedians' at head office were implicated in what today would seem to be an astonishing decision to dispose of Minton Lane's surplus ammoniacal liquor literally 'down the drain' but it would at the very least need to have had their agreement.

> Some 558,000 gallons of liquor have been put down the drains and added to the bulk of old father Tyne. We must have poisoned many salmon (5 January 1934).[84]

It was not the first time the Newcastle company had dumped by-products in the river. Jackson, the company secretary, admitted to that in his history of the company. He noted that in the 1860s, the practice of draining coal gas tar into the river greatly annoyed the many rowers of the period, at a time when that was a popular past-time and major sport.

---

83 In June 1933, F.P.T. (Frank P. Tarratt) the chief engineer of the Newcastle company, was elected President of the Institute of Gas Engineers. He was also a member of the Institute of Civil Engineers and held official positions with the National Joint Industrial Gas Council, the Federation of Gas Employers, the National Gas Council and North of England Gas managers Association.

84 In 1958, Tynemouth's MP Dame Irene Ward stood up in Parliament, described the condition of the Tyne as deplorable to the point of being indecent, and declared that 'one of my ambitions before I die is to see that the pollution of the River Tyne is dealt with'. Sadly, she died with that wish unfulfilled but, in the last twenty years, there has been a huge improvement. The Tyne is once again a salmon river and even seals periodically poke their heads out of the water. However, we should not assume that such polluting industrial practices have come to an end. Water companies are still dumping raw sewage into our rivers on a massive scale. For example, across the upper Thames alone, 102 sewage treatment works discharged effluence into rivers in 2021. About half did so for more than about 500 hours during the year and almost a quarter did so for more 1,000 hours.

The collection of tar globules on the sides of racing skiffs involved oarsmen in a good deal of cleaning work and recriminations against the Gas Company (Jackson, p.20).

It was around this time that the celebrated children's author Robert Westall used to visit the Minton Lane gasworks as a small boy. In the biographical notes he left behind on his death in 1993, there were accounts of his visits to the gasworks to see his father, the foreman fitter, in the mid-1930s.

The massive wall of the gasworks … with the colossal red-brick twin chimneys towering overhead. … It is a magical kingdom where the blacksmith's hammer rings out, where pools of beautiful slick oil, yellow, green and blue, lie on the cobbles, where carthorses stamp in gloom, where men stripped to the waist shovel coal into banks of glowing furnaces. It is my father's magical kingdom, from which he is returning with boots of a fearsome chemical blackness, and a strong whiff of benzene upon his cap (Westall, 2006 p.32).

Westall's description of his visits to the gasworks warrants inclusion because it adds another valuable dimension to the journal entries of Taylor, and the recollections of people brought up in the gasworks house, which follow in the next chapter. Together, they allow us to provide readers with a much fuller portrayal of a gasworks than anything found in Jackson's worthy but dull and brief history of the plants which made up the Newcastle and Gateshead Gas Company.

To me, aged four to five, he was the oily wizard. It wasn't that he didn't wash as much as anybody else, but mere washing wasn't enough to remove the marks of his oily trade. When he first came home he was often as black as a coal miner; his work clothes, his black greasy cap and dungarees, and especially his dreadful black sooty boots that lived beside the gas stove in the kitchen, smelt of the pit: sulphur and benzene and carbon. Even washed and dressed in his best … his smell went everywhere before him and lingered after him. On the perilous journey to the outside loo in the dark of a winter's night, with only the comfort of a wavering torch, I would be reassured on arrival to find that lingering smell of benzene. … It added to his fascination that the thumbnail of his right hand grew in five dreadful segments, from where he had hit it with a hammer while he was an apprentice. … He worked in a place eminently suitable for a wizard. It was only a quarter of a mile from home (I got the smell of benzene even when he was at work, if the wind was in the right direction) and sometimes when he forgot his bait I would be sent along with it by my mother. Even this 'bait' was extraordinary, and wizard-like. Something mysterious in a tin, wrapped always in a red-and-white spotted handkerchief. And a tall lidded can, full of an awful mixture of sugar, condensed milk and black tea leaves, which he referred to as his 'makings'.

The works, as I approached, resembled nothing I have come across since except the Black Land of Mordor in Tolkien's *The Lord of the Rings*. A cloud of brown darkness hung over it, always. My father said that was the reason he never had a cold: the germs withered in that blasted air. … The wall around the works was livid red brick, 15 feet high, with black iron spikes and broken glass on top. Above the wall thrust two immense red-brick chimneys, day and night belching wreaths of black smoke that sometimes enveloped you as you approached, leaving you coughing helplessly.

There was only one gate, and here lived my only enemy, the timekeeper, a man I deeply hated and distrusted. For one thing he had a clean white face, and a clean white collar with tie. The only work he ever seemed to do was to write things in a large book. Nothing passed the gate but he wrote it down in his book. But, far worse, he had once denied knowing who my father was, the first time I had been sent alone with the bait. What was more, he had made me give him the bait and said he would make enquiries, in a voice that hinted there would be serious trouble all round. Stripped of my sacred trust, for my mother had said that I was to give the bait to no one but my father, I went home in hysterical floods of tears.

Next time I was wiser. Holding my breath, I would duck down and creep beneath the monster's window. This was not easy for in front of that window was a monstrous metal plate, studded with screws and strange writing. The weighbridge, where the coke carts parked as they passed in and out, and my enemy would read a dial inside his office and give out yet another sheet of his endless white paper. If I trod on the weigh-plate, my enemy's dial needle would swing and he would know I was there. So, doubled-up, I would work my way along the six-inch strip of cobble between gatehouse and weigh-plate. I knew he was my father's enemy because my father called everybody else in the works by their Christian name, but this man he simply referred to as 'the timekeeper'.

But now I was safe inside my father's kingdom. Cobbles beneath my feet and, between the cobbles, huge puddles upon which the greeny-yellowy-blue swirls of oil endlessly writhed like jagged snakes. Black brick walls, crusted with soot an inch thick; glass windows smeared with a yellow oily coating so thick you could hardly see an electric light shining through. There were great black doorways from which came the heavy clink of hammers in the darkness; others in which huge, sweating engines turned endlessly, hissing softly to themselves, with no one to tend them. Some huge doorways were full of the dreadful glow of red and yellow light, in which men with shovels toiled, reduced to black skeletons by the glare, feeding the furnaces. Above my head pipes stuck out, puffing huge fat clouds of green smoke, or dripped unknown blackness that might burn your hand away as it touched you. Great stinking heaps of still hot white ash; pits full of brown bubbling water of a bottomless depth; a weathered, scarcely decipherable sign 'Number Four Retort House'. Sometimes I would wander fearless for ages, until I found a man who had time to speak to me. Fearless, for my father was lord of all this.

I have great respect for Tolkien's *The Lord of the Rings,* and yet I cannot find the fear in it that others feel. Tolkien's Hell was my Heaven. And eventually, a bent dark figure would emerge, white-eyed and white-toothed. No orc, but an honest man, because black-faced. Men with black faces were workers, and my father's friends. Men with clean faces were bosses, or worse still 'Boss's men' and my father's sworn enemies. This blackened figure would recognize me with a cry. 'It's Bobby's bairn!' Others would emerge and take up the chorus. 'Bobby's lad ... Bob's bairn. He's brought Bobby's bait!' And they would make me feel like the hero that carried the good news from Ghent to Aix. Then the burning question: 'Where's Bobby? Where's Bobby?' was passed from shed to shed, gantry to gantry, until it seemed the only question of importance in the world. Bobby was in number three retort house. Bobby was up on the dreadnamed coke-crusher. Bobby was on number one conveyor. Bobby seemed to be everywhere, omni-present, like God.

And then he would arrive, hurrying always but flustered never, ramming his way through the day's crises like a little tramp steamer butting through heavy seas, always with a man or two clustering round him as he walked, asking what was to be done, in a stream of wizardly incantation involving cranks and sumps, steam valves and condensers. Mission accomplished, I would run out of the gate wildly, at full speed across the weigh bridge, leaving my enemy the timekeeper mouthing and waving his arms helplessly behind his glass window.

The best time of all was a Saturday morning, when he came off a week of night shift to two days' holiday, while it was still dark at six o'clock in winter. … he would call at the baker's and buy bread buns fresh from the oven and bring them to me in bed, still scalding hot and dripping butter (and tasting faintly of benzene). Then he would sit for a few minutes and tell me strange things, like how … (the) gasworks was full of rats. They used to nibble the hooves of the carthorses as they slept, and the horses, that pulled the coke carts, never seemed to notice. He told me about Ginger, the works cat, who could pick out the one pool of clean rainwater from the many pools of poison, and never came to harm, but the stupid rats couldn't, and burnt their paws and mouths (Westall, edited by McKinnel, pp.35-41).

The Beginning of the End

Taylor's apprehension about the future of the Minton Lane works was reinforced during January 1934 when F.P.T. warned Mr Duncan that the company was going to take an additional million cu. ft. of COG from Consett which would require a further reduction in 'the make' in Minton Lane. Taylor commented:

> This is yet another turn of the screw which will eventually close us down as a gas-making centre. What price the gentleman's agreement then? [a reference to the employment security guarantee following the takeover] (18 January 1934).

A few days later his concern was increased further when he learned that the works' future would be an item on the agenda of the Newcastle Board.

> What news would Mr Duncan gain from F.P.T. on the question of our closing down? Frankie [F.P.T.] has hinted at the possibility for some time. Now there is something definite in the air. We are all wondering what will happen today when the Board meets and discusses our future (23 January 1934).

Taylor did not have long to wait for what was more depressing news, and it could hardly have come at a worse time for him personally. That afternoon, he was at the funeral of the grandfather who had brought him up. Mr Duncan had joined him at the graveside. Following the internment, he shared with Taylor the unwelcome news that 'F.P.T. had warned him that there was now every possibility of the Works closing down at an early date.' For Taylor, a 36-year-old who had only ever worked for the gas company, who was living in a town with an unemployment rate of over 40 per cent, it was a most unwelcome prospect.[85] However, the following morning there was no further news. Taylor wrote in his journal, 'What game are headquarters playing?' He received an answer a few days later when F.P.T. arrived at Minton Lane and informed Mr Duncan that the works would be making no gas at all during the summer months. Asked what the situation would be in the winter, F.P.T. was 'non-committal' (29 January 1934). The details of what was envisaged became clearer later that day when Taylor spoke to an official at head office.

> Mr Clough told me, in confidence, that he had been ordered to cut our estimates for 1934 by half, and when he had enquired why, he had been startled to learn that we would close down on March 31st for six months, re-opening again on October 1st. Meantime, if there was any possibility of the Board selling the Works site, that would be the end of us. … I think we have reached the last turn of the screw which came into being when the old Company amalgamated with that of Newcastle.

Taylor's characterisation of the unfolding events is convincing. Given its contract for Consett's COG, the manufacturing plant at Minton Lane was of only limited value to the Newcastle company. Of much greater significance was the Tynemouth company's customer base and distribution network. Although at the time, for public relations purposes, it had been better for the directors of both companies to describe the takeover as an amalgamation, the one-sided nature of the deal had since then been only too apparent. All the key decisions had been taken by the Newcastle company's management, and they had been consistent with a long-term policy to phase out the manufacture of gas at Minton Lane and transform it into nothing more than a storage and local distribution depot for gas manufactured elsewhere.

Taylor had been encouraged to believe that the white-collar staff in the company would not be made redundant, but he was 'heartily sorry for our workpeople; most of whom have been with us for years and years and their hope of employment elsewhere is NIL.' He added, 'And what about Mr Cowan's assurance (in writing) to Mr Hogg that no workman or official of the old company would be

---

85 Making matters worse for Taylor is that, following the death of the 'old man' (his step-grandfather) he could not even be sure that he would continue to have a home.

worse off in wages or security?' (29 January 1934). On 21 February 1934, Taylor recorded that rumours were beginning to circulate about the closure of the works. He remarked that, unusually, there had been 'no visitations from headquarters over the last two or three weeks', which led him to pose the question, 'is there any significance in this unusual occurrence?' Inevitably, the lack of official news only increased speculation and made Taylor deeply pessimistic.

> In readiness for tomorrow's fateful meeting – when the question (which I believe to be already decided) of closing North Shields down will be discussed – we had to prepare a list of men employed who were born 1878-80 [aged 53-56]. Some have over forty-years' service. Tomorrow will decide – what? Of this I am sure: they will close the Works down at the end of next month. Our men will be thrown out of employment and it is more than probable that staff members will be placed under redundancy. And once the place is closed down, I cannot see us starting up again in September. The Powers that Be will push all their worth to sell the site and plant in the interim. What a system which takes so little account of men and homes! (26 February 1934).

Later that day he wrote to a World War One comrade. In addition to mentioning his own problems, he added.

> As for the world of today, the more I think about it the less I like the prospect. We are living in a madhouse and I often wonder what is going to happen next. It just needs a spark and that will be the end of civilization. Here on Tyneside we go through days of depression with a fullness that robs us of any joy of life. Just imagine these river towns where practically the full manpower is unemployed! The shadow of redundancy is over us. They are talking of scrapping shipyards once world-famous. Many are already scrapped and the offices and buildings converted into gymnasiums for the workless. I know you will read in our optimistic papers that trade is better and soon everything in the garden will be lovely. That may apply to the prospects for the south but, as far as the north is concerned, we are doomed to poverty as the sacrifice-battalion was doomed to extinction in the World War.

Taylor's reference to the scrapping of once-famous shipyards referred to the actions of a group of shipbuilders, backed by the Bank of England and the major clearing banks, which had set up National Shipbuilding Security Ltd., and bought out shipyards as part of a scheme to, literally and physically, destroy the industry's then excess shipbuilding capacity: that same capacity which just a few years later would be so desperately needed to build warships and replace the hundreds of merchant vessels destroyed by enemy action. Just across the river from North Shields, the Palmer's shipyard in Jarrow was one of those targeted. In the very same year that the Minton Lane gasworks was being temporarily closed, the Palmer's Yard was bought and then dismantled: an action which brought devastating consequences to the people of Jarrow. Even before the destruction of the yard over 80 per cent of the working population had been unemployed. Now the yard on which they had been dependent was not only idle but incapable of ever re-opening. The plight of the unemployed of Jarrow and North Shields was made worse by the fact that they were part of a larger depressed area. In the UK in 1934, there was a significant improvement in the level of employment, but about 35 per cent of the insured workforce of Tyneside was unemployed, more than twice the rate in England and Wales as a whole.[86] In North Shields, the rate was over 40 per cent. Moreover, much of this unemployment was long-term. Fifty per cent of those registered unemployed had been without work for more than 12 months and this figure does not include those who had obtained only a brief period of work in an otherwise continuous spell of unemployment which could have far exceeded 12 months.

The situation at Minton Lane became a little clearer at the end of February. Mr Duncan attended a meeting of the shareholders in which the chairman explained that the company had 'contracted for a further million cubic feet of gas per day from Consett and that, as a consequence, one of the gasworks in the company would need to be closed down.' Subsequently, F.P.T. confirmed that Minton Lane would close on 31 March, and asked Mr Duncan how many of the workforce could be 'dispensed with'. The following day, Taylor phoned the former Tynemouth director he knew and asked him to take special care of the letter which the chairman of the Newcastle company had given the chairman of the Tynemouth company, guaranteeing the security of employment of its workforce following the so-called amalgamation. In the absence of firm information, it was inevitable that rumours would flourish. One of them was that Mr Duncan would be transferred to the laboratory at Elswick and that his on site family house would

---

86 Unemployment statistics were (and still are) generated from statistics collected for a different administrative purpose, in this instance the number of people who had paid national insurance contributions which entitled them to unemployment benefit and were now out of work and receiving that benefit. Consequently, unemployment statistics always underestimate the number of people who could or would like to be in work.

NEWCASTLE-UPON-TYNE & GATESHEAD GAS CO.

Gas Works,
North Shields.

March 2nd. 1934.

N O T I C E.

CLOSING DOWN OF NORTH SHIELDS WORKS.
COKE OVEN GAS.

It is with regret the Directors have decided to shortly cease the manufacture of gas at North Shields Works. The Works will be re-opened for some portion of next Winter to meet the seasonal demands.

Allowances will be made to certain suspended workmen.

The Engineer will take an early opportunity of meeting the men and explaining the whole position.

(Signed) Geo. Duncan,
MANAGER.

Minton Lane Gasworks Temporary Closure Notice, 2 March 1934, included in the journal of Thomas Taylor.

be used by a caretaker until the site was sold. Whatever the truth, this is all the information that Mr Duncan was able to put on his official notice.

Understandably, Taylor was bitter about the directors and shareholders of the Tynemouth company who had personally gained rather than lost by handing over the Tynemouth company to Newcastle.

> I hope the ex-directors and shareholders of the old Tynemouth undertaking are satisfied. What they gained out of the amalgamation has proved to be at the expense of 70 men and 70 homes and 70 families. Had there been no amalgamation, the works would today have been working at full pressure and been employing at least double the number of men (2 March 1934).[87]

He added this the following day.

> The Works is a place of gloom this morning. I did not like to look the men in the face. There was something pathetic in the expression, a halt in their movements – like the men I saw being drafted from camps to the BEF (British Expeditionary Force) during the World War. The shock has stricken them into a dullness and apathy and they have not yet quite realised what the closing of the Works means. They see unemployment looming ahead, their homes and families are in danger. They are helpless. Their livelihood is to be taken away from them – and they do not know why.

It seems that no one at Minton Lane was assured of continuing employment. Taylor reported a conversation with Mr Duncan, and he too did not know what his future would be. For a man with a wife and large family living in a house on site, that must have been most disconcerting. Taylor understood that Mr Duncan's

---

87 In reality, they had gained at the expense of many more than 70 households because by then the workforce had already been greatly reduced from the around the 200 people employed at Minton Lane at the time of the takeover.

options were to accept a pension, or to remain on site during the summer months at a much-reduced salary when the yard would be shut.

The first letter to the local newspaper about the closure of the works came on 5 March and was signed WEST END TRADESMAN. He or she raised the question:

> Why should we be compelled to use gas manufactured outside the borough when we have a gasworks of our own that is a benefit to the town? Are the Newcastle and Gateshead Gas Co. going to give us nothing in return for our custom? We must be one of their biggest customers and in return they intend to further cripple this badly stricken town by forcing us to purchase gas manufactured in another borough. Is this a fair deal? … Can the Town Council move in this matter? Tynemouth Corporation must be a large purchaser of gas and coke from the above company and should insist on it being manufactured within the borough.

A second letter signed HOUSEHOLDER wrote:

> Surely it is an unusual and unfair state of things to think that on the closing of the North Shields Gasworks all gas used in the Borough of Tynemouth will be manufactured elsewhere, and all money spent by consumers of gas in the borough will help to pay the wages of workers at Howdon, whilst our work people will join the already long list of the unemployed. … Why should the works be closed? There is no rival causing additional expense, and the borough is one of the largest consumers the company has outside of the city. It is certainly a great deal larger than Wallsend, which borough is now apparently to benefit at our expense. … The statement that jobs will be kept open for the workers on re-opening in the winter appears to be a very doubtful concession. How will the workers live during the intervening six months? The question presents, I think, a splendid opportunity for some of our public men with the interests of the town at heart to approach the gas company with a view to influencing them to reconsider their decision, and thus save adding to the already sad distress in our town.

A subsequent letter from John Jackson of the Newcastle company emphasised that it had been his suggestion that a representative of North Shields was co-opted on to its board. So 'I therefore suggest that any aggrieved employee should see Mr

Lishman as to what steps he has taken in their interests.'[88] Another letter drew attention to the centuries-old, often bitter and occasionally bloody relationship between Newcastle and the other towns on the river.

> ... The Tynemouth Council missed a splendid opportunity six years ago when the town lost control of the gasworks because we had not a Ralph Gardner to fight again the age-old threat of domination of the coast by Newcastle. Today, not only is the North Shields area to be solely dependent upon an outside supply of gas and the town lose a valuable rate-yielding site but, according to the Newcastle Gas Company's official statement to the press, a further 70 of the town's workpeople are to be thrown out of employment. Surely the Mayor will ... enquire if the employees of the old Tynemouth Gas Company were given any guarantee of security by the Newcastle Company before the so-called amalgamation was agreed upon. ... Another important point to bear in mind is that if the gasworks had not come under the control of the Newcastle company, the plant would have been working to full capacity and at least twice the number of workmen would have been in employment. Have the ex-directors and shareholders of the old Tynemouth Gas Company no protest to make? (*The Shields News*, TOWNSMAN, 6 March 1934).[89]

The following day, TOWNSMAN had another letter printed which drew attention to the written guarantee of security of employment which had been given to the chairman of the Tynemouth company at the time of the takeover. He urged councillors to make representations to the Newcastle Board; seek the support of Tynemouth's MP, and, if necessary, that of the Board of Trade. Similar letters of support from other local people were printed in the same edition and over the next several days. Amongst the additional points made were that the Newcastle company was making handsome profits and paying high dividends; that it had already cut the work force at Minton Lane from over 200 to 70, and that the site and plant, acquired for effectively nothing given the terms of the takeover, were of considerable value to the Newcastle company. Another pointed out that when the amalgamation was first mooted, a latter-day Ralph Gardner had tried to

---

88 This is further evidence that Lishman joining the Newcastle Board was not a formal, negotiated part of the so-called amalgamation. It was in that purely personal capacity, that he eventually became the chairman of the Newcastle and Gateshead Gas Company.

89 Taylor notes in his journal that he had written to the local newspaper under a non-de-plume (almost certainly Townsman) and used a friend's address to protect his identity.

persuade the Corporation to take over the undertaking for the good of the town and warned them what the outcome would be if it went ahead.[90]

During this period, F.P.T., the Newcastle company's chief engineer, visited Minton Lane to explain the closure to the workforce. He told them how in 1927 the company had signed a contract to take a large quantity of COG from the Consett works and that it was ultimately that commitment which had led to the decision to close the gasworks at Minton Lane. The company had found that reducing 'the make' at each of its other works to ensure it did not have an unsold surplus of gas had proved uneconomic, and so it was now obliged to close one gasworks completely, at least for a period. That, account, of course, raises the possibility that the acquisition and then closure of the Tynemouth works was planned as early as 1927, as a way of finding a market for the surplus gas for which the Newcastle company had become contracted. During the following days, Taylor and Mr Duncan discussed which of the Minton Lane employees would make up the skeleton staff that would keep the site going during the period that the manufacturing plant was shut down. 'It was a rotten job' (13 March 1934).

By the end of the month, the gasworks were still in operation. It seems likely that the postponement of the closure was to accommodate a request from a Tynemouth Council sub-committee for a meeting with the directors. That took place on 6 April and resulted in nothing more than confirmation that the works would close, but now at the end of April. But the cumulative impact of the Newcastle company's policy was already apparent in early April. Taylor's quarterly figures show that by then, Minton Lane was already receiving more COG via Howdon than it was making itself. Compared to the 108 million cu. ft. of gas it received via Howdon, it had only manufactured 91 million cu. ft. on site. By mid-April only 5 of 24 retort beds were being used to manufacture gas.

It was on 21 April that Minton Lane employees began to receive their curtly worded termination of employment letters from the Newcastle company. They stated that from one week later, the 28 April, they would be subject to only one further day's notice. In defence of their actions, the company claimed that it had never guaranteed continuity of employment, as many seemed to have assumed, but only that Tynemouth workmen would not be replaced by Newcastle employees, and that they would be taken on with the same limited security as Newcastle employees i.e., the one-weeks' notice which they were now receiving. He also added that during the Board of Trade inquiry into the amalgamation, the chairman

---

90 Ralph Gardner was a local hero who during the days of the Civil War and afterwards fought a prolonged legal and political battle against the Newcastle monopoly of trade on the Tyne, despite being unlawfully imprisoned and ill-treated by officers of the Newcastle City Council.

had conceded under cross-examination 'that the time might come when the manufacture of gas at North Shields would cease.'

Included with the letter to employees was a second piece of paper setting out the 'allowances' that would be paid to workers to compensate them for their loss of employment. For example, someone with 15-years' service would receive a lump sum of £40

NEWCASTLE & GATESHEAD GAS COMPANY.

CLOSING OF NORTH SHIELDS WORKS.

To Mr. _____   Wage No. _____

I hereby give you notice that after 28th instant, your employment with the Company will be subject to one day's notice.

_____
MANAGER.

20th April, 1934.

Minton Lane Gasworks Warning of Redundancy (20 April 1934, included in the journals of Thomas Taylor.

(the equivalent of c.£8,000 in 2022) plus the equivalent of £1 weekly (equivalent to £200) for 10 weeks, 82.5p for 15 weeks, 75p for 15 weeks and then, finally, 62.5p for 9 weeks.[91] Those who secured employment elsewhere, or were taken back on during the winter months, would have those payments reduced by up to 50 per cent. The notice also emphasised that these were ex gratia payments and that 'the Directors reserve the right to cease or alter the payment of the allowances in any or all cases and nothing herein shall restrict the right of the Company to determine the employment of any person'. Taylor wrote in his journal:

> The men were handed the official notices with their pay at five. Many were shocked – and the optimists confounded. Now they know the intentions of the Newcastle Company. The amalgamation was never intended to include the North Shields Works but only the Tynemouth Gas Company's huge area.

By then, only five retort beds were in use and the volume of gas manufactured had fallen from 914,000 cu. ft. on 15 April to 569,000 cu. ft. by the 19 April. However, the final blow came suddenly two weeks later. Mr Duncan received a phone call from the former manager F.C.W. during which he was instructed to close the works immediately.

> This was a bombshell and took us off guard. We could not close down the complicated plant like switching off a light. Mr Duncan was upset – but

---

91 These sums of money would be taken into account in the calculation of the household means test if the recipient claimed public assistance of any kind.

he tackled the work at once. We are definitely finished tonight and that seems to be the end of everything. Will we start up again? At the moment I cannot realise what this will mean – or that the Works, as a works, is now idle. Memories of twenty-years came crowding into my mind. We reeled under the long-expected blow …Home … Security of employment … (9 May 1934).

The retorts were charged for the last time at 8p.m. that day, and at 6a.m. the following morning all valves were closed. By then, 30 of the remaining staff had been paid off; 16 had been re-allocated to the yard's distribution function, and six re-located to the Howdon gasworks. A skeleton staff of about 30 remained.

It was during those summer months, in a town with an unemployment rate of over 40 per cent, that the Council sought ways to reduce its spending. One of them was by not lighting its streetlamps until later in the evening and turning them out earlier in the early mornings. To that end, it willingly accepted an offer from the gas company to install clocks on its 1,274 'uncontrolled' gas lights, which it would pay for in annual instalments over the next 20 years. Potentially, that would make the town's five gas lighters redundant, but the Council undertook to try to find them alternative employment.

The Minton gasworks did re-open for the winter and gas was again manufactured from September 1934, but still at a level far below the capacity of the gasworks and again just during the winter months of peak demand.

NOTICE
NOTICE IS HEREBY GIVEN THAT
GAS-MAKING OPERATIONS
WILL COMMENCE ON THESE WORK
ON OR ABOUT MONDAY
FIRST SEPTEMBER 24th.
WORKMEN WHO WERE DISPLACED
WHEN THE WORKS WERE
CLOSED DOWN FOR THE SUMMER MONTHS WILL BE
RE-INSTATED AT THE CONVENIENCE OF
THE MANAGEMENT.

After the retorts were started up again, Mr Duncan sent this letter to the company's chief engineer.

I have pleasure in placing on record that carbonising operations were resumed on these Works on the 24th instant, after the manufacturing plant had been inactive since May 10th last. This gratifying fact is not only appreciated by myself, but is also shared by all the workmen and members of my staff, who join me in tendering thanks to the Chairman, Directors and other Officials of the Company, who by their decision to re-open the North Shields Station have given us once more an opportunity of occupying our accustomed places in the general economic scheme of things. We sincerely hope that as a result of our coordinated efforts, the North Shields Works will justify the Board's favourable consideration in its further deliberations on future policy.

The favourable consideration only lasted until the end of the winter months. Once again, the chairman of the Newcastle company announced at the AGM that manufacturing at North Shields would not continue beyond the spring. This is how the decision was reported in the local Shields newspaper.

The North Shields manufacturing station of the Newcastle and Gateshead Gas Company is to be closed again shortly.

Addressing the shareholders at the annual meeting of the company at Newcastle today, Mr John E. Cowan, chairman, said that under their contract for COG they were compelled to purchase a larger quantity in 1934 than previously and therefore it became necessary to close the North Shields manufacturing station during the summer. They re-opened it for this winter and would close it again in the spring (*The Shields News*, 26 February 1935).

Tragically, the North Shields station of the now Newcastle company received a further mention in the North Shields local newspaper for a different reason after it had re-opened for the winter months of 1935. In November, when the coke-breaking machinery stopped suddenly, 54-year-old Joseph Bage was found dead in its claws. It was later concluded by the coroner that he had been overcome by carbon monoxide poisoning, 'accidentally inhaled', whilst working as a retort coal charger. His duties involved re-filling the retorts with coal after the coke residue had been removed onto a two-foot-wide belt three inches below floor level. After losing consciousness, Bage had fallen onto the 50 feet a minute conveyor belt and was carried head-first for about 300 feet into the machinery. His body could only be released by dismantling the coke breaker: an operation which took eight hours.

The source of the carbon monoxide appears not to have been established but what seems evident is that, whereas when working as designed the retorts would have been filled by an automatic process, with just a small number in operation the retorts were being filled and emptied manually.

Whatever the local circumstances in North Shields, the gas industry nationally was still flourishing. The figures released at the British Industries Fair in 1938 showed that despite the growing popularity of electricity, 40-45 per cent of domestic lighting, and over 60 per cent of streetlighting, was still by gas. The industry had close to 12 million consumers and there were 8 million gas cookers in use. Over 400 trades made use of gas in some way ranging, 'from vast engineering concerns to small fish frying establishments.'

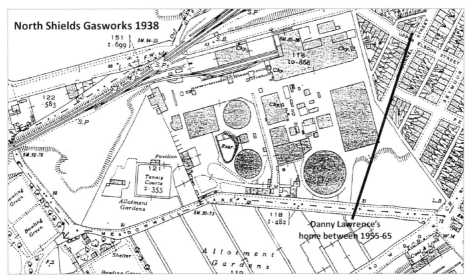

Site plan of the North Shields gasworks in 1938, shortly before the outbreak of war. Note that on this map, Minton Lane is still known as Meadow Well Lane. Source: Wilkinson, J. B., Desk Study and Historical Report. Former Gasworks Site at Minton Lane.

The Second World War

Early in 1939, the gas industry began to move onto what would be a war-footing. The new chairman of the Newcastle and Gateshead company, Sir Cecil Cochrane, following the death of both the previous chairman and vice-chairman, announced that:

> Due to the unsettled state of Europe and this being a vulnerable district, we have been asked by the Government to do work which is considered essential to enable us to continue the supply of gas in the event of damage to one or other of our works or to the coke ovens supplying us with gas. A large

expenditure is involved, and the Government is making a grant towards this on a percentage basis. The company has also to carry out a considerable amount of work for the protection of its employees and the plants for which no grant will be received (*Shields Evening News*, 28 February 1939).

Preparation for war was also evident in the work of local Air Raid Patrol (ARP) units which carried out an exercise in North Shields in May 1939. It was a huge operation, carried out during a black-out, involving all senior local government officers and others, including rescue, demolition and decontamination squads, and electricity, gas main and water repair gangs. The exercise was repeated in September.

These defensive measures were more than matched by the Luftwaffe's preparations for its offensive actions. Tyneside was easily reached from many of its air bases, and it was an obvious target, and not just because of its many war-related industries, such as shipbuilding, engineering, and armaments. The Tyne was also of direct military significance with Royal Navy vessels in the river for repair or preparation for a return to sea. It was also a strategic river for the importation and exportation of goods and materials essential to the war effort. North Shields, at the entrance to the river, was an easy target and German documents discovered after the war include an Ordnance Survey map of the area, and related aerial photos, identifying the main targets in North Shields, which included the gasworks. As Bolger notes, as well as multi-bomber raids, there were sporadic attacks by single 'nuisance raiders' and 'tip and run' attacks and, because North Shields was located at the entrance to the river, it was a suitable place for enemy crews to drop any remaining bombs before heading home (Bolger, 2019 p.162). The heaviest bout of bombing was in April to October 1941, but it continued until 1943.

In the same month that war was declared in 1939, a Fuel and Lighting Order came into operation which rationed coal, gas, and electricity. The rationing of coal was comparatively easy to enforce. Consumers had to register with a specific coal merchant, and it was the merchant who regulated the supply. However, unlike the rationing of coal and most other commodities, the onus for ensuring that gas and electricity rations were not exceeded lay with the consumer. Once informed of what they were allowed to use, each consumer was expected to learn how to read his or her gas and electricity meters and, if they exceeded their ration, notify a fuel overseer. There was no incentive to do so. The opposite was the case because an overseer had the power to disconnect a consumer and take proceedings against him or her for breaching the regulations. The penalties for a breach could be either a fine or imprisonment or both. The introduction of such gas restrictions in the north-east led to an official protest from the Newcastle and Gateshead Gas Company. It pointed out that as one of the largest coke producing areas in the country, so much coal gas was being generated as a by-product that it was being 'liberated into the air... [so] the rationing of gas in this area is quite unnecessary.' That remark laid bare the problem which had confronted the gas manufacturing plant on Minton Lane since the 1927 takeover. The supply from the Durham coke ovens was considerably more than the gas being consumed. As a sales representative put it:

> Nobody will quarrel with the principle of rationing, but for it to be introduced at this stage for gas consumption in an area like this is sheer stupidity. We've got far more coal gas than we can dispose of. With the black-out, gas consumption has fallen by about 30 per cent. Why then should we be rationed in our own district when collieries would welcome more trade.

Unfortunately, for the Newcastle and Gateshead company, having that information made so public, sat uncomfortably alongside the fact that just a few months earlier it had announced an increase in the price of gas. That increase provoked a particular protest from the Council of the stricken town of Jarrow, across the river from North Shields, which had become known nationwide following the well-publicised march to London of a delegation of the unemployed in 1936. Nor did the admission that the company had more gas than it needed sit well with the handsome profits and maximum dividends that had been declared earlier in the year. It was an obvious reminder that the Newcastle and Gateshead Gas Company was a private monopoly and that its shareholders were doing very well from their investments whilst many others in the area were struggling just to put food on the table.

That embarrassing admission that the company had more gas than they knew what to do with was, inevitably, a consideration in January 1940 when the Newcastle and Gateshead company put forward a Parliamentary Bill to not only take over the Morpeth Gas Light Company but also erect a new gasholder at South Gosforth, 170 feet (52m) high and 160 feet (49m) in diameter. As the chairman explained to shareholders at the 1940 AGM, if the company wished to continue expanding it had no other option but to extend its territory northwards and eastwards. The new gasholder was needed because, despite 30,000 gas streetlights not being lit because of the black-out, the bad weather had pushed gas consumption to record levels. Plainly, gas rationing was not yet having much impact in the north-east! Although opposed by Newcastle, Tynemouth and other local authorities, the Bill was eventually passed, although the gas company did make a concession to erect a 110 ft (34m) rather than the originally proposed 170 ft (52m) gasholder.

The first North Shields employee of the Newcastle and Gateshead Gas Company to lose his life during the war was 31-year-old Gunner David Fraser, who had worked for the company since leaving school. He was called up in December 1940 and killed by enemy action as early as February 1941. The following month, it was the turn of the Minton Lane gasworks itself to experience enemy action. Other raids followed. Details of them will be described in the next chapter but the overall effect was to curtail the ability to produce gas in Minton Lane for periods. No full account of the scale of the damage was ever published but we know from a subsequent report by the company secretary that, during one of the raids, the Minton Lane site was hit by seven high explosive bombs and 'terrific' damage caused. Comments made after the war by gas company officials also revealed that the output from the yard was all but lost for periods.

Despite some having maintained in 1939 that there was no need to ration gas in the north-east, by 1942 there was a widespread acceptance that being economical with gas was vital for the war effort. In a lengthy article on ways to economise, the *Newcastle Evening Chronicle* explained how much gas was needed to accomplish ordinary domestic tasks. At the time, over half of an average consumer's gas went on cooking. Less than 20 per cent of what was used for cooking was used to heat water and yet, despite that, people were recommended to:

> Wash [clothes] fortnightly if possible, use no more hot water than necessary to cover clothes, and change some of Friday's cleaning to Monday to put soapy water to good use. Steep dirty clothes overnight, don't rinse under running hot water, scrape all grease off plates before washing (*Newcastle Evening Chronicle*, 23 March 1942).

Large advertisements were also placed in newspapers by the Ministry of Fuel, urging the public to exercise 'drastic economy' to ensure that gas was available in sufficient quantity for industry.

Gas companies had long been regulated by the government because of the inherent dangers of coal gas. However, the range of controls was increased further during the war years. To comply with gas rationing, gas companies now had to urge domestic customers to use less. There was also now more direct intervention in labour relations in the gas industry. Under the Essential Works (General

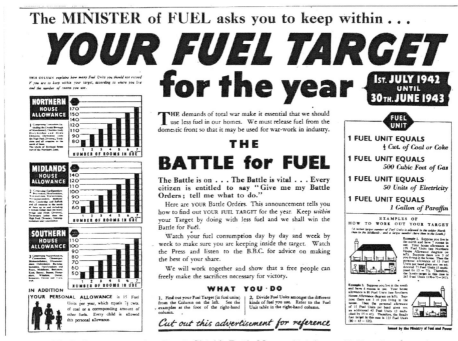

Ministry of Fuel advertisement placed in the Shields Daily News *of 24 August 1942 urging domestic consumers of gas to stay within their assigned target. Note that the target varied a little between the North, Midlands and the South in an acknowledgement of average temperature differences.*

Provisions Order) of 1942, employees could be prosecuted if they frequently arrived late at work. Just such a prosecution took place in July 1942 when an employee at Minton Lane was charged by the Ministry of Labour and National Service for being persistently late between 7-29 April and 18-30 May, and as a result missed 'a total of 7½ hours' work. The employee pleaded guilty but refused to pay the fine and was sent to prison for two months (*Shields Evening News*, 20 July 1944). Another employee was fined at the Tynemouth Police Court in 1944 'for having on or about December 26th 1943 left his employment with the Newcastle and Gateshead Gas Co. at the North Shields Gasworks without the permission in writing of the National Service Officer'.

In the final year of the Second World War, an article by J. Stanley Bell in the *Newcastle Evening Chronicle* paid tribute to the contribution of the local gas industry to the war effort. He maintained that at that stage the Newcastle and Gateshead company was 'rated among the six largest concerns in Britain today'. It was a £5 million company with seven gasworks supplying 25 local authorities covering 284 square miles with 1,700 miles of gas mains. Bell noted that of the approximately 2,000 employees in 1939, 559 had volunteered or been conscripted. Twenty-five had lost their lives and another ten had become prisoners of war. To help replace the men who had joined up, women were enlisted to perform a variety of roles including meter reading and the maintenance of domestic gas appliances, as well as manual work at the gasworks. The single photo in the piece, showed the Minton Lane purifying plant which had received a direct hit. Focusing on that was appropriate because, as Jackson explained in his history of the Newcastle and Gateshead Gas Company, the North Shields gasworks had been the worst hit of the company's sites. We know from the detailed records maintained by Inspector Harold White, the Deputy ARP Controller for the North Shields area, that the air raid warning was sounded 253 times and bombs dropped on 31 separate occasions. As a result of the air raids, 225 people were killed and 475 injured. At least 310 high explosive bombs were dropped on the town, along with 19 parachute mines and about 18,000 incendiary bombs (Bolger, 2019 p.167). At least 166 properties were destroyed; a further 281 damaged beyond repair, and 1,303 described as seriously damaged. Approximately 10,000 more were slightly damaged. For those of us who grew up in North Shields in the 1940s, bomb sites were a part of an urban landscape that we took for granted. In addition to dealing with the damage to roads and pavements, a huge amount of repair work had to be undertaken as a matter of urgency to deal with bomb damage to gas mains and gas pipes. As we explained in an earlier chapter, there was a danger that the continued use of gas would draw air in from broken mains and create an explosive mix of gas and air. To reduce the risk, valves had been installed so that damaged mains could be isolated, and specialist mobile repair teams were organized to deal with them. Damaged gas pipes had to be replaced, gas appliances removed and where possible replaced, in addition to all that was needed to get the gasworks back in working order after the worst of the bombing. All this work along with the continued manufacture of coal gas, was so important to the war effort that no technically qualified gas employees were allowed to enlist, or be conscripted, without permission from the Ministry of Labour.

Living in the gasworks house in the early years of the war was the Minton Lane manager, George John Duncan, and those of his family still living at home. It is the Duncan family's occupancy of the house, starting at the end of the Great War in 1918, through the final years of the Tynemouth Gas Company to the ignominy and repercussions of the takeover, and then the bombing raids on North Shields, which are described in the following chapter. However, it will begin with the circumstances which led to the building of the gasworks house, and a short account of its earlier occupants.

Chapter 8

The Duncans of Minton Lane

AFTER THE design of the Minton Lane gasworks had been agreed, the directors of the Borough of Tynemouth Gas Company asked George Livesey to design a suitable house for the manager (BTGC DM 26 Sep 1870). However, they considered what he proposed to be too expensive and so, at the time of the 1871 Census, the new manager, Livesey's brother Frank, was lodging with a shipowner and his family in Tynemouth. The issue of constructing a house on site was considered again in April 1873, when the directors charged Livesey's replacement, along with the company secretary, to 'get a plan and specification of a house on a smaller scale to lay before the directors.' As we noted in an earlier chapter, given that the estimate for the originally designed house was not much more than twice Livesey's annual salary, the reluctance to adopt the original proposal seems penny-pinching.

We have been unable to determine precisely when the more modest house was built other than it was between 1873 and 1879, when it was occupied by the then current manager, James Kemp. He was summarily dismissed and required to 'quit the house he now occupied in the Company's Works as manager, on or before the said Saturday the 22nd November 1879.' He was succeeded by the 22-year-old engineer William Hardie, who by then had already served three years as assistant manager at the Redheugh gasworks. We know from a newspaper report that he was living alone in the house in 1887, except for a 65-year-old widowed housekeeper, and that he continued to live in the house until sometime between 1901 and 1911, by which time he was living with his sister and two Scandinavian servants in one of the grand seafront houses on Beverley Terrace in Cullercoats. Prior to that, he had been elected to the Council in 1904, made Mayor in 1908, and Chairman of the Finance Committee in 1910, a position he held up to the time of his death in 1918.

Hardie's place in the gasworks house was taken by his deputy, Frederick Willis, with his wife, two children and a servant. However, on his promotion to engineer and manager after Hardie's death, he moved from Minton Lane to

Monkseaton. The gasworks house was taken over by the company chemist, George John Duncan, who also assumed the role of works superintendent. It was he and his large family who lived in the gasworks house during its most eventful years.

Duncan Gas Industry Links

Like Hardie, Duncan had family connections to more than one gas company. So delving into his family history is useful because it gives us clues to the kind of people who were drawn into the gas industry in its early stages. His great-grandfather George Duncan was born in the Northumberland market town of Alnwick in 1803, around the time that gas lighting was first being advocated by such pioneers as Murdoch, Clegg, and Winsor. He moved, aged 17, to another Northumberland market town, Morpeth, in 1820, at about the same time that North Shields set up its first gas company.[92] George established a bakery, opened a shop, and later also became a flour dealer, before going on to serve as a councillor, the Mayor of Morpeth and member of the Board of Guardians (which provided relief to the poor).[93] He and his wife Isabella had eight children: four boys and four girls. Only the boys took up occupations. What is interesting is that, like their father, they learned trades but then sought to move on from them. The eldest, John, trained as a boot and shoemaker then set up a business in Amble but, like his father, was enterprising and, in addition, bought a small ship. In fact, in several newspaper announcements relating to family events, he is described only as a ship owner. Unfortunately, his 140-ton brigantine *The Wave Spirit* was destroyed by fire in 1868 and, although he is still described as a shipowner and shoemaker in the 1871 census, he had by then established himself as a successful licenced auctioneer and appraiser.[94] Thomas, the second boy, trained as a printer and bookbinder but chose instead to take up the post of Rates Collector and later Inspector of Nuisances with the Morpeth Local Board of Health (although, as the extent of the work in that second role grew, he relinquished it). His many newspaper advertisements indicate that he also undertook private work as a debt and rent collector and commission agent. The third son, George, became a tailor but seems to have died in his twenties.

It was the youngest son, William Duncan, born in 1831, who took over his father's bakery and flour business and followed in his footsteps by becoming

---

92 About 20 miles south of Alnwick and about 20 miles north of North Shields.

93 There is still a Duncan's yard in Newgate Street, Morpeth, on the site of the original bakery and shop.

94 Like his father George, John was a keen gardener, won prizes in local competitions and in 1862 was reported to have grown a 2lb carrot, 16 inches long with a girth of 9 inches!

a councillor and Mayor of Morpeth. In addition, he became a director of the Morpeth Gas Company in 1874. Established in 1833, it seems to have been less preoccupied with making money for the directors than both the gas companies of North Shields. For example, the directors did not receive any fees until 1852 and, even then, only in terms of a limited free allowance of gas, provided they attended two-thirds of the directors' meetings. Initially, at least, those meetings were frequent. In the first year of the company's existence, they numbered 42.

After William's death in 1899, he was succeeded in the baker's business by his son, also called William Duncan. After the gas company was reconstructed in 1902, he too was invited to become a director and he served in that capacity from 1908 to his death in 1931. The newly constituted company adopted a notably cooperative stance towards its employees. A Savings and Provident Fund, established in 1909 just after William joined the Board, enabled employees to share in company profits. Those who chose to do so received returns of between 7 and 9 per cent. In the same year, the directors chose to provide a purpose-built house for the company manager and 'cottages of a superior class' (actually substantial semi-detached houses) for the company's principal workmen, near to but not on the site of the gasworks. They were officially opened in 1910 by William who was by then the Mayor of Morpeth, and it was the Mayoress, his wife, Mary Ann, who declared the houses open by hoisting the Union Jack over them.

The remarks made by the Morpeth Gas Company's chairman, Ralph Crawford, on that occasion are worth noting. He emphasised that the company had not built the cottages with purely philanthropic motives. They had land which they thought could not be put to a better purpose than that of building houses on it for their principal workmen, whose presence near the gasworks was particularly advantageous if there was any kind of emergency. The history of the company records him as adding:

> The relations between the Company and their workmen had been of the most satisfactory character: and it was hoped that their condition would be improved by the occupation of these cottages. Though he was not going to make a political speech, he could not help saying that those who tried to set capital and labour at variance were no friends to either, for it was an axiom that no capital could be fruitful without labour, and there could be no employment for labour without capital (Morpeth Gas Company, p.33).[95]

---

95 Similar remarks were being made by the chairman of the Tynemouth Gas Company at a time of industrial unrest.

With such links to the local gas company, it is not surprising that other members of the extended Duncan family became involved in the industry.

Such family connections in the early phases of the gas industry were not uncommon. Thomas Livesey (1807–1871) joined the company which became the South Metropolitan Gas Company in 1839. His sons George and Frank both followed him into the industry. George joined the South Metropolitan Gas Company in 1848 working initially as an assistant to his father. He was promoted to general manager in 1857 and the post of engineer in 1862. He remained in that post until he was elected company secretary by shareholders, at which point his brother Frank gave up his position in North Shields and succeeded him as the company engineer.[96]

In the north-east, there were also two generation of the Hardie family in the gas industry. William Hardie Snr, who for almost 40 years was the company secretary of the Newcastle and Gateshead company, had married a daughter of the manager of the Redheugh gasworks, and had two sons follow him into the industry. William served as the engineer and manager of the North Shields company for an equally long time and his younger brother Thomas, like his maternal grandfather, became the manager of the Redheugh gasworks. Moreover, their sister Mary married W. D. Gibb, the engineer for the Newcastle and Gateshead company. When the Centre for Technical Education in Newcastle introduced a course in gas manufacture in conjunction with Rutherford College (later to become Newcastle College), there were three members of the Hardie family on the organizing committee: the brothers William (from the North Shields company), his brother Thomas (from Redheugh), and William's brother-in-law W. D. Gibb (from Newcastle and Gateshead).

There was also an established professional as well as family network amongst those involved in the gas industry, both in terms of seeking and giving advice, and being invited to the opening of events at one another's companies. This reflected a set of shared interests amongst those involved in the gas industry, which was of particular significance given the growing competition from the electricity industry at the time. So, for example, the directors of the Morpeth company often sought the advice of Thomas Hardie, the brother of the North Shields company's manager William Hardie. An additional example of the network is that when the Morpeth company celebrated its centenary, Frederick Willis, the former Engineer of the Minton Lane works but by then the Assistant Engineer of the Newcastle and Gateshead company, was one of the invited guests. In short, Hardie, Willis and others were part of an established network of professionals with common interests.

---

96 https://en.wikipedia.org/wiki/George.Livesey

In the case of the Duncan family, even before George's youngest son William became a director of the Morpeth gas company, his older brother Joseph Ferguson, had served an apprenticeship as a plumber and gas fitter. However, our research suggests that Joseph was not as successful in business as his brothers William and Thomas were in their respective fields. We know from advertisements, such as the one below in the *Alnwick Mercury*, that, like his brother Thomas (the shoemaker, shipowner, and later auctioneer and valuer), that at some stage in the 1870s he established a business in Amble, describing himself not only as a plumber and gas fitter but also tin-plate worker.

It was there, in April 1877, that Joseph's first child George John was born. However, as the following advertisement in the *Morpeth Herald* shows, within a year Joseph Ferguson was back in Morpeth, and had opened a business in a side street, again offering his services as a 'plumber, gas fitter and tin-smith'.

JOSEPH F. DUNCAN,
PLUMBER AND GAS-FITTER,
TIN-PLATE WORKER,
QUEEN STREET, AMBLE,
Begs respectfully to inform his friends and the public generally that he has commenced business as above, hoping by prompt attention to all orders entrusted to him to merit a share of their support.
Repairs of all kinds punctually attended to.

Joseph Ferguson Duncan advertisement in the Alnwick Mercury, *17 March 1877.*

By the time of the 1881 census, when he was described as a plumber, gas fitter and tinsmith, he was running his business from one of the town's main streets: the same street on which his brother William was now running the family bakery. That move would suggest that Joseph's business was doing reasonably well but, if so, his success did not seem to last. By 1891, he had not only moved from Morpeth but was no longer running his own business. According to the census, he was *employed* as a plumber and *gasmaker*,

JOSEPH T. DUNCAN,
PLUMBER, GAS FITTER, TIN-SMITH, &.,
WANSBECK STREET, MORPETH,
BEGS respectfully to inform the Inhabitants of Morpeth and neighbourhood, that he has commenced business as above; hoping by strict attention to all orders, combined with {moderate charges, to merit a share of public support.
Repairs of all kinds done on the shortest notice.
BEST REFINED PARAFFIN OIL.

Joseph Ferguson Duncan advertisement in the Morpeth Herald, *23 February 1878.*

and living in Stagshaw, a hamlet three miles from the Hexham gasworks. It is possible that this physical move, and the change from being self-employed to becoming an employee, could be related to his failure to win a contract to lay a new water main in Morpeth.

By 1901, Joseph Duncan was living in North Shields, about 30 miles from Stagshaw, and working for the Tynemouth Gas Company as a 'gas main and service layer', indicating that he did not work *in* the gasworks and held only a relatively menial role in the company. The occupation of 'gas mains layer' still exists and according to the National Careers Service even experienced workers can only expect to earn about the average wage. Although Joseph does not

EXTENDING THE WATER MAIN IN COTTINGWOOD LANE.

The tenders for laying a new water main in Cottingwood Lane were opened, and were as follows:—Mrs. Daglish, for the main alone £7 5s, for the 2in flush valve £1 5s—whole work, £8 10s; Joseph Duncan, main £7 2s 6d, valve £2 12s 6d—total, £9 15s; Thos. Cranston, main £8 8s, valve £2 11s 6d—total, £10 19s 6d; Jas. Henderson, main £6 5s, valve £2—total, £8 5s; T. R. King, main £7 10s. Mr. Henderson's tender was accepted.

This brought the meeting to a close.

The public notice of the outcome of tenders submitted for extending the water main in Cottingwood Lane, Morpeth, Morpeth Herald, *18 February 1882.*

appear to have needed to live close to Minton Lane, between 1901 and his death in 1918, all three of the modest properties he lived in were only a short walking distance from the gasworks.[97]

Joseph and his wife Margaret had six children. One died as a baby and another in infancy. The only surviving girl became a dress maker. Of the three boys, one became a watch maker but the oldest, George John, and youngest, Joseph Henry, followed their father into the gas industry. Both qualified as gas chemists. Tragically, Joseph Henry's promising career was cut short. After being educated at the local grammar school, qualifying as an analytical chemist, and holding posts with the Sunderland Gas Company and the Commercial Gas Company of London, he volunteered for military service at the outbreak of the First World War. Whilst serving with the Northumberland Fusiliers he was killed in Flanders in October 1915, aged 25.[98]

Unlike his younger brother, George John was educated in Morpeth and eventually qualified as a chemist by attending evening classes whilst working for the gas company by day. However, he seems to have served an apprenticeship first because in 1901, aged 23, he was working as a plumber and gas fitter, at the Minton Lane gasworks. He was still described in the same terms when he married Ann Elizabeth Ingram (a daughter of the manager of the local water works) in 1904.

According to Alice (the baby in the photograph), George John Duncan would have preferred to have taken up a very different occupation. She explained in her

Left to right: 1907, George John, his grandmother Mary Ann Duncan (née Clark) holding his first child Alice Duncan, and his father Joseph Ferguson Duncan. At the time, both George John and Joseph Ferguson were gasworks employees. Duncan later became the company chemist, superintendent and finally manager of the Minton Lane gasworks.

---

97 For the benefit of those familiar with North Shields, the addresses were Stormont Street, Chirton West View, and Lovaine Place West.

98 He was one of 1,700 men from the Borough of Tynemouth killed during the war (Jackson, D. p.65).

memoirs that her father 'had always really wanted to be a doctor'. She added that the top shelf of their double glass-fronted bookcase was filled with medical books. However, even if someone with his background could have secured a place at medical school, the costs of his studies would have been prohibitive. Instead of pursuing his dream, George Duncan concentrated on advancing up the hierarchy at the gasworks. Apparently, not long after starting work at Minton Lane he was asked by the then manager, William Hardie, what job he hoped to have. His answer was, '*Your* job Sir'! After working during the day, he went to evening classes and in due course, like his younger brother Joseph Henry, qualified as an analytical chemist.

> Father worked in the gasworks and travelled backwards and forwards on a bicycle. He was frequently out at night school for years, and he eventually qualified as an analytical chemist (Alice).

At that point, his eldest daughter told us, he took the letter notifying him of his success and nailed it to the door of the Minton Lane gasworks offices! By 1915, he had become the company chemist, and was able to count William Hardie as a work colleague, although it was still some years before he fulfilled his ambition to be the gasworks manager. Like his younger brother Joseph Henry, George John volunteered for military service at the outbreak of World War One. At the AGM of the Gas Company in March 1915, the impact of the war was the first item on the agenda.

> As a consequence of the war in which we are engaged, the year under review has been one of great events, and naturally this company, in common with other gas companies, has experienced considerable anxiety, and we have had to accustom ourselves to new and novel experiences. Forty-five of our men, including Mr Duncan, the works chemist, have joined the colours [volunteered to enlist in the army]. I'm sure it is the wish of all of us that that by the early and victorious termination of the war, these men may be enabled to return safely to their homes (*Shields Daily News*, 5 March 1915)

Although Duncan volunteered when war was declared, we have no evidence that he saw active service. Initially, because of the large number of volunteers, the government chose to introduce a maximum age of 30 for recruits, at a time when Duncan was already 37. When the age limit for both volunteers and conscripts was raised to 35 in 1916, Duncan was still too old at 39. In any case, even if his age had not been a factor, it might have been judged that he was more useful to the war effort in his key role in the gasworks than as a combatant. That he did not do active service must have been a relief to his parents and family, especially after the death of his brother Joseph Henry at Flanders in 1915.

The Minton Lane Gasworks House

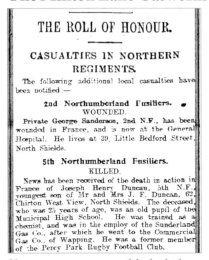

Newspaper announcement of the death of Joseph Henry Duncan, Newcastle Journal, *15 October 1915.*

In 1918, when Frederick Willis was promoted to chief engineer and works manager after the death of William Hardie, he moved out of the gasworks house and away from North Shields into the suburb of Monkseaton.[99] He was followed into the gasworks house by the company chemist, George Duncan, with his still growing family. Their move from Walton Avenue, in the still largely rural Preston Village, to a house on an industrial site must have been made with mixed feelings. For George Duncan, although it meant no more pedalling back and forth to work and an increased income, it came with more responsibility and much longer hours of work. For his wife, Elizabeth, it meant leaving her established neighbours behind. As her eldest child Alice explained: 'The neighbours were all business people: Smurthwaites, the market gardeners; Jamieson the pharmacists; Middletons, the decorators; Hastie-Burton, the builders; George Swan, the cyclists and, as they were young families, the same as we were, we were all very friendly.' The only obvious advantage for the family was that, although their Walton Avenue house was a substantial four bed-roomed terraced property, the gasworks house was a little larger and detached. Their move was made on 7 November just a few days before the signing of the armistice on 11 November 1918, and a month before the sudden death of Duncan's father, who had been a gas company employee.

We have been unable to find a still photograph of the Minton Lane house. The best we have is a frame from a Super 8 film shot in 1972 by a friend brought up in the area. It corresponds closely with the sketch drawn by Lorna Duncan, the youngest of the ten Duncan children.

---

99 His son was suffering from tuberculosis and a move to a suburb nearer to the sea was obviously preferable to living on an industrial site in an industrial area.

Lorna Duncan's sketch, from memory, of the gasworks house on Minton Lane. Note the close proximity of the then three gasholders.

Lorna Duncan, her eldest sister Alice, and our late friend George Brigham who lived in the house shortly before it was demolished, have provided us with detailed descriptions of the interior of the house. George Brigham's schematic floor plans are based on his recollections of when he lived in the gasworks house with his parents in the 1960s. The alignment of the house explains why the relatively narrow frontage on Lorna's sketch does not give an appropriate impression of the house's size.[100]

In her late 80s, Alice described the gasworks house in astonishing detail.[101] It revealed the many ways it differed from other properties in the neighbourhood.[102] Compared to the cramped and often squalid dwellings alongside the river and on the bankside, it was of a markedly superior quality. The nearer 'Tyneside flats' to the east of the site were comparable to the two-up-two-

We need to emphasise that although of poor quality, this image of the Minton Lane gasworks house and the adjacent allotment gardens is the only one we have been able to locate and is taken from a single frame of a Super 8mm film shot 50 years in 1972 by Dr George Thomson. The gasworks offices are to the left and the house is little right of centre. To the right of the house is the then only remaining gasholder. Behind it are several gasworks' buildings including the retort house and one of its two chimneys.

---

100 As a qualified, experienced, and well-regarded draughtman, George was uncomfortable drawing plans without dimensions and having to rely on his memory. However, he was persuaded to provide us with this schematic plan of the house and its surrounding area which has proved extremely useful.

101 She dictated her memories into a cassette recorder. They were then transcribed by Danny Lawrence.

102 It would be inappropriate to include her description here, but it is provided in Appendix 6.

down dwellings built in much of the rest of the country. They provided decently built, self-contained accommodation that many people still live in today, although, in almost all such cases, they have now been 'modernised'. At the time (and even into the 1970s) these small upstairs or downstairs flats were without bathrooms, indoor toilets, and plumbed supplies of *hot* water.[103] Back in the early part of the twentieth century, the contrast between these Tyneside flats and the three-storied detached gasworks house led one of Alice's school friends standing in the entrance hall of the house, to exclaim, 'Eeh, this house is just like a palace!' It was not only the generously laid out ground floor which was in marked contrast to her friend's small flat. Had her friend ventured upstairs, she would have been even more impressed with the three bedrooms, bathroom, and separate toilet on the first floor, along with a telephone and speaking tube; and that the two main bedrooms were heated by gas fires and the

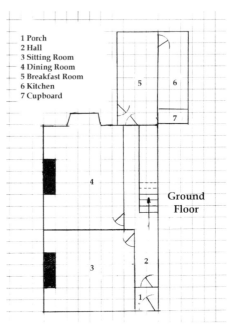

1 Porch
2 Hall
3 Sitting Room
4 Dining Room
5 Breakfast Room
6 Kitchen
7 Cupboard

Ground Floor

George Brigham's site plan, drawn from memory in 2018, of the ground floor of the gasworks house on Minton Lane.

smaller bedroom by pipes leading from the hall below. On the floor above, were two large attic bedrooms with fireplaces, in addition to a smaller room and landing so big that in later years it was used as a dining area and study when the whole of the top floor served as a separate flat for part of the household. Alice's friend would also have been impressed that unlike the residents of the Tyneside flats who shared small backyards but did not have gardens, the gasworks house had both a vegetable and flower garden, a lawn and even a wooden chalet that had previously served as a home for the son of Frederick Willis who suffered from tuberculosis.[104]

Family Life in the Gasworks

What follows in this section may only be indirectly relevant to the industrial activity on the gasworks site, but is included to illustrate that most people,

---

103 They did have plumbed cold water, something still not enjoyed by thousands of families in North Shields until after the slum clearance programmes of the 1920 and 1930s.
104 Some Tyneside flats were constructed with tiny front gardens.

including those who lived in the gasworks house, had a daily life of toil which, to some extent, could be mitigated by the gas appliances available for rent or purchase.

Moving to Minton Lane meant the Duncan children had to change schools, lose their school friends, and move from a village location on the outskirts of the urban area to living on a noisy, dirty and polluted chemical factory site. Yet, whatever reservations the children may have had, as the next section will illustrate, the accounts they left behind suggest that they found ways to make use of their new industrial surroundings to enhance their childhood. What they could not escape, was the domestic discipline which gave them all a share in the numerous chores that had to be carried out in the Duncan household. Lorna noted:

> Daddy was frequently called out during the evening and also during the night as he was on duty 24 hours a day, and mother's hands were never idle. She made almost all of our clothes, sewing and knitting every minute that was available. Mending was done in the precious hours of so-called relaxation and there was always plenty of that. Materials for clothing were mainly wool or cotton – manmade fibres either had not been invented or were not in common usage. As we went into the dining room to say good-night we left any of our clothing that required mending on the arm of mother's chair. It was usually done by the next morning.

Mrs Duncan was kept busy despite having 'a daily' to help her in the house, and a window cleaner courtesy of the gas company. Because of the smoke from open coal fires, windows became dirtier, more quickly, than today. For those who lived on or near the gasworks site, they had to be washed even more frequently to keep them clean.

> Fortunately, we had a lady coming in regularly to clean the windows. I remember her always wearing a hat and a grey shawl around her shoulders, even on her way home. Perhaps she had no coat; lots of people had not in those days. Mother always made her a cup of tea halfway through her work and they would sit and chat for a little while and then Mrs. Tait would go back to her window cleaning. The windows were all sash windows. The outsides were cleaned by pushing up the bottom half of the window and climbing half out so that you could sit on the outside sill looking in and hanging onto the window with one hand while cleaning the window with

the other. The outside of both windows could be cleaned by pulling one down and pushing the other one up and then pushing the clean one up and the dirty one down. It was a hazardous and most unenviable task (Lorna).

Despite such help, the children's contributions remained vital to the smooth running of the household, just as they had been in Walton Avenue. What is noteworthy about Alice's account of those chores is how many references she made to their ample supply of hot water, something not available to those who had to obtain their hot water by boiling kettles or pans over an open fire or on the hob of a gas cooker. She also made a point of noting that keeping the brass carpet stair rods bright was made more difficult because of the 'tarnishing from the works' fumes.'

> We each had our allotted chores to do. The boys had to polish the brass stair rods and clean shoes. Washing the dishes was an on-going chore as meals during the week were staggered because there were three different age groups. The two top age groups attended different schools at different times and different distances. The dishwashing chore was the one least liked, although there was an abundance of hot water. To soften the water a knob of washing soda was put into it. All spoons and forks had to be washed first in the hottest possible water, and promptly dried whilst still hot and polished as far as possible. The blades of the knives were cleaned every day with powdered bath brick. There was no stainless steel in those days. Every week, all spoons and forks had to be cleaned with *Meppo* then washed in very hot water to keep their brightness. We used to be irritated by what we considered to be mother's fuss over everything being correct.

The Duncan girls also mentioned the benefits of access to a gas water heater on each Monday's washing day, as well as the benefits of having ready access to plumbed hot water. Most families were not so fortunate until after the Second World War when boilers of various kinds became expected features in domestic dwellings. Until then and, for many, well into the post-war period, piped hot water remained a luxury. Readers must remember too that, prior to the second half of the twentieth century, and in marked contrast to today, electrical appliances played only a small role in most homes. To drive home to her own children how tough life had been when she was young, Lorna described Monday's washing day in some detail.

Young people today would have great difficulty in believing the laborious and lengthy task that washing clothes was before the Second World War. It was a full day's work. At about six o'clock in the morning the boiler in the washhouse was filled with cold water and the fire underneath prepared and lighted. We were very fortunate because instead of a fire beneath the boiler we had a large gas ring which heated the water much more quickly. The first boiler full of water was used to fill the large wooden tubs that the white clothes were 'possed' in before being rinsed ready to be boiled.[105] The next boiler full of water was for the coloured clothes and the next for the really dirty ones, and so on. Several tubs of water were needed for rinsing, the tubs being emptied by being rolled into the yard and tipped over into the sink. This procedure must have been carried out at least a dozen times on a washing day for such a large family as ours. Between each wash or rinse the clothes were mangled. This means that they were squeezed between two large wooden rollers which were turned by a handle at the side; the possing and mangling all using manual labour. Clothes were dried hung on lines in the yard, or on wet days hung indoors on clothes horses and pulleys, wooden rods pulled up and down from the ceiling by ropes. When dry they were then put through the mangle again to get as many creases as possible out of them. They were then ironed with 'flat' irons before being aired and put away. Flat irons were heated on the fire or gas ring: their temperature being tested by spitting on them. When ironing anything like a shirt, the collars and cuffs were done first before the iron cooled, which it did quite quickly so another iron had to be used. Of course, one iron was not enough to be in use at any one time. One or two were heating up while one was in use. How does that compare with the modern method of putting a load of washing in the machine, switching it on and going back to find it washed, dried and, in many cases, ready to wear? I well remember us still busy ironing at nine or ten o'clock at night, the whole day having been devoted to the washing.

Gas fires were also time saving. Most houses until at least the middle of the twentieth century relied on open coal fires to provide them with heating. Interestingly, that also appears to have been the case in the gasworks house even though gas fires were installed and the Duncans did not have to pay for their gas.

---

105 'Possing' was done with a wooden pole with a handle at one end and a heavy wide base at the other. The poss stick was pushed down quickly on to the clothes several times to help agitate the dirt from them.

Alice and Lorna recalled what was involved in lighting, maintaining, and cleaning out coal fires, before they could be lit again the next morning, a process already described above in chapter two. But, even in this respect, the Duncans were more fortunate than most other families in North Shields.

> The fires [downstairs] were all open fires. We were extremely fortunate in that one of the many perks of Daddy being manager of the gasworks was that we received free coal, sticks with which to light the fires and, of course, as we lived at the gasworks, free gas: all the lights being gas lights. The fire in the breakfast room was lit on most mornings. ... The box below the inglenook housed the sticks which were delivered regularly by workmen from the yard. There the sticks were kept dry, ready for quick ignition each day.

The Gasworks Playground

The Duncan children may not have had any electric or electronic devices to hold their attention, but Alice emphasised that they were never bored. Her account of how they spent their spare time is evidence of how little impact electricity had made on people's lives in the first half of the twentieth century. It also indicates how the Duncan children treated their less than salubrious surroundings as an adventure playground.

> There was one word which none of us ever knew the meaning of and that was – boredom! Any indoor leisure time during the winter could be spent in playing Happy Families, Ludo, Snakes and Ladders or Chess. Of course, in the 1920s we had our radio set. This was a crystal set tuned in with great diligence and much patience. It was set on a side table by the fireplace in the dining room and woe betide anyone who dared to run or make any noise in that room, because the slightest vibration used to knock the 'cat's whisker'. Of course, earphones had to be worn to hear it. The 'cat's whisker' was so named because it was a very fine piece of wire which had to be manipulated carefully against the crystal to acquire the correct wavelength.[106]

Today, we spend a lot of time *listening* to music on all manner of electrical devices. For the Duncan family, what mattered more was *making* their own music. As Lorna (who became an accomplished pianist, accompanist, and secondary school

---

106 BBC radio broadcasts were not introduced until the 1920s.

music teacher) explained, her father's interests extended far beyond the chemistry of coal gas production.

> Father's hobby was making violins. These took a great deal of time and patience. As father explained, the purity of sound of the finished instrument came not only from the strings used but the depth of the inside of the belly, which was obtained by careful, gradual shaving of the inside. As this operation was performed on the kitchen table, we were interested in it though not understanding it at the time. The instrument was finished with a special German varnish. He made five of these violins. He endeavoured to make each have a more mellow tone than the one before. As well as his own home-made violins, he had two very good ones. His older one he had played from boyhood. He possessed another old one, dated 1750, which he said he wouldn't sell for any amount of money! Although music was a great part of our lives from birth and we enjoyed hearing the violin, none of us had any desire to play it. Father loved his violin but only seemed to play it late at night, perhaps just before they were going to bed when, of course, it would be quiet. … As I have said, music was always a great part of each of our lives. The keys of our piano needed to be rubbed with a damp wash-leather each day. Professor G. Wood was considered part of the family although his visits several times a week late at night meant grumbles from those of us who had to prepare a supper on a tray. After that, piano and violin music until midnight were our lullabies! This was apart from our own singsongs. It was a good thing that we had no neighbours!

Lorna had lots more to add on that subject.

> Each week we had several musical evenings, father playing the violin and a great friend of his playing the piano. This friend was a professor of music called George Wood. He was a wonderful pianist. I believe that I got a lot of my love of music from him as well as my father and the rest of the family. Father taught himself to play the violin, playing so well that he was able to play Mendelssohn's Violin Concerto to an exceptionally high standard. Many a night I fell asleep in bliss while listening to Mr. Wood and Daddy playing that marvellous composition, and even now, whenever I hear it, I cannot help thinking of those magical days when almost all the music we heard was live music and most people were performers as well as intent listeners. Some of the violins that Daddy played he made himself, shaping the special wood and mixing and heating the glue which was a special

mixture. Most of the family could play the piano, Phyllis and Elizabeth doing exceptionally well. We could all sing too and many a song was enjoyed with the whole family together in the sitting room.

Outside the house, Alice recalled that in what she called the leisure garden (to distinguish it from the vegetable and fruit garden), 'there was a hefty wooden erection of a swing', and the wooden chalet in which the previous manager's tubercular son had lived. 'That was a marvellous place to play.' Lorna added: 'It was very like a magnificent Wendy house. We loved playing in it, as it was just like a real house. It had curtains up at the windows; linoleum on the floor and a gas stove which we could light, and we often made toffee there. I expect mother was very grateful that we could play there and keep out of her way.'

Alice also recalled that going from the inside to the outside of the main house was not always done in the most conventional way.

> The first flight of 12 stairs led to a landing, leading to a double width staircase of four stairs. … On the right-hand wall was a large, coloured glass sash window through which we had a great game – climbing on to the kitchen flat roof and trying to jump down for a dare (by the boys) onto a handful of grass they laid down. … A great joke of Henry's when he was about eight was to go into the lavatory, fasten the door leaving the notice 'engaged'. He would then climb out the window, down the drainpipe and go away. When he was sought, he would climb in again.

Alice continued:

> Somewhere along the line we acquired two goats as playthings. The boys fixed two old dolls pram wheels onto a wooden box and harnessed the goats, taking turns racing round the gasholder. Another pastime was climbing girders and catching pigeons nesting there, as well as sailing paper boats round the water surrounding the holder (which stank).

Lorna made similar points to Alice but emphasised even more how much freedom they enjoyed in those parts of the gasworks site which, in terms of health and safety, ought to have been out of bounds.

> We were allowed a considerable amount of freedom in the works itself so long as we did not go in during working hours. Occasionally we broke this

rule in order to go into one of the shops to 'blow the buzzer'. The 'shops' were buildings where the workmen repaired or made various pieces of equipment for use in the yard. In one of these shops was a lever which blew the buzzer and we thought that we were very adult when allowed to pull it, hear the roaring sound and then the movement of all the feet, wearing heavy hobnailed boots trundling either in or out of the works. If we were up early enough to blow the first buzzer of the day, which was not very often, we would hear the sound of even more feet, some of which belonged to poor people who pushed wheelbarrows, some of which were home-made, clattering up the cobbled road as soon as the 7.30 a.m. buzzer sounded. They were then able to go up to the top of the yard where there were piles of coke which they were able to buy cheaply. … In our early years I believe we looked upon the yard or works as we frequently called it, as our playground. The most interesting part was the offices which bordered the street or to give it its correct name Minton Lane. At the entrance where the workmen clocked on were the cards which they stamped in the clocks so that their working hours could be checked. I'm afraid that their cards were occasionally very incorrect at times as we transgressed by playing at stamping several cards with peculiar times on them. Fortunately, the secretary could easily tell what had happened and we were not reprimanded.

Most people think of only gasholders when they hear the word gasworks but there is much more. There were large areas which to us were playgrounds. Three gardens in different places provided us with fresh vegetables, us when children with small garden plots, and some of the workmen with allotments. As most of the coke and coal was transported by horse and cart there were stables to house the horses, a trough for their drinking water and bales of hay and straw for their food and bedding.

A pond filled with stinking, dirty greasy water provided the boys with a wonderful boating lake – as long as they did not fall in. Often, we visited the furnaces where the coal was heated to a certain temperature to drive off the gas. The coke was then transferred on conveyor belts to be piled up outside. There were also large, covered areas where the purifiers were. As you can imagine we had marvellous times playing there and knew the yard as they say like the back of your hand. The holders provided us with wonderful climbing frames.

Lorna's familiarity with those gasholders was to prove of great value during a bombing raid in 1941, and her ability and bravery in climbing them in dangerous circumstances earned her a certificate of commendation signed by the Prime Minister, Winston Churchill, himself. Her confidence in climbing also developed from games with her brother Joseph Henry (nicknamed Boco).

On the grassed area my brother and I played various games. When we played cricket, I was almost always the bowler as Boco liked to bat. Occasionally a ball would go up on the roof. As there was a convenient drainpipe up the wall, we were able to climb up to retrieve it. I say we but I did not find it so easy. I was good at climbing but found that negotiating around the large coping stones at the top, forming strong guttering very difficult. Once, when I thought that I was doing very well, I lost my grip just as I was going over the coping stone and fell head over heels to the ground. I knew nothing then of slow-motion films. If I had known, I would have thought that I was in such a film. I still remember falling just as if it was in slow motion. Several members of the family, including my parents watched me fall and were amazed to see me get up as if nothing had happened.

Lorna went on to describe other things that the children enjoyed about living on the gasworks site.

Behind the house there were other things to interest us. One of the things was a hen run. The hens belonged to a previous manager of the works. They were looked after by one of the workmen, who fed them and collected the eggs. We enjoyed going with him, to 'help' him. Eggs in those days were neither as plentiful nor as cheap as they are today and I'm afraid we sometimes asked for an egg. He promised us that if there was ever a day when there were six eggs, he would give us one. After waiting for several weeks and not receiving an egg we, Margaret, Jean, Boco and I, decided that we had to do something about it. We would go into the hut where the hens slept and count the eggs before the keeper arrived. Guess who was the person elected to crawl through the small opening that the hens used for entry? The smallest person – and that was me. One day there were seven eggs. I could only just get through the tiny space and getting back with the precious egg and then over the fence without breaking it was not easy for a young person as I then was. That egg was treasure trove to us. We carried it upstairs to the attic, where we slept, to discuss what we were to do with the said egg. How were we to cook it? How were we to share one egg among four of us? In the middle of this discussion we heard the stairs creak. This creak we knew only too well. It was the sound that usually sent us scurrying back to bed at night when we were supposed to be asleep – but this was morning. What could Daddy want at this time of day? Had he discovered our guilty secret? It was summertime and in our attic bedroom was a strong trunk which our older brothers, George and Ingram, had recently brought back from camping. This was usually kept locked but at the time was still open, so we quickly slipped the stolen egg inside. I think that Daddy was surprised to see us all in the attic at that time of day but said nothing. He had actually come upstairs to lock the trunk as it would not be needed again until the next summer. The smell that emanated from that trunk the following year was unimaginable. We kept the story of the egg a secret for many years. Also behind the house was a pigeon ducket, where our older brothers George and Ingram kept their pigeons, most of which were very tame. They were also homing pigeons and Ingram sold one on several occasions as it always returned home. Whether or not he returned money to the buyer I don't know. They multiplied over the years and eventually went to live on the gasholder but came down to be fed by us. Naturally, some were tamer than others and would come onto our hands to be fed. One, particularly tame, somehow broke its leg. Daddy managed to make a splint with match sticks so that after a few weeks it was able to move about again but always had a limp. It became a family favourite as it was so friendly after that. The family cat one day caught it as it was no longer able to move as quickly as the others. Jean was furious with the cat and gave it a good smacking, which was a bit unfair as the cat was only following its natural instinct. Round the back, as we called the ground behind the house, was a patch of ground where we each had a plot. We were always encouraged to cultivate these plots to create a love of gardening but I'm sorry to say that my interest was never very strong and my plot of the garden never very attractive. Part of this ground was never cultivated but we did play on it. We dug a deep hole at one spot and called it a cave, where we sat telling so-called ghost stories, rattling bones or shaking stones on a shovel to create an atmosphere whenever we came to a particularly frightening part of the story.

Lorna also described many of the games that they played as children, but I have not included any references to them because they do not relate even indirectly to the gasworks house or site. The same is true of her recollections of family pets.

However, one does warrant a mention because of its well-publicised experience with one of the gasholders. He was Mac, a wire-haired terrier.

He became the most loyal and wonderful family member that anyone could wish for. Whenever Daddy went around the works Mac, as we called our dog, went with him, especially when he was called out at night which was very frequently. He would stay with him until he came back into the house. He was not allowed upstairs at all but when he thought that everyone was asleep we would hear him creep upstairs and sleep at one of the bedroom doors. At the first sound of anyone on the move he was away downstairs. He used to set each of us to school or work. When we thought that he had accompanied us far enough we told him to go home, and he would watch us until we were out of sight before returning. If, on the way home, he met another member of the family he would accompany them until instructed to return. … At the beginning of the swimming season we went to the baths in Hawkey's Lane on the opening day which was always a Sunday. The water was cold, or should I write freezing, but this did not deter us. On one of these opening days we were so keen to have our first dip of the year that we did not notice that Mac had followed us. He slipped in unnoticed by the staff too and had his photograph taken standing on the end of the springboard. It was printed on the front page of the local paper the following day, and we were very proud to tell people that he was our dog. … Wherever we were, Mac was with us. He was very protective when we went down to Tynemouth to swim in the sea, which we occasionally did before going to school, getting up at about six o'clock, walking the two miles to the beach, having a swim and walking the two miles back for a quick breakfast of the usual porridge. This was followed by another long walk to school. Mac walked all the way to the beach and back with us besides swimming with us in the sea, always staying as far out as the person who was swimming farthest out and staying in the water until the last swimmer came out. What sense do animals have to tell them of any possible or imminent danger? Perhaps it won't be long before scientists can tell us now that they can separate genes from egg cells and clone animals. … In spite of Mac belonging to such a large family and feeling responsible for all of us he was really Daddy's dog, spending most of each day with him at work, going around the works late at night, as well as walking with him to and from the newsagents each lunch time. One night as usual Daddy went out on a tour of the yard. He was away much longer than on previous evenings but eventually returned without Mac. He had been looking for him for some time before coming home and, not being able to find him, thought that he must have returned. 'He'll soon come back' we said, 'He never stays out on his own' – but he did not return. 'I'm going to see if I can find him' Daddy said, getting worried. He retraced his steps until he came to a gasholder that was being repaired. The holder had been emptied of gas so that the crown was almost level with the ground. In order to inspect the holder one of the metal plates near the centre is removed. Around the holder there is a space about two feet wide which, when in use is filled with water; this of course gets very dirty and contaminated with gas. As the holder was being repaired this liquid had been drained off. What was left in the bottom was filthy, gaseous, and therefore dangerous. Daddy had jumped over the gap to check that all was well, expecting Mac to wait for him as he usually did. He was thinking about this when he thought he heard a faint whimper. Yes, there it was again. Shining his torch down to the bottom, about 20 feet below he could see nothing but the filthy slime. Trying once more he thought he saw a slight movement. Getting a long piece of rope and a workman to help him he was lowered down to the bottom. Even then it was difficult to see Mac, he was so covered in black sludge and by this time appeared lifeless. Daddy must have had a gruelling task getting up that narrow gap covered in slime, carrying a slippery inert dog in his arms but with his determination he accomplished the rescue. On his return we were all aghast, looking unbelievingly at the black figure before us. We could hardly distinguish man from dog. When we did it was all hands to the buckets of hot water to try to get them both cleaned. Daddy was soon in the bath but getting Mac cleaned was a much more difficult task. We lost count of the number of times we filled buckets, emptied dirty water and mopped up spills and splashes. Eventually, we decided that we could not get Mac any cleaner. His coat was stained and though he seemed to be recovering a little he was obviously suffering the effects of inhaling fumes and had injuries to his hind quarters. We wrapped him up and made him as comfortable as we could, going to bed praying that he would recover. It was several days before he was able to move on his own and he was never as fit as he had been, but he still had his loving and playful nature. From then on he walked with a limp, but he did not let this disability stop him from joining in with the activities that he had always enjoyed so much. Daddy fortunately did not appear to suffer too much from the after-effects of his very courageous rescue. We were all very proud of him, especially when his bravery was recognized by the Royal Humane Society, who awarded him a certificate.

Although not pets, any description of the gasworks site would not be complete without a reference to the company's horses. As Lorna explained:

In the 1920s there was very little motorised transport. The coal and coke from the gasworks were carried by horse and two-wheeled cart. There were three horses, each with their own stable, which were quite a distance from the house. At the end of each working day the horses were loosened from the carts and their harnesses and walked to the troughs where they could get a drink. This was where we were able to ride bare back on the horses, a journey of about two hundred yards. To us, who were still quite small, the horses seemed huge, but that made us feel quite grown up. We remained on the horses until they were in the stables for the night. They had a long working day as they usually began at 7.30a.m., finishing at about 5.00p.m. My brother Henry occasionally decided that he would like to have a ride to school on one of the carts, so would wait at the bottom of the road until one came. Sometimes he was late for school as there was no set time for the carts to leave the yard. What colour he was on arriving at school after riding on a coal cart I shudder to think.

Dog Rescuer

DOG lovers in the borough of Tynemouth would read with a sense of pride the exploit of Mr George Duncan, the 60-year-old manager of the North Shields Gas Works in descending 30 feet to the bottom of the well of the gas container at the works to rescue his pet dog. Fortunately, neither master or dog were any the worse for their unexpected adventure.

The accompanying photographs are those of Mr Duncan and his wire-haired terrier, Mac.

A local newspaper report of George Duncan's rescue of Mac, his wire-haired terrier. Unfortunately this, the only cutting kept by the family, is not labelled with either the source or date, but would have been sometime during 1937, a year which has not been digitised by the British Newspaper Archive. This poor-quality image is the best available.

Education and Occupations

Minton Lane was in the catchment area for the local authority Western Board School. However, a family connection with the headteacher of the more highly regarded Queen Victoria Primary School (another Board School) enabled the Duncan children to attend there instead. It had the advantage of being close to the home of their widowed grandmother, whose husband Joseph had been employed at the gasworks. All ten of the Duncan children subsequently went on to secondary, rather than the minimal elementary education available to most children. They did so after passing the examination for admission to the selective Tynemouth Municipal High School, which had been opened in a fine new building in Hawkey's Lane in 1909.

None of the Duncan children followed their father and grandfather into the gas industry, although three became chemists of a different kind. George the oldest boy signed indentures with a Wallsend pharmacist on leaving school. He qualified in 1930 and was the first permanently appointed pharmacist to the North Shields Preston Hospital. He remained there for 42 years until he retired in 1973. His brother Ingram followed his example and worked for the North Shields pharmacy and manufacturing chemists Williamson and Hogg. [107] On qualifying he remained in the retail sector. Mary, after working with Williamson and Hogg, became a dispenser with a local GP, in the days when family doctors dispensed their own medicines. Elizabeth, Margaret and Lorna went to college and became schoolteachers. Phyllis became an award-winning shorthand typist and then teacher of commerce. Jean was a nursery nurse, who also trained as a hairdresser. Alice did a year's nursing training before she married. Joseph Henry was a student on a Durham University medical degree course when he joined the Royal Air Force (RAF) after the outbreak of the Second World War. Like the uncle he was named after, he was killed in action. [108]

The Bombing of the Gasworks

Lorna Duncan recalled that her mother had been nervous about the possibility of having to move into the gasworks house during the First World War, because Zeppelins had twice made runs over it in 1915. If she was also apprehensive about living on an industrial site, her concern would have been reinforced in 1927 following the explosions of two gasholders in Manchester, each containing 1.75 million cubic feet of gas. It was reported that the iron sheeting of the holders had crumpled like paper. Although there were no fatalities, 23 people were treated for burns or shock. Had something similar happened on the cramped Minton Lane site, it might have involved not just the workforce but Mr Duncan's wife and children, because the gasworks house was so close to the gasholders.

By the outbreak of the Second World War, it was a smaller Duncan family living at the gasworks house. George had moved away on his marriage in 1930 and

---

107 The same Williamson who was the chairman of the Tynemouth Gas Company.

108 His reconnaissance aircraft was shot down by a U-boat in the Atlantic. His name is recorded on a memorial unveiled by the Queen at Runnymede. Lorna, who as a child had adored and been inseparable from Joseph Henry, attended the occasion along with her father George Duncan.

Alice had done the same in 1931. By the time Ingram married in 1936, his mother Elizabeth was seriously ill, and died two months later, at the tragically young age of 59. Mary was the next to marry and move away in 1938. Lorna recalled how the remaining Duncan family 'were like all the population of the United Kingdom, gathered around the 'wireless' [radio] on that momentous Sunday morning, hoping against hope to hear good news' but 'the fact that my boyfriend had been recalled to duty just a few days after returning from his annual fortnight's training in the Territorial Army should have been enough to substantiate our fears.' Lorna explained that the Duncans were conscious that living in the gasworks put them in a vulnerable position, 'the three large gasholders being a prime target for enemy bombers.'

> Shortly after listening to the broadcast telling us that we were at war; the siren, warning us of the approach of enemy bombers, sent us tearing into the kitchen, to crouch together under the table, where we thought we would be safest. At home at the time were three of my sisters and my youngest brother, living with father. He was so worried about us being so close to danger that we were soon despatched to live with friends, the families of our boyfriends, as we were all courting at the time. My brother, being almost 21 was called up into the RAF. As the expected air raids did not materialise, we were allowed to return home, at least my sisters were. By that time, I was at college. I was then at the gasworks only during the holidays.[109]

Lorna Duncan in the garden of the gasworks house adjacent to one of the site's three gasholders.

By Christmas, Lorna had two more married sisters. Elizabeth married in August 1939 and Phyllis in November. By then, Joseph Henry, the youngest Duncan boy, was not the only member of the family in danger in the services or on the high seas. The husbands of Elizabeth, Jean, Margaret, and Lorna were in the armed forces, and Phyllis was married to a merchant seaman on the Atlantic convoys.

---

109 At that stage, Lorna was training as a primary schoolteacher. Later in life, when a qualified schoolteacher she was awarded an LRAM (Licentiate of the Royal Academy of Music) teaching diploma and went on to teach music at secondary school level.

The winter of 1940-41 was very severe. A headline in the local newspaper described TYNEMOUTH'S FEBRUARY SNOWSTORM MOST DEVASTATING FOR 54 YEARS.

The snow continued to fall with the inevitable result that some train and bus services ceased altogether. Local streets became blocked, and shopkeepers and householders with the assistance of soldiers and men engaged by the Corporation endeavoured to make roadways passable. This produced a remarkable sight with heaps of snow three and four feet hight in line with pavements all over the town. ... Roofs and wires had to stand an enormous strain and there was considerable damage to property. ... A number of cars and vans were snowbound and had to be left exposed to the weather. Numerous families were unable to secure deliveries of bread and other necessities for a couple of days [this in a society without fridges and freezers where essential shopping was done daily] (*Shields Daily News*, 3 March 1941)

Working in such conditions left George Duncan in poor health.

Father had great difficulty in the works as the pipes kept freezing up. Even in fine warm weather he worked for arduously long hours, often going around the works checking that everything was satisfactory well after 10 o'clock. In freezing weather, when people needed extra gas for heating, his work was trebled, and emergencies were frequent. One evening he came back to the house at about 11.00p.m. We had a meal ready for him, but he had barely sat down to it when we heard the sound of running water under the floorboards in the kitchen. He tried to lift the floorboards to get at the fault but was too physically and mentally exhausted to do anything and we had to get one of the workmen to repair the burst pipe. The following day, Father collapsed at work suffering from double pneumonia and bronchitis. It was weeks before he was anything like well, but he insisted on going back to work (Lorna).[110]

George Duncan was still far from fully recovered when there was a huge bombing raid on Tyneside on Wednesday, 9 April 1941. Between about 23.20 and 4.50

---

110 Pneumonia (and even more so double pneumonia) was a particularly serious illness in the first half of the twentieth century. It was the most likely infectious disease to prove fatal and the third cause of death overall. By 1943, sulphonamides (popularly referred to as M&B because they were developed by the pharmaceutical company May and Baker) were used twice to treat Winston Churchill when he developed pneumonia. The more effective antibiotic drug penicillin was not available for doctors to prescribe until later in the 1940s.

the following morning, 116 enemy aircraft dropped an estimated 152 tonnes of high explosives and many thousands of incendiary devices. One of the many areas hit was the Minton Lane gasworks. That did not come about by chance. The gasworks can be clearly identified, along with other prime targets in North Shields, on the Luftwaffe map shown opposite. Fortunately, of the three high explosive bombs which hit the site, only one did significant damage to functional parts of the gasworks. It fell on the tracks leading from the railway main line into the gasworks. Another fell on the tennis courts of the recreation area just beyond the gasworks house. The main threat came from the approximately 200 incendiary devices that rained down on the gasworks and, at that time of day, it fell to the family who were on hand to help deal with them, along with the company foreman Joseph Callaghan and the few other workmen on site. Present in the house that night, other than George Duncan, were his daughters Phyllis, twins Margaret and Jean, with her fiancé George McDonald, and Lorna, home for the Easter holidays. This is Lorna's account of what happened that night.

In April I returned home for the Easter holidays. There had been only a few air raids in the months prior to that holiday … [and] the gasworks were up until that time unscathed. But on the evening of 9th April 1941, I had been in bed for a short time when the siren sounded. We knew that the enemy had the gasworks as their target when we heard the terrific sound of hundreds of 'tin cans' falling around the house. Pails of sand and buckets of clay had been placed at strategic places around the house and in the works but there were so many incendiary bombs to be extinguished that we (Daddy, Phyllis, my twin sisters Margaret and Jean and Jean's fiancée, who was on leave, myself and the workmen who were on duty) were soon digging in the soil of the garden for anything to put over the flames. The works were quite extensive with furnaces, purifiers and workshops as well as three gasholders and a water gas plant. Besides these there were stables for the cart horses, large gardens to the north and south and two tennis courts.

We were in the vicinity of the tennis courts when we heard the unmistakable whistle of a high explosive bomb. Flinging ourselves to the ground we waited for what seemed like an eternity for the end of the salvo. Then, rising to our feet, we were showered with debris, mud and stones which had been thrown up by the bombs. The gods were certainly with us that night for no one was killed.

German Stadtplan of North and South Shields showing military targets
Archive Reference: TWAS DX111/1

TYNEMOU

⚡ Dampfelektrizitätswerk 🏭 Gaswerk 🚞 Ziegelei

🚂 Eisenbahnwerkstätten, Bahnhofsanlagen

⊕ Krankenhaus ⚓ Schiffsbauerei und Reparatur

The Luftwaffe map highlighting bombing targets in North Shields, including the gasworks (Gaswark) indicated by the added white line at the bottom of the image. Courtesy of the Tyne and Wear Archives.

Although, presumably for reasons of wartime morale, the events at Minton Lane were not described in detail in the local newspaper at the time, they were described later in June 1941 after two of those present that night had visited Buckingham Palace to receive awards for their bravery.

> Mr Duncan, then in the vicinity of No.3 holder, extinguished several (IBs) on the ground at the rear of his house and shortly afterwards noted a glare from the crown of the holder. He climbed to the top, put out and sealed two burning escapes and located and sealed a third heavy escape which had not ignited, using clay, plates and tools stocked in readiness on the crown of the holder. Though hostile aircraft were constantly overhead, attracted by the fires which were then raging elsewhere, he remained on top for half an hour, during which some high explosive bombs were dropped in the vicinity, including one which wrecked the approach to the weighbridge. Stoppage of the leaks at three separate points involved further journeys to get clay and plate, the difficulties being increased by the high camber of the crown and wet and slightly frozen surface of the plates. After completing temporary repairs, Mr Duncan had great difficulty in getting down to ground level owing to exhaustion. He is 64 and had not yet fully recovered from a recent serious attack of pneumonia. … Subsequently he was instrumental

in ensuring the recovery of the works foreman, Mr Callaghan, who had been overcome by gas, to whom he administered oxygen.

Mr Callaghan, after attending to incendiaries near the water gas plant, including one inside the building which had fractured the oil pipeline, had noticed flames coming from the crown of No.1 holder (used for water gas). He climbed to the top and with difficulty extinguished and sealed off the escape with wet clay. In this case the bomb had burst open the seam and repeated efforts were necessary to effect repairs. In making these attempts single-handed Mr Callaghan suffered severe gassing. But he eventually succeeded and managed to reach the ground where he was partly revived by being walked up and down by his mates. He appears to have been on top of the holder when a HE bomb dropped on the railway [track into the gasworks]. Having previously noticed incendiaries at No.3 holder, Mr Callaghan, though still suffering from the effects of the gas, climbed to the crown, apparently just after Mr Duncan had got down, and finding a slight leak on one of the damaged plates added more wet clay to stop the flow but, beginning to feel a relapse, he went down to the ground where he was later discovered only semi-conscious.

Valuable assistance in the raid was given by Miss Lorna Duncan, daughter of the manager (*Shields Evening News*, 14 June 1941).

This is how Lorna continued her account of her contribution that night.

After hours of exhausting work, we returned home but Daddy was soon called out again as some incendiaries had been seen on another holder. He was on his way to deal with the trouble when I saw him. His face was grey! There was no way he could have done any more that night, so I sent him home and taking three of the workmen with me, set off for the holder. I knew the yard as they say, 'like the back of my hand', so knew exactly where to go but when I arrived at the vertical iron-runged ladder I had only one companion. Dressed only in my nightdress, dressing gown and slippers, I picked up the bucket of clay which was strategically placed at the bottom of the ladder and began my ascent, followed by the workman. The crown of the holder was frosty and of course curved so the workman's hobnailed boots slipped on the surface. It was impossible for him to reach the hole from which the gas was hissing fiercely, so I went alone. The handle of the bucket was made of wire, which was cutting into my hand, but the hole had to be plugged. Leaning to one side away from the hissing gas, I took a lump of clay and tried to put it in the hole. Naturally, it fell straight through. The only way that I could plug that gap was to build a wall of clay around the edge of it and gradually build it into the middle, making a mound of clay. I believe that it held until a secure repair could be made.

The magnitude of Lorna's achievement that night can be better understood by comparing it to how it was recommended that such emergency repairs should be carried out. In an article in the *Gas Journal*, published just a week before the bombing, Leonard Bott, in *Extinguishing Flame and Repairing Gasholders*, described how *four men* could repair a breach in the crown of a gasholder with clay. He warned how in frosty weather [as it was on the night of the bombing] 'the clay and ropes for hoisting it should be protected at the foot of the ladder because, even if fine weather, if the clay is on top of the holder it is liable to be forgotten and become dry' and 'during the frosty period the rope is liable to become stiff'. Lorna, we must remind readers, had no rope and carried the clay up the vertical ladder of the gas holder in a bucket with a wire handle (*Gas Journal*, 2 April 1941 p.15).

Terrible though the situation was at the gasworks on 9 April 1941, things were much worse in other parts of the town. To put the events in Minton Lane in perspective, what follows are sections from the official account of the raid on the Borough of Tynemouth.

Enemy Air Raid 9/10th April 1941 – A report to the Emergency Committee by the Chief Constable and ARP Controller, T. Blackburn, dated 17 April 1941.

I have to inform you that at 23.25 on the 9th April 1941, the public warning was sounded in this Borough. The 'Raiders Passed' signal was given at 04.50 on the 10th April 1941. During the 5½ hours the warning was in operation enemy aircraft flew over the Borough at intervals, and there was heavy anti-aircraft gunfire during the whole period. The raid commenced with a shower of IB [incendiary bombs] in the high part of the town, and a small number of HE (high explosive bombs) were also dropped. Between 00.30 and 01.30 more IBs and HEs were dropped at intervals at the Timber Storage Yards [very close to the gasworks], and Docks at the riverside [and in the centre of the town, the raid ended with a further shower of IB and HE mainly on the Timber Yards and Docks.

So far as can be ascertained, 35 HE, mainly of heavy calibre, fell and exploded, and thousands of IB were dropped. With the exception of four bombs, all the HE dropped were of a very heavy calibre. The craters averaged

70' to 80' [21m – 24m] across and 25' [8m] deep. The blast effect from these bombs was tremendous and far reaching. The four bombs mentioned as exceptions to the very heavy ones were of a medium type, with craters about 25' [8m] across and 3'to 8' [1m – 8m] deep. The blast effect in these instances was very great having regard to the size of the craters. Of the heavy bombs above mentioned, five were of an exceptionally heavy type. The craters being in the vicinity of 120' [37m] across and 30' to 35' [9m – 11m] deep.

In the course of the raid, 35 persons were killed, these consist of 17 adult males, 13 adult females, and five children under 16 years. Reports received up to the present show that 101 persons were injured, 15 seriously. Of the persons killed there was one soldier, one Police Constable, one First Police Reserve (Ex Inspector), and one male and one female of the Whitley Bay First Aid Services. Of the persons seriously injured, there was one Police Constable, one Special Constable and five Civil Defence Personnel. Of the persons slightly injured, there were two Police Sergeants, two Police Constables, three Special Constables and 13 Civil Defence Personnel. The following is a resume of the damage caused to buildings so far as can be ascertained at the present.

Totally demolished	22
So badly damaged demolition necessary	41
Seriously damaged but repairable	99
Slightly damaged exclusive of glass	513

Several hundreds of shops and houses in all parts of the Borough had windows blown out or broken. Among the premises mentioned above are Preston Hospital and the Public Assistance Institution, which received a direct hit on the south-west part of the building demolishing the X-Ray building and killing three members of the staff and one patient, as a result of which many of the inmates were evacuated from the Hospital to the Linskill Senior School and have since been evacuated to other areas. First Aid Headquarters was severely damaged and put out of action as a result of a HE falling in close proximity. Two persons were killed at this incident. The Royal National Lifeboat Station was completely destroyed. An Anderson shelter received a direct hit, and four persons inside were killed. A schedule of major incidents is attached hereto.

IBs caused numerous small fires in the timber storage yards [opposite and very close to the gasworks]. These developed into five major fires and later into a conflagration, which extended for about one mile along the river front to the west of the main part of the town. Every effort was made to extinguish the conflagration before dark on the 10th instant, and the situation was well in hand but at about 10.00 a.m. a breeze sprang up and increased the danger. At 10.30 Mr C. Thomas, the Regional Fire Inspector, arrived and took charge of this incident. He called for assistance and aiding parties, consisting of two units (each) from Newburn, Gosforth, and Blyth. Military Assistance was also obtained, and the soldiers were employed removing timber from the danger area. By 14.00 the fire was under control and extinguished at 18.00.

At about the same time as the timber yards were becoming a serious matter, three large fires developed very rapidly in the centre of the town, involving three large shops within a space of 80 yards. The water supply was insufficient because of the nearness of the buildings, and it was obvious that extra pumping appliances for relaying water would have to be obtained. At 03.23 I requested Whitley Bay Control to send all available fire appliances to assist in fighting fires which had developed. They replied that nine units would be immediately despatched. These arrived quickly, and the fires referred to above were soon under control. The fire float was also brought into operation for these incidents to pump water from the river. They were extinguished at 07.00 when the Whitley Bay aiding party was released.

In addition, several hundreds of small fires were started in all parts of the town, and these were speedily dealt with by the Fire Service, Police, Wardens and Civilians who tackled bombs as they fell, saving, without doubt, hundreds of properties. Over 100 calls were received at the Fire Station and it is estimated that at least 400 minor fires were dealt with. The Mobile Water Carriers recently acquired by the Fire Authority proved invaluable during the course of the raid in dealing with fires where the water was off or the supply insufficient. In all, 43 appliances were used from this Brigade, and 15 aiding Units were employed in dealing with fires. At 03.00 the position regarding the fires was giving cause for anxiety, by 04.00 the position had eased, at all other times the situation was well in hand.

The work of the emergency services was greatly hampered after about 1.30a.m. because virtually all police box telephones were by then out of order, and many of the exchange lines from Fire Stations and Air Raid Warden Posts were inoperative. Despite the additional risk to life, human messengers had to be used to replace them. The Rescue and Demolition Services were called out to seven incidents; the Repair Services to two; and at one incident the Decontamination Squad was required. In addition, two Rescue Squads from Wallsend and one from Whitley Bay were sent to incidents in North Shields. These 15 services in all also succeeded in rescuing 11 people alive who had been trapped in bombed buildings and recovered 15 bodies from the debris. The last was not recovered until 23.00 on Saturday, 12 April, three days after the bombing began.

The gasworks was only one of the industrial undertakings damaged by that night's bombing. As well as the 15 high explosive bombs and numerous incendiary devices which fell on the land, docks and timber yards along the riverside owned by the Tyne Improvement Commission, incendiary bombs fell on Smith's Docks and Cookson's Lead & Antimony Works though, in both instances, they were dealt with effectively by their own ARP personnel.

Following the bombing raid on the gasworks, the acts of bravery of George Duncan, Joseph Callaghan and Lorna were recognized in several ways. George Duncan was made an MBE (Member of the Order of the British Empire), Joseph Callaghan was awarded the George Medal (the first person in North Shields to receive one), and Lorna received a commendation for bravery from Winston Churchill. Shortly after returning to college, she was summoned to the office of the principal. 'No one was more surprised than I was to learn that journalists had arrived to question me and to take photographs, because of the raid on the gasworks.' Mr Duncan and Lorna received their awards at Buckingham Palace in June. In July, the bombing raid on the gasworks became the focus of a BBC radio drama-documentary, at a time when BBC radio was the

George Duncan's MBE (left) and Lorna Duncan's commendation signed by Winston Churchill (right). Unfortunately, our efforts to locate either Joseph Callaghan's George Medal, or an image of it, have been unsuccessful.

main medium of communication for the British population, with tens of millions of listeners. The first sheet of the original script is included below, and the full text of the document is set out in Appendix 4. Later in July, George Duncan, Joseph Callaghan, and Lorna were made presentations by the chairman of the Newcastle and Gateshead Gas Company. Mr Duncan received an inscribed silver salver, Joseph Callaghan a wallet containing an undisclosed sum of money, and Lorna an inscribed 'beautiful silver and enamel dressing table set.' Mr Callaghan duly received his George Medal at Buckingham Palace in October and was made an honorary member of the Royal Society of St George in November.[111]

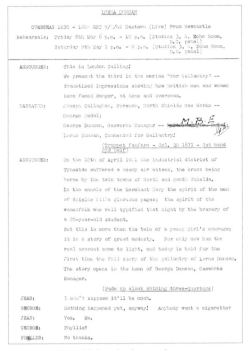

First sheet of the BBC radio drama–documentary, featuring Lorna Duncan and the bombing raid on the Minton Lane gasworks, 9–10 April 1941. It was broadcast live on Saturday 9 May 1941.

Although George Duncan may have been proud of his MBE and pleased with the gift from the company, it did not compensate him for the major setback to his health. On the advice of his doctor, at the age of 64, he was urged to apply for early retirement. It was not only granted but in recognition of his exceptional service to the company on that horrific night his pension was doubled. However, the ordeal at the gasworks was not yet over.

Rather than remain in North Shields, which was still being bombed, George Duncan rented a furnished house in Rothbury, Northumberland, for himself and the family still living with him at the gasworks. His own furniture remained at Minton Lane until he rented a larger unfurnished house in Alnwick. In late September he returned to North Shields to oversee the packing. The return coincided with what at the end of the war *The Evening News* described as 'perhaps the worst raids of all'. Enemy aircraft shot down barrage balloons and were able to then dive-bomb the town. The raid began before the usual siren warning of a raid and many people were still on the streets and in places of entertainment. On the 30 September, 38 HE bombs led to 61 deaths, numerous serious injuries, and widespread damage. It included North Shields Railway Station; the adjacent Prince's Theatre (a cinema), and the nearby offices of the local newspaper. Behind those premises, a group of houses including one lived in by Danny Lawrence's paternal grandmother were destroyed.[112] Elsewhere in the town centre, there was major damage to the town's then two main shopping streets, Saville Street and Bedford Street. A little

---

111 Joseph Callaghan retired in September 1958 after working at the Minton Lane gasworks for 51 years. He died in 1965.

112 Who fortunately, and unusually, was not at home that night.

further away, on Coach Lane, the Wesleyan Methodist Church was damaged and set on fire and extensive damage done to Queen Victoria School, the primary school which the Duncan children had attended and where Margaret Duncan was teaching at the time. She had been scheduled to be on fire duty that night but fortuitously for her had exchanged her shift with another teacher so she could help with the packing at Minton Lane. Beyond the town itself, there was bomb damage to the Whitehill Point Ferry Landing, and as many as seven HE bombs fell on the Albert Edward Dock and the railway tracks leading to it. Other residential areas hit included Morpeth and Rothbury Terraces, Wallsend Road, and Waterville Road, where Danny Lawrence's maternal grandparents were living. A single HE bomb also fell between Regent Terrace and Queen Alexandra Road, close to what had been Preston Colliery. Homes were damaged, a shelter was hit, and two more people lost their lives.

Bomb damage to the Queen Victoria School in Coach Lane, North Shields. Apart from the obvious external damage, several classrooms were no longer useable and so pupils were transferred to Western Board School. Even partial repairs were not authorised until 1942. More extensive repairs were approved in 1943 but pupils did not return to the school until February 1944. The boundary wall fronting onto Coach Lane was not replaced until 1947 (Pears and Ripley, Background Information, *section 10).*

The Duncans were even more fortunate to escape injury during the 2 October raid. Eight of the 28 bombs that fell that night hit the old cemetery on Albion Road where George Duncan had been waiting to meet a friend (presumably to say their final goodbyes before he moved to Alnwick). Although he was unharmed, he returned to the gasworks only for it to be hit by four HE bombs. They fell as the removal men were closing the doors of their second removal van. The gasworks house was only slightly damaged during the raid but there was serious and extensive damage to the gasworks plant and production came to a halt for a considerable time. Whilst detailed written accounts appear not to have survived, some indication of the scale of the damage is revealed by the series of photos which we include courtesy of the website *North Shields 173*. George Duncan must have been appalled at having to leave behind such scenes of devastation in the gasworks which he had looked after so diligently

Examples of the damage to the Minton Lane gasworks following the bombing raid on 2 October 1941. Above: the damage can be seen below the arm of the crane in the upper part of the image. Below: the huge damage inflicted to the area to the right of the relatively undamaged retort house. Images courtesy of Peter Bolger and https://northshields173.org.

Examples of the damage to the Minton Lane gasworks following the bombing raid on 2 October 1941. Above: note the rear and chimney of the retort house to the left. Below: the remains of the gasworks bomb shelter. Fortuitously, it was empty when the bomb hit. Images courtesy of Peter Bolger and https://northshields173.org.

since 1918. At the same time, the Duncan family must have heaved a big sigh of relief when the all-clear sounded on 3 October and they were able to leave the gasworks for the last time.[113]

Over the next year, the three remaining single Duncan sisters were married: Jean in July 1942, Margaret in September, and Lorna in December.[114] The following year, they would have been greatly relieved that they were no longer living in the gasworks house, and that it was Ernest Wearne rather than their father who had to live through and deal with the aftermath of the raids on the 12th and 13th of March 1943. They resulted in major damage. Though it has not been possible to obtain detailed information, it is known that, amongst other things, the purifier house was completely destroyed.

Although there was no loss of life at the gasworks during the bombing raids, a terrible fatal accident did occur at the works on 3 March 1942, when 61-year-

---

113 There were only three deaths in North Shields during that October raid. South Shield bore the brunt of the bombing.

114 George Duncan enjoyed a long and happy retirement. He married again at the age of eighty and died at the age of eighty-nine.

Assessing the scale of the damage to the Minton Lane gasworks following the bombing raid on 2 October 1941. Images courtesy of Peter Bolger and https://northshields173.org.

old John Jones Cummings was crushed between a coal hopper and a charging machine. He had worked there for 44 years, mainly on the same job, so was hugely experienced but, during the wartime conditions, might have been unusually tired. The accident occurred when wet and sticky coal was not running well from the hopper into the charging machine. He climbed the ladder to clear it, after putting the lever of a compressed air machine into the neutral position. However, for some reason, the machine started to move and, although a workmate saw what was happening and pulled the lever into the reverse position, it was too late to save Cummings. When questioned by the coroner, his workmate explained that it was the usual practice to put the lever into neutral in such circumstances and that he had never before known it to slip out of neutral. Another witness described how he had found Cumings and concluded that he had climbed from the ladder into the hopper and 'was in the act of getting back on to the ladder when the machine ran away', and that Cummings was caught between the machine and the coal hopper. 'I think the cause of the machine moving was the lever had slipped from neutral and fallen into full speed position which caused the machine to run away and jam Cummings. I have now received instructions to cut off the air, which would prevent a repetition' (*Shields Evening News*, 16 March 1942).[115]

Newcastle and Gateshead Gas Company officials revealed after the war that the output from the Minton Lane gasworks was all but lost for a time after the bombing raids. Fortunately, the impact of the damage for gas customers was not nearly as great as it would have been had the Tynemouth company not been taken over in 1927. Without access to the wider network of the much bigger company, the town of North Shields and the surrounding area might have been without gas for significant periods.

---

115 This was not the only significant accident at the gasworks during the Second World War. For example, George Turner, was admitted to Tynemouth Jubilee Infirmary on 20 February 1944 suffering from burns to his face and hands.

Chapter 9

Rationalisation, Nationalisation and Privatisation

UNTIL 1949, the bulk of the British gas industry was owned and run by numerous privately-owned undertakings, although in some areas gas was supplied by companies owned by local authorities. Both during the war and the period of reconstruction afterwards, there was widespread acceptance that for the sake of efficient production such fragmentation could not continue. When a Labour government brought the whole of the gas industry into public ownership on 1 May 1949, politicians in all parties represented this as a fundamental change. Whether approvingly or disapprovingly, they subscribed to the essentially Marxist view that it is who *owns* the means of production which matters most. The tacit assumption was that taking the industry into public ownership would transform it, whether for good or ill. A less well-known alternative viewpoint, derived from the work of the German sociologist Max Weber, is that what matters most is not who *owns* but who *controls* industries, and this is a better basis for understanding what happened to the gas industry for at least the first decade after it was taken into public ownership.

Rationalisation and 'Nationalisation'

Taking the industry into public ownership was not at the expense of the shareholders of the private undertakings, such as the Newcastle and Gateshead Gas Company. Intensive lobbying on their behalf resulted in compensation based on the average market value of their stock at six dates in either 1945 or 1947, whichever was the more advantageous to them. They received their compensation in the form of 3% *guaranteed* British Gas stock. The municipal owners of gas undertakings had more reason to complain. At the annual meeting of the Association of Municipal Corporations in March 1950, the Lord Mayor of York complained about the 'ever-increasing control of Whitehall'. He reminded his audience that local authorities had recently lost their hospitals (which after 1948 became part of the NHS), their civil airfields, and their profitable trading departments such as gas and electricity.

Although members of the post-war Labour government were ideologically predisposed towards public ownership, there was also widespread agreement amongst all those concerned with the future of the gas industry that public ownership or something comparable was the most sensible course of action for entirely pragmatic reasons. Their main concern was the industry's fragmentation. A few committees had already discussed the problem but the most significant was set up in June 1944 by the coalition government, and chaired by Geoffrey (later Lord) Heyworth, the chairman of Unilever. Heywood's committee concluded that the industry needed to be fundamentally rationalised and, as in 1948 public ownership was the only proposal on the table, there was no concerted resistance to it. On the contrary, the industry bodies that had formed themselves into the British Gas Council gave an assurance to the Minister of Fuel and Power in 1947 that they would cooperate with the Labour government's proposals and, within the industry, public ownership appears to have been widely accepted as both inevitable and sensible. By the time the Bill to take gas into public ownership was introduced, the coal and electricity industries had already been taken out of private hands so there was an established precedent for such fundamental change. That did not stop the Conservative opposition fighting the Bill on behalf of gas companies' shareholders. The final session in the House of Commons lasted for 51 hours, a then record time (Peebles, p.26-7).

The UK entered the war with 1,079 distinct gas areas. The majority were private companies but to the extent that 25 per cent were municipal undertakings there was nothing new, in principle, about gas being publicly owned. Although it became common to refer to the now publicly owned industry as having been *nationalised* that was actually a misnomer. The *form* the newly organized industry took after the Gas Act of 1948 resembled the private part of the industry more than the municipal, and it was certainly not run nationally. On the contrary, it was divided into 12 *autonomous* regional boards. Moreover, each regional board was broken down into smaller geographical units. The National Gas Council did have some significant functions, but it was made up of the chairs of the regional boards.

Despite the gas industry now having a new and more uniform structure, it was inevitable that there would be a great deal of continuity, not least because the plant used to generate gas was the same as in the days before it was taken into public ownership. There was also a great deal of continuity in personnel. 'Manny' Shinwell, the Labour Minister for Fuel and Power, had promised that 'the industry would be run by people who knew all about it' and that proved to be the case. Most top managers made themselves available for re-appointment. In the case of the Northern Gas Board (NGB), the North Shields born John F. Jackson, who had been company secretary and solicitor to the Newcastle and Gateshead Gas Company, was appointed to the key role of company secretary to the newly established regional board.[116]

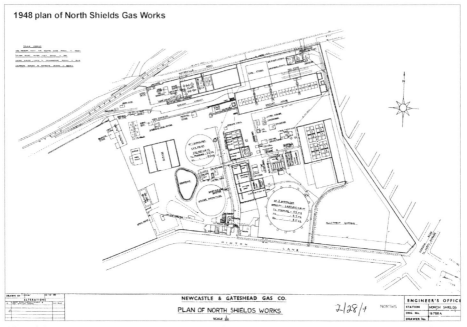

1948 plan of North Shields Gas Works

Plan of the Minton Lane gasworks in 1948, just before the 1949 nationalisation of the gas industry. Source: Wilkinson, J.B., Desk Study and Historical Report. Former Gasworks Site at Minton Lane.

When the anonymous 'Pleb' wrote to the local newspaper in 1942 advocating public ownership of the gas industry, he or she insisted that the main difference would be the disappearance of the profit motive (*Shields Evening News*, 15 December 1942). Yet, after the industry became publicly owned, the language of

---

116 The NGB, which covered Northumberland, Durham, parts of Cumbria and the North Riding of Yorkshire, should not be confused with the misleadingly named North-Eastern Gas Board which was responsible for the East Riding of Yorkshire and parts of the North and West Ridings of Yorkshire, including the city of York. The NGB covered a significantly bigger area than the Newcastle and Gateshead company. It comprised the following former private and municipal companies: Annfield Plain and District Gas Company, Appleby Corporation, Bishop Auckland District Gas Company, Blyth Gas Company, Brancepeth Colliery, Carlisle Corporation, Cleveland Gas Company, Cockermouth Urban District Council, Darlington Corporation, Guisborough Gas Company Ltd, Hartlepool Gas and Water Company, Hexham Gas Company, Houghton-Le-Spring District Gas Company, Keswick Gas Company, Maryport Urban District Council, Middlesbrough Corporation, Newcastle-Upon-Tyne and Gateshead Gas Company, Northallerton Consumers' Gas Company Ltd, Penrith Urban District Council, Redcar Corporation, Richmond Corporation, Shotley Bridge and Consett District Gas Company, South Bank and Normanby Gaslight and Coke Company, Spennymoor and Prudhoe Gas Company, Stockton-on-Tees Corporation, Sunderland Gas Company, Whitehaven United Gas Company Ltd, Wigton Gas Light and Coke Company Ltd, and the Workington Corporation gas company.

profit and loss was still employed. From the outset, the bottom line of the NGB's accounts was critical to the decisions made. There were many other elements of continuity. Key decisions made by the private companies at an earlier stage meant that initially the newly publicly owned bodies had limited room for manoeuvre. For example, although the price of coal had gone up some time before 1949, the private Newcastle and Gateshead company had chosen not to increase the price of gas accordingly, in the way it would ordinarily have done. It had no need to do so because it knew that public ownership was on the way. The company had also deferred undertaking repairs and building new plant for the same reason.

From its inception, the NGB could not provide enough gas when the demand was high. This was particularly the case during the frequent periods when coal was in short supply. The consumption of gas was, by 1951, 100 per cent more than it had been ten years earlier. The combination of these circumstances led to frequent reductions in gas pressure. That was not just a problem for those in industry, cooking food or heating water. It was also a problem for those still reliant on gas lighting. That included schools in the Wallsend area. It led one councillor, after seeing pupils struggling to see their blackboard in winter months, to demand that gas lighting be replaced by electric lighting. Her motion was passed unanimously (*Shields Evening News*, 21 December 1950).[117]

Not all the local gas supply problems could be attributed to decisions taken by the Newcastle and Gateshead company before it was taken into public ownership. Like other industries, in the immediate post-war years, the NGB suffered from shortages of materials and key components. Most significantly, on Tyneside, the delays in obtaining key equipment originally promised for 1948 meant that developments at the Howdon gasworks had to be postponed until the change in ownership. The revised plan, announced in January 1950, singled out Howdon to become the largest self-contained carbonising plant in the whole of the area covered by the NGB. In addition to producing 8 million cu. ft. of gas daily from 500 tons of coal in the carbonising plant, it was also to have a water gas plant producing an additional 4 million cu. ft. of gas daily. Moreover, as part of an ambitious plan for a gas grid in the area, there were to be two 12-inch high-pressure gas mains from Howdon across the river to Jarrow, utilising the pedestrian Tyne Tunnel on which work was completed in 1951. As part of the scheme, Jarrow was to have a new 3 million cu. ft. gas holder. However, there were to be losers as well as winners. The South Shields manufacturing station was scheduled for eventual closure.

---

117 Five years later, Wallsend agreed to move from gas to electric streetlighting.

Although the coal, gas and electricity industries were all now in public ownership, they were not being run in conjunction with one another, as part of a national plan. On the contrary, they continued to compete against one another, just as they had done when the industries were in private ownership. Crucially, the gas and electricity industry relied heavily on coal to generate electricity and produce coke and coal gas, making it almost inevitable that it would be in short supply, especially in bad weather when it was even more difficult to mine. Electricity power cuts were not uncommon and there was often a huge unmet demand for gas. When the famous comic actors Laurel and Hardy came to tour the UK in 1947, they had to register for their ration books by candlelight. When they were staying at the Royal Station Hotel in Newcastle, the outside temperature was -13°C. But, when the American Oliver Hardy phoned his wife in California, he learned the temperature there was 27°C. He went to tell Stan Laurel and found him huddled over a small coal fire. When he told Stan his wife was basking in sunshine, Stan picked up the last piece of coal, threw it on the fire and using the opening words of the popular morale boosting song of the time declared, 'Ah well, *There'll Always Be An England*' – and they burst out laughing.

The competition for coal had led to relentless price increases which continued into the 1950s. In that decade, the price of gas to domestic consumers increased by 65 per cent. Overall, despite the growing demand, the actual domestic consumption of gas declined by 7 per cent. However, like all averages, this single figure masked significant local variations. That was conspicuously the case in the area formerly covered by the Tynemouth Gas Company, where the situation was much worse. At a meeting in January 1949, Mr. J. White from the Minton Lane gasworks, in explaining why the area was suffering from low gas pressure, pointed out that because of the wartime damage to the Minton Lane gasworks, and delays on the extensions at Howdon, it had only been possible to increase the company's productive capacity by 28 per cent at a time when there had been a 70 per cent increase in the demand for gas.

The crucial extensions at Howdon came perilously close to being wrecked in May 1952. Sparks from the retort house ignited its bitumen-lined roof and only prompt action by fire tenders from Wallsend and Tynemouth brought it under control without significant interruption to gas production. It was the second fire the Wallsend brigade had been called to at the works in a two-week period, and another followed just a few days later in the sulphate plant in which firemen were obliged to wear breathing apparatus. The new facilities finally opened on 23 September 1952. In a speech at the event, Rowland Lishman, the North Shields man who was a former director and vice-chairman of the Tynemouth

Gas Company before eventually becoming the chairman of the Newcastle and Gateshead company, remarked on the huge difference between the gasworks he knew as a boy and the modern plant at Howdon. He reminded his audience that he remembered men, stripped to the waist, working 12 hours a day, seven days a week, shovelling coal into retorts. One gas employee who would certainly have agreed with Lishman was Jack Yhearm who retired in 1953. He told a reporter on the occasion that 'In the old days it was slavery: 12-hour shifts and seven-day weeks' (*Shields Evening News*, 21 July 1953). Lishman also insisted at the opening of the Howdon plant that the days of the obnoxious-smelling gasworks were over, 'Today, one can live next door to one of these works and scarcely know it', although that was not a view shared by the residential neighbours of the Howdon gasworks! Lishman further explained that the new works would become a centre for the distribution of high-pressure gas which would eventually extend as far north as Morpeth and as far south as Sunderland. When working at full capacity, 250 workers would be producing 12 million cu. ft. of gas every day. Among the daily by-products would be 5,000 gallons of tar (*Shields Evening News* and *Newcastle Evening Chronicle*, 23 September 1952).

Unfortunately for the reputation of the Gas Board, and the consumers affected, the increased supply of gas from Howdon did not finally resolve the problem of the low gas pressure in Tynemouth and Whitley Bay. Some pipes to houses were partially blocked by naphthalene, because the new Howdon plant had been put into operation without all the necessary preparatory work being completed. As a result, weary of earlier unmet reassurances, a decision was made in Whitley to gradually switch from gas to electric streetlighting. By early 1953, the first batch of new sodium electric lights were installed and declared a vast improvement on the gas lights they replaced. A similar gradual shift from gas to sodium electric streetlighting began in North Shields around the same time and similar replacement schemes began in Wallsend in 1957.

Local Problems

In his *History of the British Gas Industry,* Williams argues that 'nationalisation' gave the industry the ability to compete technologically and commercially with its main fuel rivals, coal and electricity. That may have been the case eventually, but not during its first decade. It is true that some *rationalisation* of the industry took place which would never have been possible had the industry remained in private and municipal ownership. In the 11 years from 1949 to 1960, as many as 622 gasworks were closed because they did not warrant modernisation. However, gas continued to lose ground to the electricity industry in terms of customers and, in the area around the Minton Lane gasworks, it was also losing a prolonged public relations battle.

The main concern of those living near to Minton Lane was not low gas pressure. It was the discharge which they complained had been falling from a chimney since 1945. Trying to resolve the problem on behalf of local residents became an issue taken up by Tynemouth councillors on a cross-party basis in February 1950. At a meeting in May, the Gas Board's Divisional Manager explained that 'the nuisance' was caused by using low grade coke, produced on site, in the water gas boilers. He anticipated that the problem would disappear in three months' time, when it was planned to fire the boilers with liquid fuel. One candidate in the local elections was not satisfied with this answer. She described the yard as 'that ever-present menace to health.' She added that she had heard talk about transferring it to Howdon and she would try with all her might to hasten the move – 'short of carrying it to Howdon on her back' (*Shields Evening News*, 4 May 1950). The promised resolution of the problem did not take place. A letter to the local newspaper in October 1951 complained that 'twice in a week I have been almost blinded passing through the grit showered over Waterville Road by the gasworks.' The writer went on to draw attention to the promise that had been made the previous year but emphasised that 'it seems nothing has been done.' She then added further to the embarrassment of the Minton Lane management by remarking on 'the discharge of what seems to be sewage across the pavement from the same establishment' (*Shield Daily News*, 29 October 1951). Interestingly, it was a local councillor, not a company employee, who responded to the complaint. He noted that the Gas Board had not yet been able to secure the liquid fuel it hoped would solve the grit problem and added that once the extension in Howdon was complete 'the gas producing unit nearest to the houses at North Shields will cease operating except at peak periods' (*Shields Evening News*, 3 November 1951). Whilst it was true that it was planned to reduce the manufacturing capacity of the Minton Lane yard, and that it would continue to play second fiddle to Howdon, the councillor chose not to mention that a naphthalene washing facility had been installed during 1950, and that an experimental liquid purification unit was under construction.

Another local critic of the gas industry had a different kind of complaint to make. To try to improve access to coal supplies, the now publicly owned gas and electricity industries were building up their own collier fleets. David Robinson, a partner in the North Shields Stag shipping line, and chairman of the North of England Shipowners' Association, complained at its 1951 AGM that this was at the expense of private carriers, and was in danger of putting them out of business (*Shields Evening News*, 6 April 1951).[118] The situation seems to have changed little by 1957 when the then President maintained that because a large proportion of coal was being transported in colliers belonging to the gas and electricity industries, 'it is unlikely any independent coasting company would now contemplate building a ship suited only to the coal coasting trade' (*Shields Evening News*, 1 July 1957).

What public ownership of the industry could not change were periodic expressions of concern about the safety of coal gas. On 22 July 1950, a gas explosion just about 100m from the gasworks caused extensive damage to a downstairs flat, and to two adjacent properties. It occurred after an employee of the company was sent to deal with a complaint about low gas pressure. Three people were admitted to hospital following the explosion, including the employee who received burns to his face. On 3 August, the displaced tenant wrote to the local newspaper, pleading with the Council to rehouse her and her son, both of whom had been injured in the explosion. Apparently, her near-death experience did not make a difference to the priorities of the local authority which was struggling with a huge unmet demand for council housing. With just one child (and a husband at sea) she did not have 'sufficient points' to qualify for one (*Shields Evening News*, 3 August 1950). Another incident occurred in May 1951 at the location of the popular local department store D. Hill Carter and Co., and the manufacturing business of the local pharmaceutical company Williamson and Hogg's. A series of small underground explosions led to gas and electricity being cut off to the premises in the area, whilst the cause of the explosions was investigated. More embarrassing still for the publicly owned company was a series of explosions at the Jarrow gasworks in 1953. The top 50 ft. of its 120 ft. chimney was blown off and the remainder damaged. Houses in the vicinity 'quivered with the shock, which roused sleeping families and brought them rushing to their doors.' Another witness described how 'the whole room lit up briefly with the flash' and another that 'everything seemed to reek of gas and soot was floating around.' Fortunately, although some brickwork fell into neighbouring streets, most of it came down inside the gasworks perimeter and there were no injuries (*Shields Evening News*, 7 January 1953). Further embarrassment followed in April when the NGB was prosecuted by the Ministry of Fuel and Power for supplying gas from the new Howdon plant which contained sulphuretted hydrogen (H_2S).

---

118 For an account of North Shields' shipping companies, including the Stag Line, see Lawrence, 2016, pp. 58–70.

'Though it is a nationalised industry it should be treated no differently from a private body and the public should know what is going on' said the Ministry solicitor. Howdon gasworks admitted supplying to the public gas containing sulphuretted hydrogen on September 17 last year – better known in your schooldays as the stuff stink bombs are made of' explained Mr Beezley. 'It could have caused the public very considerable discomfort and inconvenience' he added. Defending, Mr Clifford Cohen, said the machinery at the works was new and elaborate. The gas goes through four purifiers. One valve had been left open by mistake which meant that the gas went through only one purifier (*Shields Evening News*, 21 April 1953).

The company was back in the news for another unfortunate reason in August. A North Shields' employee was sent alone to make a temporary repair to a heavy escape of gas from a 4 ft. deep trench on a housing development. He passed out in the trench with his face 'full against the leaking gas pipe' and would have died had his plight not been spotted by a six-year-old girl playing nearby. She saw his feet protruding from the hole and enlisted the help of a thirteen-year-old girl before running to find the site watchman. Although only able to walk with two sticks, he literally fell into the trench to move the unconscious man and, with the help of the older girl, managed to get him out of the trench (*Shields Evening News*, 10 August 1953). All three received commendations from the Royal Humane Society. Tragically, just months later, in January 1954, another North Shields man died from an escape of gas at the Minton Lane gasworks. His daily routine involved entering a pit under the governor house to run off surplus water from a gas main. That involved opening a *water* cock, but the release of water was always accompanied by an escape of gas. When another worker heard the escaping gas, he pulled the victim out of the pit but, later, told the coroner that 'the gas affected me towards the end, and I was more or less paralysed in my arms and legs.' Though still alive when pulled from the pit, the victim died from coal gas poisoning shortly after reaching hospital. A verdict of accidental death was recorded but, following the incident, the NGB instituted changes in all its gasworks so that water cocks could, in future, be opened at ground level.

The Beginning of the End for Coal Gas

Even in the days when the Howdon plant was state-of-the-art for the manufacture of coal gas, there were indications it might have a shorter life than the once state-of-the-art gasworks at Minton Lane in North Shields. By the 1950s, alternative energy sources were being sought which did not require good quality coal.

For example, attempts were made to utilise low grade coal by processes which 'gassified' it completely without leaving any coke or tar residue, an approach with origins in the closing years of the nineteenth century. Over a hundred such small plants were subsequently built around the country but failed to produce gas of a sufficient calorific value to be used more widely. Two more radical approaches were announced by a now Conservative Minister of Fuel and Power in July 1954. The one which did not hit the headlines, but which was more immediately relevant to the gas industry, was the manufacture of gas from oil in two large, dedicated plants in the South-East and West Midlands. More such plants followed but, even as late as 1960, 90 per cent of all gas consumed in the UK still came from traditional manufacturing methods. The more dramatic innovation was the announcement of the world's first civil nuclear power programme. Calder Hall at Sellafield in Cumbria opened in 1956. At its peak in 1997, 26 per cent of UK electricity was generated by nuclear power stations.

That there was a need for more energy sources became abundantly clear over the winter months of 1954-55 when, despite the new supplies from Howdon, there were still problems of low pressure in the NGB area during cold spells. It became such a matter of concern that the Conservative MP for the Tynemouth constituency raised the issue with the Minister for Fuel and Power in the House of Commons on 21 February 1955. She asked if he would publish the report of the Northern Area Gas Consultative Council about the low pressure and at times failure of the gas supply altogether during a recent cold spell. The answer she received was that publication was not a matter for the government: an indication of the 'hands-off' policy the new Conservative government was adopting towards the publicly owned industry, and how far short it was of being truly 'nationalised'. At a subsequent meeting, the NGB defended its record, and claimed the problem was caused by the success of the accelerated housing programme, which had increased the demand for gas more than could have been anticipated. Its spokesman added that during the unusually cold spell, many consumers had turned on their gas ovens and used them as space heaters when they could not get supplies of coal. Making life more difficult for the gas companies in 1955 was a rail strike which obliged them to hire 'a huge fleet of lorries' to keep up the supply of coal to local producing units including the Minton Lane gasworks. 'The same lorries are being used to remove coke and other by-products from the gasworks to prevent any congestion of storage space' (*Shields Evening News*, 4 June 1955).

This was not the happiest of times for the Newcastle division of the NGB. In April 1955, it was summoned for unlawfully allowing waste products to flow into the river from the Howdon gasworks. Readers may recall that in 1934 Taylor noted in his journal that 558,000 gallons of surplus ammoniacal liquor had been poured 'down the drains' and finished up in the river. It seems that a similar practice was still taking place 20 years later. Following complaints about a half inch thick 'oily, tarry substance' fouling the area in and around a shipyard in Willington Quay, the river police traced it to a submerged sewer where the oily substance was 'bubbling up and stretching up the river for about 600 yards'. They then discovered it was emanating from the effluent chambers of the Howdon gasworks. In the same year, the whole industry became the subject of an enquiry by the BMA. Whilst suicides using coal gas had long been common, the BMA was concerned at the 20 per cent increase in deaths from *accidental* gas poisoning.

At that time, the NGB could boast that it had the lowest gas prices in the country but announced in July 1955 that they would soon increase substantially because of a further rise in coal prices. The chairman conceded that the increase of 3d a Therm was 'undeniably a shocker' but pointed out that since being taken into public ownership in 1949, the cost of coal to the Board had risen by 80 per cent (*Shields Evening News*, 11 July 1955). Later in the year, the NGB's Consultative Council, warned that not having a cheap and plentiful supply of gas was making it difficult to attract new industries to the north-east. It noted the obvious irony that it was because so much of the coal mined in the NGB's area was being exported to the Continent, that prices at home were so high. This again pointed to the absence of a coherent government strategy for the UK's publicly owned energy industries and reinforced the need for additional sources of energy.

This general situation was not helped by an incident in February 1956 at Derwenthaugh, by then a National Coal Board's (NCB) plant. A 70-ton coke-discharging truck was derailed and, because of the awkward angle at which it was lying, could not easily be put back on track with a crane. Instead, a combination of NCB and workers from British Railways had to work through a bitterly cold night, and further falls of snow, to right it, using diesel jacks. For a few days, until the ovens were working again, the effect on industry in the north-east was devastating. Fortunately, domestic customers and hospitals received their supplies of gas from elsewhere and were unaffected.

The future of the Minton Lane site was in jeopardy at this time as the NGB sought to keep costs down by focusing on its more efficient plants. Ten had already been closed and another 27 were scheduled for closure. As it happens, those who lived in North Shields, in the immediate vicinity of what was known locally as the 'gas yard' would have been happy to have had the Minton Lane site included in those destined for closure. Several complaints were printed in the local newspaper in March 1956. Amongst other things, the correspondents complained about the grit that fell from the retort houses chimney, as others had done in 1950.

At regular intervals the residents in this area have to contend with a most nauseating smell of gas permeating our homes and nostrils, but the smell is as nothing compared to the herculean task of the women folk to keep on top of the grit and grime which collects on floors, window ledges, curtains, sideboards and cupboards, hardly a day goes by without I hear remarks passed by my neighbours complaining about the filth which accumulates in their homes from the adjacent gas yard. From being a child I was given to understand that it was advisable, especially in the evening, to keep his bedroom window open in order to enhance a good night's rest and good health. No doubt that is sound advice. But living in this area I sometimes wonder if it is not more beneficial to keep the window shut to keep out the dust we must surely be breathing. Goodness knows what effect this polluted air has on the chest.

It is commonplace when walking up the town end of Waterville Road to find one's shoes making a half to one-inch footprint in grit and dirt which has settled there from the smokestacks of the gasworks and it is most unpleasant when a particle of coke finds its way into one's eye. ... Some three or four years ago I approached a man who was then one of our councillors and was informed that measures had been taken to contact the authority concerned, and that in all probability when the new extensions to the Howdon gasworks were completed, production at the North Shields yard would either cease or be extensively curtailed. However, possibly because we need all the gas we can produce, that state of affairs never materialised. We all realise that gas producing plant is most essential (we moan especially when gas pressure is low due to severe weather conditions or breakdowns) but surely in this modern scientific age some steps could be taken to minimise the wholesale outpouring of this most injurious and abominable filth. SOOTY (*Shields Evening News*, 13 March 1956).

The letter spawned several more in response, with one exception all echoing the same point. For example:

Regularly every two hours night and day this retort house comes into action and every period brings forth clouds of dense evil smelling smoke together with showers of the grime and grit mentioned but like Sooty I agree that the smell, bad and foul though it is, is at least tolerable – it's the dirt that comes with it that causes the real grievance and I contend is a real grievance which is crying out for instant strong action. ... To bear this out any member of the Health Committee is welcome to come along to my home any day and actually see the grime on floors and furniture and door frames before my wife does the daily mopping up (*Shields Evening News*, 22 March 1956).

The same year saw further substantial increases in the cost of gas which helped the NGB to declare a profit in 1957 compared to the loss in 1956. However, the chairman insisted the improved financial results were also due to increased efficiency, by concentrating gas production in fewer units and extending the gas grid. He announced that in the coming years the South Shields gasworks would be closed completely, and the North Shields retorts brought into use only in the winter months (as had been the case in the latter part of the 1930s). This, however, did not mean that Minton Lane would be at a standstill. During this phase, additional facilities were still being added to the site. Ernest Wearne and his family had moved out in 1955 and been replaced by the Jarmy family. Like George Duncan, Harold Jarmy was a chemist rather than an engineer. He had previously worked with the Newcastle branch of the company and appears to have managed the site jointly with Vincent Reed. Both also had responsibilities in South Shields and Howdon initially, but Reed shifted his focus exclusively to South Shields in 1960. Gas continued to be manufactured to some extent at Minton Lane during the 11 years that Jarmy lived there. His daughter Carol remembers the coke heap on site being as 'high as a house'.

Following the gas industry being taken into public ownership, several significant changes were made at Minton Lane between 1941 and 1976, during the periods that Ernest Wearne, then Harold Jarmy and finally George Brigham occupied the gasworks house. Not all involved a reduction in facilities. Although the number 1 gasholder was dismantled, the purifier building reduced in size and some oil tanks removed, they were replaced by a benzole plant and compressor house. Other changes included the former carburetted water gas purifier being replaced by a garage, and naphthalene and ammonia rotary scrubbers added, as well as tar and liquor pumps, alongside the site's northern boundary. In addition, petrol tanks were added to the area between the number 1 gasholder and the site of the by then dismantled number 2 gasholder (Wilkinson, p.13).

North Sea Gas

Looking further ahead, the outlook for sites like North Shields and even Howdon was not promising. Given the relentless rise in the price of coal, the gas industry was still searching for alternatives. A contract was signed in 1958 between the National Gas Council and the Constock Liquid Methane Corporation of America to ship natural gas to the UK in liquid form. It arrived in the *Methane Pioneer*, a converted cargo ship and the first ocean-going natural gas tanker in the world.[119]

A report by the British Productivity Council in May 1953 had recommended that the UK should follow the lead of the United States and start prospecting for natural gas.[120] It noted that coal gas accounted for only 5 per cent of gas sales in the USA, compared to 99.7 per cent in the UK. US natural gas was also so comparatively cheap that the companies which provided it had no need for pre-payment meters. In contrast, in the UK, it was necessary to replace existing pre-payment meters with models more suitable for rising prices. By then, penny-in-the-slot meters needed to be emptied every 6 weeks instead of the 12-week interval before the war. Meters installed in new homes by 1953 could use only 6d or 1s coins (the equivalent of £1.88 and £3.76 in 2022). The rise in the cost of coal gas, primarily because of the increasing cost of coal, was not just an issue for low-income families. It was threatening small businesses with high fuel bills. So, for example, in May 1953, a baker told the annual conference of the National Chamber of Trade that many small bakers like himself were close to bankruptcy because, although the price they could charge for bread was still controlled by central government, that price cap took no account of increases in the cost of fuel.[121] That too was a matter which concerned the British Productivity Council, and it made the obvious point that although all three energy industries were in public ownership, they competed against one another just as they had done when in private hands. Far from eliminating wasteful competition, the three industries had failed to carry out the coordination that had been argued would be possible under public ownership.

The advantages of natural gas may have been obvious but the UK, though well-endowed with coal, simply did not have a ready supply of natural gas as did the USA. In the early 1950s, no one was able to anticipate that, within two

---

119 An old friend, Nick Kostalas, was third engineer on her in 1964. Subsequently, two specialist vessels were built in the UK, the *Methane Princess*, and *Methane Progress*.

120 The British Productivity Council was set up by the government in 1951, with the aim of increasing Britain's industrial efficiency. Its government funding continued until 1973 when it underwent a major reorganization and became a collection of Local Productivity Associations.

121 Comparable to what is happening to the government-imposed caps on fuel prices in the UK at the time of writing.

decades, the UK would enjoy access to natural gas on a scale that would enable it to end coal gas manufacture completely. What the industry did initially was import liquified gas in a converted cargo ship from the United States, and then in purpose-built vessels from the Sahara. However, the discovery of a huge gas field in the Groningen province of Holland in 1959 increased hope that gas reserves might yet be found nearer to home and gave geologists valuable information on what kind of strata were most likely to be productive. It was that knowledge which prompted exploration in the North Sea. Although it was done by private companies granted licences by the government, the publicly owned Gas Council was in a strong position to capitalise on the discoveries, in a way the pre-war fragmented private gas industry would not have been. What emerged was a system in which the prospecting companies extracted the gas but then delivered it to shore bases run jointly with the Gas Council. The first licences were issued in 1964. The first major find, the West Sole field, followed in 1965, and by the middle of 1967 gas was coming ashore at Easington, in Co. Durham.[122] That led to growing confidence that similar finds would be made in other parts of the British sector of the North Sea. Against that background, in 1966, an ambitious decision was taken to switch the whole industry from coal gas to natural gas. It is most unlikely that such a bold step would have been taken had the industry not already been in public hands, and the Labour government of the day not been led by Harold Wilson, who believed that the UK's future depended on advances in science and technology. In his famous speech to the Labour Party conference in 1963, he began by reflecting on the pace of technological change and its implications for industry. In ending he uttered the lines for which the speech is most remembered. To prosper, a 'new Britain' would need to be forged in the 'white heat' of 'scientific revolution'. Switching the whole industry to natural gas was a momentous decision in keeping with Wilson's vision. It did not make immediate financial sense. The scale of investment and innovation needed to extract and distribute natural gas was enormous. Moving from being a *manufacturer of* coal gas to a *customer for* natural gas also meant writing off the considerable investment in the modern plants constructed to make gas from coal and oil that had been made after the industry had been taken into public ownership.

It is difficult to exaggerate the scale of the technical challenges involved in extracting North Sea gas. A huge engineering programme was also required to handle the gas once it came ashore. New terminals were needed; high pressure

---

122 Perhaps appropriately because Easington had been the constituency of 'Manny' Shinwell (later Baron Shinwell of Easington) who had been the first Labour Minister of Fuel and Power in the post-war government when the industry was taken into public ownership.

pipelines had to be laid; new compressor stations and control systems had to be designed and installed, and local distribution systems adapted, as necessary. Though enormous in themselves, these were not the only demanding challenges to be overcome. Another set had consequences for gas consumers because the composition of natural gas varied significantly from coal gas. Coal gas was made up of about 50 per cent hydrogen, 35 per cent methane, 10 per cent carbon monoxide, and 5 per cent ethylene. In contrast, although the composition of natural gas varies depending on the locations from which it is derived, the methane content is much higher at between 60-90 per cent (with significantly varying proportions of the other four main constituents: ethane, propane, butane and carbon dioxide). One key consequence of this marked difference is that despite having twice the calorific value of coal gas, natural gas requires twice as much air to burn effectively. So, the decision to switch to natural gas obliged the industry to embark on a massive programme to convert gas appliances. *All* gas burners in business premises and homes had to be modified or replaced, at no cost to the consumer. This immense project represented what is arguably the biggest feat of engineering in the UK since the end of the Second World War, and yet the main body of the conversion was completed within ten years. It was an extraordinary achievement. When the changeover began, it was only possible to estimate how many appliances were involved. In the event, 35 million were eventually identified, with a total of about 200 million burners, in 13.5 million premises. In domestic properties alone, an astonishing 8,000 *types* of gas appliances needed conversion. The overall cost of the conversion programme was in the region of £500 million, which in *economic cost* terms is the equivalent of about £17 billion in 2022. When the conversion began, 90 per cent of our gas still came from coal. Ten years later, when the conversion programme was all but completed in 1977, the days of coal gas were not just numbered but over.

By then, the industry was being managed in a different way. The principal role of the original twelve area gas boards was to manufacture gas. With the switch to natural gas, and gas now being fed to the area boards rather than being manufactured by them, it made sense for the management of the publicly owned industry to be more centralised. That change of direction was initiated in 1969 by the same Labour government which had made the historic decision to switch to natural gas two years earlier. Its Bill lapsed when Parliament was dissolved for the May 1970 general election but, during a period of still consensus politics, the Conservative Government which replaced Labour introduced its own Bill in Parliament with the same objective which was to put full responsibility for the gas industry into a new statutory body, the British Gas Corporation. In essence, the brief of the Corporation was to make more of a reality of the term 'nationalisation' which, although in popular use, did not accurately reflect how the publicly owned industry had been organized.

Despite this greater centralisation, as before, the now national British Gas Corporation still exercised its responsibilities through regions, with the same boundaries as the original area boards, each with its own chairman and vice-chairman appointed by the Corporation. The main impact of the reorganization at this regional level, which coincided with the ongoing switch to natural gas, was on the industry's plant and workforce. There was a reduction in the number of gasworks from 192 in 1967 to 35 in 1977; and the size of the workforce fell over the same period from 123,000 to 100,000. The reduction in the number of manual workers fell more dramatically, from 24,000 to 1,500. Over the same period, there was an increase in the number of customers from 13 million to 14 million, most of them domestic users. Moreover, their average consumption of gas increased from 211 to 453 therms per year.

This period of national change coincided with changes at the local level in North Shields. Harold Jarmy left Minton Lane to take up a position in at the NGB's headquarters at Killingworth, in Northumberland, in 1966. The house was then left vacant until 1967 when George Brigham moved in: the same George Brigham (but now supervisor gas engineer) who had been injured in a gas explosion in 1933. Prior to that he had lived with his family in the flat above the gas showrooms in Whitley Bay, as the inspector in charge of gas fitters. When it was proposed to change the use of the building, he was offered the Minton Lane gasworks house. His daughter recalled that it was refurbished for them. The most significant change was the installation of central heating. Such a large house, without modern insulation, demanded what she described as a 'huge, free-standing probably industrial boiler', which helps to explain why the Duncan children used to find their attic bedrooms so cold in the inter-war years.

At the stage the Brigham family moved into the Minton Lane house in 1967, there were still two gasholders in use. The smaller one was dismantled about 1974, towards the closing stages of the programme of conversion to natural gas. In the pit where it had been, hundreds of nineteenth century earthenware and glass bottles were found. Why they were there remains a mystery. The larger gasholder continued to be used. Elizabeth Matthews (née Brigham) recalls that when it was full, 'you could hear it bubbling and bouncing. You could hear the creaking as the holder rose and fell.' At that point, she remembered, her father would ring the Howdon works to ask them to lower the pressure. Elizabeth also remembers that gasholder for a quite different reason. During a summer holiday, she held a birthday party for her son in the garden of the gasworks house. George Brigham's grandson understood that he should never go through the gate that led to the huge gasholder. His friends did not, and the adults spent the afternoon 'stopping seven and eight-year-olds from climbing up the holder! We did get them all back safely to their parents, but never entertained the idea of a party in the garden again.' The gasworks' stores were also still in use at this stage, mainly for the benefit of those employees responsible for fitting, maintaining, and repairing gas boilers, water heaters and gas fires in homes and commercial premises.

The gasworks perimeter wall overlooking Minton Lane.

As early as 1967, when the conversion to natural gas programme was first announced, the councillors and officials of the County Borough of Tynemouth anticipated acquiring at least part of the Minton Lane site for their own use. It was reported in the local paper that both the Housing and Education Committees had declared an interest in the site to the Town Planning Committee, and that the matter had been referred to the Borough Surveyor for his verdict on what land would be left for housing if a new primary school was built on the site. In early 1971, about 60 per cent of the land was duly sold to the County Borough of Tynemouth and advertisements placed in local newspapers inviting contractors to indicate if they wanted to submit tenders for the demolition of the site's buildings. The advertisement explained that the work would involve the clearing and levelling of the site together with the complete demolition of all the structures and chimneys, removal of foundations, filling in of tanks and cellars, and the removal of approximately 3,000 cubic yards of gas.

View of the gasworks site from the north i.e. from the direction of Waterville Road, showing the retort house and adjacent area after it had fallen into disuse. This area is now occupied by the Waterville Primary School.

In December 1971, two steeplejacks climbed on to the retort house to demolish the iconic chimneys. A local newspaper reported:

> Brian Hogg and his partner Harry Ford give a new meaning to that old sign 'Danger – men at work.' They are 'Danger men – at work.' Brian and Harry are steeplejacks and yesterday they were 100 feet above North Shields, knocking down the chimney of the old Minton Lane Gasworks. … Brian who is 31 thinks this chimney is a picnic. He has knocked down a 300 – footer before. But 100ft or 300ft, it's much the same if you fall (*Newcastle Journal*, 3 December 1971).

The demolition of the retort house and other buildings followed.[123] What remained on the remaining part of the site were stores, offices and workshops, and the number 3 gasholder. Access to the site from Howdon Road was bricked up, leaving the large gate by the gasworks house the only entrance.

---

123 Elizabeth Matthews (née Brigham), and others, had some regrets about the disappearance of these iconic structures from the local landscape. 'I thought that the old retort buildings were beautiful when we lived there. Void of any production and now just shells, wandering around them on a summer's evening with the sun setting through one of the high round windows was delightful.'

Brian Hogg at work dismantling a 100-feet (30.5m) Minton Lane retort house chimney on 2 December 1971. Note the remaining gasholder in the background. Image courtesy of Dave Morton and The Newcastle Chronicle and Journal.

12 Upper Elsdon Street

Harry Ford sitting at the top of the 100-feet (30.5m) Minton Lane retort house chimney, overlooking Upper Elsdon Street, on 2 December 1971. Marked on the image is the 12 Upper Elsdon Street Tyneside flat where Danny Lawrence lived with his parents between 1955-1964. The six flats have since been converted into three houses. Image courtesy of Dave Morton and The Newcastle Chronicle and Journal.

In 1972, a plan was unveiled to build 50 private houses on the Council-owned part of the site, in addition to a school. By 1973, it was announced instead that Shepherd Construction of York were to build 83 dwellings, but none of them materialised. All that was built on the former gasworks land was a replacement for the Western Board School. Progress on it was delayed, we have been led to believe, initially because of problems with the toxicity of the soil, and again in early 1974, with the school half built, because the contractors went into voluntary liquidation. The school was eventually completed and is still in use. The area which had originally contained the tennis court, hit by a high explosive bomb in 1941, and the two smaller Victorian gas holders, early purifiers and tar and liquor well is now a playing field (Desk Studies, p.3).

Commercial use was still made of the remaining part of the gasworks site. It became a centre for gas emergency services in the north-east and was embroiled in a much publicised and unusually unpleasant labour dispute over a pay claim in 1973.

> North-East gas workers warned that if threats were carried out against any workers, gas supplies would at once be cut. The decision was taken at a meeting of workers at Minton Lane, North Shields – distribution centre for the emergency services in the north-east. The men also decided that they would continue to strike on a week-by-week basis until their wage claim was settled. Gas workers' strike leader, Mr Jack Wonders, received more threatening letters today. One, addressed to his wife Mrs Irene Wonders, yesterday contained a bomb threat. Two letters postmarked London and a postcard from Sheffield contained the latest threats today. One which was sent in an official OHMS [on Her Majesty's Service] envelope threatened to blow Mr Wonders and his gasmen 'to hell' and added 'We are on our way up to deal with you and your mob.' The other letter, from New Cross, and signed by 'a housewife' accused Mr Wonders of being a traitor and in the pay of Communists. He has taken the threats so seriously that he has moved his two grandchildren from his home in St James Terrace, Percy Main, to a secret address (*Newcastle Journal*, 24 February 1973).

George Brigham moved out of the gasworks house in 1976 (although he did not retire until 1978). The house remained empty for a time before being demolished. There was still some recruitment to the much-reduced staff in Minton Lane. For example, in 1979 the regional Gas Board advertised for two drawing office assistants, one of whom was to be based at Minton Lane. But indications of these residual functions at the Minton Lane site are nothing more than that. Already struggling to survive before the conversion to natural gas, the Minton Lane gasworks, as a gasworks, was doomed, like that of many other gasworks, when the decision was taken to go over to natural gas. Nevertheless, even after privatisation, it remained the base for emergency work for some time. The final days of the site will be described in the last section of this chapter.

Privatisation

The committee of inquiry which preceded the gas industry being taken into public ownership had concluded that the industry was in urgent need of fundamental reform and rationalisation. So, although the legislation to take the industry out of private hands was taken by a Labour government sympathetic to public ownership, the legislation owed more to pragmatic than ideological considerations. That explains why the Conservative governments of 1951, 1955 and 1959, were content to keep the industry in public ownership. When Labour was returned to power (between 1964-71) it embarked on the wholesale switch from coal gas to natural gas and the related process of setting up the British Gas Corporation, although, following a general election, it was a Conservative government under Edward Heath which completed that process. This phase in British politics is often referred to as a period of relative consensus between the two main parties. The differences in their policies were not insignificant but they shared a consensus on many important issues.

The remarkable success of the conversion programme seemed to suggest that there was little wrong with the way the gas industry was organized. Yet just a few years after the conversion programme was completed, the publicly owned gas industry was privatised. It was part of a phase in British politics in which pragmatism gave way to ideology and consensus was replaced by conflict. Whereas public ownership had followed a thorough investigation by an independent committee, the Conservative government of Margaret Thatcher, elected in 1979, announced its intention to privatise the gas industry in 1981 without any comparable inquiry. Choosing to do so was part of an ideologically driven programme to reduce the role of the state.

The first phase of privatisation took place between 1979 to 1983 and included British Aerospace and Cable and Wireless. The second took place between 1983 to 1987 and, in addition to the gas industry, included Jaguar, British Telecom, Britoil and the remaining elements of British Aerospace, and Cable and Wireless. Despite the underlying assumption that the benefits of market forces derive from competition, the Gas Act did not provide for any form of competition when the assets of the state-owned British Gas Corporation were transferred to British Gas plc (BG) in 1986. A private monopoly replaced a public monopoly. That obvious fact encouraged critics of privatisation to claim that it was undertaken more to raise funds for the Treasury (so that the Conservative government could meet its election pledge to reduce levels of income tax) than any conviction that there were inherent benefits in a privatised gas industry. That view was supported by no less a person than the former Conservative Prime Minister, Harold Macmillan. He accused the Thatcher government of privatising publicly owned assets as the equivalent of aristocratic families selling off the family silver to help make ends meet. He subsequently clarified his remark by emphasising that although he was not against privatisation *per se* he was against the government treating the huge amount of money raised by the privatisation as if it was tax revenue.

Within just a few years, Britain's state-owned energy industries of coal, gas, and electricity, were privatised. Only the nuclear industry remained in state control, but the newly elected government seemed to have little interest in it. Although the Labour government of 1978 was planning to build 10 advanced PWR nuclear power stations, after the election of a Conservative government in 1979 that programme was wound down. Only one PWR was ever built. What the programme of privatisation and deregulation in the energy sector added up to, was the UK losing most of its ability to plan for its energy future. It became almost entirely dependent on market forces. Predictably, encouraged by the government, the private energy sector chose to take full advantage of the ready supplies of North Sea natural gas (and oil). The result was that within just 20 years, the UK had again become a net importer of natural gas. Given the by then planned closure of most of our coal fired power stations, along with the decline in the capacity of our nuclear power industry following its eventual privatisation in 1996, by the twenty-first century, the UK was increasingly vulnerable to fluctuations in international energy markets. [124]

Initially, following gas privatisation, for all but large industrial customers, British Gas plc was a private monopoly. It was not until a recommendation from the Monopolies and Mergers Commission in 1988 that the industry was significantly restructured. What has followed are several major but increasingly difficult to follow changes in the ownership and management of the UK's increasingly

---

124 During Mrs Thatcher's period as Prime Minister the state-owned nuclear power plants would have also been privatised had it not been for the private sector's reluctance to take on the problems of demolishing old reactors and reprocessing nuclear fuel and other radioactive materials. Although the plants were eventually privatised in 1996, the privatised company British Energy collapsed within six years and the plants were sold to the French company EDF which, ironically, is largely state-owned.

fragmented gas industry. Fortunately, there is no need for us to do more than outline them here, to trace the route to Minton Lane's fourth and final owners.

In 1997, in preparation for the opening-up of the gas supply markets to competition, BG was split into two companies, Centrica and BG plc. Centrica became responsible for the retail business of BG but soon began to diversify. It developed a credit card (Goldfish), acquired the motor vehicle breakdown Automobile Association (AA) when it was sold off and became a private company, and also an Australian telecoms business. It then moved into the North American energy industry. However, within a few years Centrica had shed itself of most of this diversification and from 2005 announced it was going to concentrate on the energy sector. It went on to become a major international player although in recent years its shares have fallen in value.

At the time of the 1997 split, BG took on responsibility for exploration and production, and the distribution business was given the name Transco. However, as early as 2000, there was a further demerger. BG became the BG Group, and Transco became the Lattice Group. Then, within two more years, the Lattice Group had merged with National Grid plc to form National Grid Transco.[125] At that point, the gas distribution network was divided into eight regions. In 2002, the Lattice Group merged with the National Grid Group, who operated the national gas transmission system (and some electricity transmission) to form National Grid Transco plc. In 2005, that company sold four of its eight gas distribution networks and renamed their remaining gas distribution business as National Grid plc. Northern Gas Networks (NGN), one of the four that was sold, was acquired by CK Infrastructure (formerly Cheung Kong Infrastructure). Today, NGN is owned by a consortium of three companies. They are CK Infrastructure; Power Assets Holdings Ltd (a global investor in energy and other utility businesses); and SAS Trustee Corporation (a pension fund for government employees in the Australian state of New South Wales).

What is clear, from even this cursory outline of the gas industry's recent corporate history, is that it bears no resemblance to the local and community-based ownership which created the Minton Lane gasworks. To that extent, it is a prime example not only of what has happened with the privatisation of the UK's utility industries, but of what is now known as globalisation. Once upon a time, the gasworks in North Shields were an expression of local pride as well as a way of making money for local shareholders. Today, the ownership of the gas

---

125 The BG Group went on to develop a portfolio of major gas assets in Egypt, Trinidad and Tobago, Kazakhstan, as well in the North Sea. However, in 2015 it was acquired by Royal Dutch Shell at a time of uncertainty for both companies because of the declining interest in further exploration.

industry is so fragmented that many of the people who have a stake in it may not even know that is the case. Unlike the original shareholders of the North Shields and Borough of Tynemouth gas companies, they have no interest in the areas the company services. Without local shareholders, it is now left to company employees to take an interest in local communities: an interest that was once the province of owners and employees alike.

It is difficult to overstate this contrast between the original ownership of British gas companies and the patterns of ownership which have emerged since the gas industry was privatised. The contrast illustrates the now enormous complexity of a market in which international players compete against one another to sell both gas *and* electricity to consumers. Moreover, the fluctuating fortunes of Centrica at the international level, and the failure of the municipal Robin Hood Energy company set up by Nottingham City Council which went into administration in 2021 with debts of £62 million, both illustrate that the industry is now no longer as stable as it was in the simpler days of the Tynemouth Gas Company.[126]

The Final Days of the Minton Lane Gasworks

Following the conversion to natural gas and then the privatisation of the industry, less and less use was made of the Minton Lane site. Over a period of years, it was cleared of its surviving buildings and structures, and then the vertical supports of the one remaining gasholder. Still left at ground level, however, was the gasholder's huge dome and, below ground, the supporting structure of the gasholder.

Those entrusted with the final clearance of the site were conscious not only of the need for an environmentally sensitive approach to their task, but also that the local community valued the site's fine brick perimeter wall. That presented them with a problem because a section of it was bowing in on itself. Rather than just make it safe by replacing the dangerous sections with modern fencing, NGN temporarily made use of crash deck protection, a form of scaffolding built to withstand falling materials, to act as a barrier to protect those working on the site. Then, in the final stages, special braces were fitted to the worst sections of the wall to make them safe for the future.

Work began on the demolition of the final Minton Lane gasholder in September 2016. After removing the water from its base, a visual scan revealed that the supporting structure of the crown was predominantly wooden. Sonar pulsing techniques were used to reveal the hidden layout of the gasholder, to give

---

126 Former Robin Hood Energy customers strengthened Centrica's customer base, in the same way that the Newcastle and Gateshead Gas Company's customer base was strengthened after it acquired the Tynemouth Gas Company in 1927.

the engineers a better assessment of the structure's stability and strength. That, in turn, enabled them to remove the metal crown in a way which minimised the risk of the wooden supporting structure collapsing.

During the subsequent demolition process, those involved were impressed with the quality of the structure that had been built over one hundred years earlier. Following the damage to the gasholder during the 1941 and 1943 bombing raids, it had been necessary to install a new sheet metal crown on top of the original, greatly increasing the weight which the wooden structure had originally been designed to support. To minimise the risk of it collapsing under the combined weight of the old and new crowns, NGN made use of two huge mobile tower cranes and cut the roof sheeting into wedges. However, once the wooden structure was exposed, it became apparent that there was little cause for concern because, despite its age, it was still remarkably robust. The images in the colour gallery include a sequence of selected stages in the demolition of the gasholder. They reveal what an extraordinary structure our forebears had created.

Over the demolition period, 470 tonnes of metal and concrete were shipped offsite for recycling. The demolition and site clearance had also involved the removal of almost 11,000 cubic metres of contaminated water, 82 tonnes of oil, and 54 tonnes of contaminated sludge. The void left by the gasholder, was filled with 23,000 tonnes of recycled aggregate. By July 2017, the work was complete. All that is now left of the large and impressive gasworks which once covered the Minton Lane site is the perimeter wall and an imprint on the ground where the final gasholder had been.[127]

Other than the perimeter wall, all that remains of the once so important gas industry in North Shields and surrounding areas are a few back lane streetlamps which escaped the removal programme. In nearby Whitley Bay, there are still ten sewer gas streetlamps of the 17 erected between 1900-1910. Although designed by Joseph Edmund Webb to burn off putrid sewer gas, they had to be supplemented by coal gas supplied by the Tynemouth Gas company.[128]

---

127 Although cleared, the gasholder section of the site still belongs to NGN. The remainder is owned by National Grid Properties (NGP). After the restructuring of the gas industry at the end of the 1990s, British Gas Property was established to manage, remediate, reuse, and sell surplus land. In time, these operations have been transferred to NGP. Only the area belonging to NGN has been cleared of toxic materials.

128 For more information about sewer lamps see The Webb Lamp Co. Ltd. and its Sewer Gas Extractor and Destructor Lamp: www.xenophon.org.uk/historywebblampco.html and the YouTube video of Paul Bradley, of North Shields: https://www.youtube.com/watch?v=vL5QL3IWfxw. In London's Carting Lane besides the Savoy Hotel there is a sewer gas lamp which burns 24 hours a day. It was erected originally to keep sewer smells away from the hotel's bedrooms!

Left: The remains of a gas streetlamp in a North Shields back lane which was not removed and has been allowed to deteriorate.
Right: One of the ten (of 17) surviving and well maintained (but no longer operational) sewer gas lamps in Whitley Bay. Although designed to burn methane from the sewers they had to be supplemented with coal gas from the Tynemouth Gas Company.

The NGN employees tasked with clearing their part of the site with its one remaining gasholder were aware that it had once been important to, and still held interest for, some members of the local community. For that reason, in 2016, they invited those with a past association with the Minton Lane gasworks to share their memories and memorabilia. That is how, for the first and only time we, together with Lorna Duncan's eldest daughter, Hazel Iliffe and her husband Alan, passed through the Minton Lane perimeter wall where the gasworks house had stood for 100 years,

It was a moving experience for Helen and Hazel, granddaughters of George Duncan, to stand beside the enormous gasholder that had towered over the gasworks house that had been the Duncan family home for over two decades. The visit also helped the four of us appreciate the wonderful engineering achievements that had taken place in Minton Lane and elsewhere in North Shields over the previous two hundred years. Although by 2016 we understood why the UK was turning its back on carbon-based fuels, we were equally conscious that we should never forget how much is owed to those who designed, invested in, and laboured in the coal and gas industries, which brought so many benefits, to so many people, for so long. It was that visit and those thoughts which created the urge to write this book.

Chapter 10

The Future

NGN'S REMOVAL of the remaining gas holder at Minton Lane in 2017, along with similar projects elsewhere, represented a symbolic end to what had been a 150-year *coal gas* industry. What we were unaware of at that time was that NGN had already embarked on the first stages of a series of projects with the ultimate prospect of replacing the by then 50-year-old *natural gas* industry with one using the environmentally clean gas *hydrogen*. The need for such a radical change came primarily from the growing evidence that worldwide greenhouse gas emissions from the use of fossil fuels were causing dramatic and dangerous changes in the Earth's climate, and that in the UK a substantial proportion of the emissions were generated by the large majority of homes using natural gas for cooking and heating.[129] However, the need for a radical alternative also came from the UK's vulnerability to the international market for natural gas. That became increasingly obvious with the succession of huge increases in the price of gas in the early 2020s. Clearly, it was not only necessary for the UK to move to cleaner sources of energy. It also needed to be more energy independent. The advantage of switching from natural gas to hydrogen is not only that it is carbon-free but that, because it can be produced in the UK like renewables and nuclear power, it can help to bolster our energy security and reduce our dependence on energy supplies from overseas. In the Chancellor of the Exchequer's 2022 autumn statement, he emphasised the huge significance of the UK's exposure to international energy price rises. 'This year we will be spending an extra £150 billion on energy compared to pre-pandemic [2020] levels, equivalent to paying for an entire second NHS through our energy bills'. To help families meet the huge increase in their energy bills over the coming winter, he allocated £55 billion for an energy support package,

---

129 The gases in the Earth's atmosphere produce an *advantageous* insulating 'greenhouse' effect. Without them, there would be extremes in temperature. However, the additional greenhouse gases produced by human activity have the *disadvantageous* effect of trapping more heat which is now melting ice fields, increasing sea levels, and creating more frequent extreme weather events. Carbon dioxide and methane emissions are the most concerning of these additional greenhouse gases.

along with a comparable level of support for the subsequent 2023-24 financial year. Not surprisingly, of the Chancellor's three priorities for growth, the first was energy security.[130]

In 2008, a Labour government passed the Climate Change Act which included a commitment to reduce UK greenhouse gas emissions by 2050 to a level at least 80 per cent lower than in 1990. Then, in 2019, following more dire warnings from climate scientists, a Conservative government went further and announced a legally binding commitment to bring UK greenhouse gas emissions to net zero by 2050 by both cutting carbon emissions and introducing offsetting methods such as planting trees and carbon capture and storage.[131] This is a hugely ambitious target, because even before the subsequent commitment to ban sales of new petrol and diesel vehicles by 2030, there have been warnings that the UK will be unlikely to be able to produce sufficient electricity to power the increasing number of electrical and electronic devices which use it. For example, in October 2022, the National Grid warned that the UK might not be able to import sufficient electricity to make up for shortfalls in our supply and so arrangements were made to keep some coal-fired power stations on standby, and give financial inducements to businesses and households to reduce their use of electricity at peak times: an arrangement activated in January 2023 following a period of unusually cold weather combined with low wind speeds.

Although it is difficult to keep up with the accelerating pace of research and development into alternatives for fossil fuels, major strides had already been made before the momentous commitment to net zero by 2050. However, as the table below illustrates, changing weather conditions mean that renewable sources of energy do not generate consistent levels of electricity. For example, wind power generated only 16 per cent of Great Britain's electricity in August 2022 but 36 per cent in October. Electricity generated by solar energy contributed 7 per cent in August 2022 but only 3 per cent in October. Overall, within the same three-month period, the contribution to Great Britain's electricity

---

130 What he did not acknowledge is how earlier government decisions have increased the UK's vulnerability. From 2013, there had been a series of government cuts in support for home insulation. From 2015 the government introduced an effective moratorium on further onshore windfarms even though they provide the fastest and cheapest way to provide more renewable energy. In 2017, the cost-cutting decision of the government to cease providing support for Centrica's *Rough* storage facility reduced our gas storage capacity to 2 per cent compared to about 25 per in the case of our main European competitors.

131 The 2023 Conservative government has been widely accused of retreating from the commitment. In June, an Environment Minister resigned, accusing the Prime Minister of being uninterested in the environment. Subsequently, in September, permission for up to 100 new North Sea drilling licences was announced and net-zero target dates relaxed.

supply from zero-carbon sources varied between 39 per cent in August and 57 per cent in October. Such a drawback in renewable energy supplies would not apply to the same degree if we made extensive use of tidal wave power, but the government-sponsored programme to develop it was only just beginning at the time of writing.[132]

Since 1991, over 30 gas-fired power stations have been constructed in the UK. The fact that they can generate electricity almost immediately when they are started up is particularly valuable when renewable energy levels are low and explains the significant variations in the amount of electricity they generate. For example, in 2022, almost 48 per cent of our electricity was generated from gas in August. In October, it was 36 per cent.[133]

Constituent elements of Great Britain's electricity supply by percentage

Date	Solar	Wind	Nuclear	Gas	Other	% Zero-Carbon
Aug 2022	7	16	15	48	14	39
Sep 2022	5	24	15	44	12	44
Oct 2022	3	36	14	36	11	57

The 'others' were coal, biomass, hydro-electric and imported electricity.
The % Zero-Carbon column *includes the contribution from hydro-electric sources.*
National Grid Great Britain's monthly electricity stats | National Grid ESO

The hope in the 1950s that nuclear power would provide us with limitless energy has never come close to being realised. Despite decades of research, beginning as long ago as 1958 with the ZETA project at Harwell, the use of nuclear *fusion*

---

132 In November 2021, the then government Business Secretary indicated that only tidal power *could* became a key part of the *next generation* of renewable energy projects. There are currently about ten tidal power stations in operation around the world, including the 680-tonne turbine in Orkney generating 2MW of electricity for the locality, as well as power for an onshore electrolyser generating green hydrogen. The first substantial tidal power plant has been in operation on the River Rance in France since 1966, with a capacity of 254MW. The capital costs were recovered in 20 years. Projects to harness waves as distinct from tidal energy are underway in the UK but only on a small scale.

133 There are three types of gas power stations. Open cycle fast turbines (OCGT) burn gas to drive turbines which produce electricity. Combined cycle gas turbines (CCGT) are like OCGTs but, in addition, heat water to create steam that drives another turbine to produce more energy. Combined heat and power stations (CHP) are similar but also use the heat from the engines for other purposes, such as district heating or to power chemical services such as oil refineries.

is still not commercially viable.[134] Britain's programme of generating power by nuclear *fission* has, however, been relatively successful. Between 1956 and 1967, 27 nuclear reactors were built, and the UK was producing more electricity from nuclear plants than either the USA or France. In the 1970s, when it became apparent that the initial gas-cooled Magnox and AGR (advanced gas-cooled) reactor designs were less efficient than PWR (pressurised water) reactors, the USA and France embarked on ambitious programmes to build a series of them. It appeared as if the UK was going to do the same when in 1978 the Labour government accepted the recommendation of the Central Electricity Generating Board that we should also adopt the PWR design for our next generation of nuclear power stations. However, the Conservative government elected in 1979 chose not to build a new generation of nuclear power plants and all but abandoned further developments in the industry. Of the planned ten PWR reactors only one, Sizewell B, was completed.[135]

That was just one of the several fundamental changes which took place in the UK's energy industries in the 1980s. The cumulative consequence of them is that we lost the ability to plan our long-term energy future in the way that had been possible when the industries were in public ownership. Instead, following the programme of privatisation and deregulation of energy markets, the UK became exposed to the vagaries of international market forces.

The short-term advantages of the then relatively cheap natural gas (and oil) from the North Sea encouraged its use at the expense of the development of alternative sources of energy. However, by the end of the twentieth century the bonanza was coming to an end and, although we continue to extract gas and oil from fields in the North Sea, the UK is again a net importer of gas and oil, and reliant on energy markets beyond our control. Moreover, unlike some other countries, we are not as well cushioned against the extremes in energy prices that emerged for natural gas in 2022. The UK has no equivalent to Norway's enormous publicly owned 'sovereign wealth fund' which was created with revenues from sales of gas and oil from its sectors of the North Sea. In contrast, British governments chose to use its revenues for short rather than long-term advantage. The ready availability of natural gas was also the key factor in Conservative governments failing to develop our nuclear energy industry. In 1978, like the French, the UK

---

134 In December 2022 it was announced that a breakthrough had occurred during a fusion experiment at the US Lawrence Livermore National Laboratory when more energy was released than had been put into it. However, even 'with concerted efforts and investment, a few decades of research on the underlying technologies' would still be needed to build a power plant.

135 A decision to go ahead with Sizewell C was announced in November 2022.

generated about 6.5GW of power from its nuclear plants. By 1990, the French supply from nuclear power had grown almost nine-fold to 56GW. Over the same period, the UK supply less than doubled to 11GW and even that has now fallen as some of our ageing plants have had to be 'retired'. Today, the French have 61 nuclear power stations, all the advanced more efficient PWR type. The UK has only six, all but one of which are of the original, less efficient gas-cooled type. Plans to kick-start our nuclear energy industry have not gone well because we have lost most of the industry which built our initial large-scale nuclear power stations, and we are dependent on other countries for both technical expertise and financial investment. That has led to a fundamental rethink of what remains of our once leading nuclear industry. Instead of one-off large-scale nuclear plants, we are increasingly focused on building a series of small-scale, easily replicated, nuclear power plants, designed by Rolls Royce with government-support, which promise to be both technically easier and more cost-effective to construct.

Because of the extent of the UK's reliance on natural gas, the UK's independent advisory Committee on Climate Change recommended the adoption of a carbon-neutral by 2050 target but accepted that there would be a continuing need for *gas*. However, ideally, the gas would be one that does not contribute further to the problem of greenhouse gas emissions. The favoured alternative is hydrogen. It has the advantage of not producing carbon dioxide when burned, whilst still offering all the benefits of natural gas. It is easily stored, responds instantly to peaks in demand and can deliver high temperature heat for industrial needs.

The availability of hydrogen will have the additional benefit of giving domestic and commercial customers an alternative to using electricity, as well as providing a central heating option for those for whom heat pumps are not viable. Alternatives to electricity are necessary in industry too. Whilst battery-powered electrical vehicles may be suitable for many purposes, they cannot provide sufficient power for the kind of heavy equipment used by companies such as JCB. For that reason, it has already adapted established engine technology to produce a motor that can run on hydrogen (rather than a hydrogen fuel-cell), which can match the performance of a diesel-powered equivalent.[136] Other noteworthy developments (albeit outside the UK) are the hydrogen trains built by the French company Alstom which were introduced in Lower Saxony in Germany in 2022, and BMW's two test hydrogen vehicles, the iX5 and Hydrogen 7.

---

136 A JCB backhoe loader powered by a hydrogen combustion engine made its first fully public appearance in 2022 during the Platinum Jubilee Pageant. Other JCB hydrogen-powered vehicles are in development.

The degree to which hydrogen is environmentally friendly overall depends on how it is produced. That is why, although it is an invisible gas, references to hydrogen often now include a colour label. The large underground pockets of white hydrogen which exist, generated by several different natural processes, are yet to be exploited commercially but its potential to generate electricity has been demonstrated in a village in Mali since 2011. Green hydrogen, generated from renewable energy sources, by electrolysing water (H_2O) and splitting it into its constituent elements of hydrogen and oxygen is becoming available The advantage of green hydrogen, like that of white hydrogen is that no unwanted greenhouse gases are generated as a by-product. Blue hydrogen, in contrast, is produced mainly from natural gas using a process in which it is combined with steam. Though a cheaper process, its main disadvantage is that it produces carbon dioxide as a by-product which must then be subjected to some form of carbon capture, usage and storage (CCUS).[137] Nevertheless, despite this disadvantage, the UK's Hydrogen Strategy published in 2021 accepted that a 'twin track' approach was necessary.

> To meet this ambition, the UK has committed to a 'twin track' approach to hydrogen production, supporting both electrolytic and CCUS-enabled hydrogen, ensuring we support a variety of different production methods to deliver the level of hydrogen needed to meet net zero (*Hydrogen Strategy*, p.33).[138]

The gas industry has been remarkably innovative throughout its long history but the move towards a hydrogen future means that it is now facing new challenges of a kind that were all but ignored during the nineteenth and twentieth centuries. Climate change may now be high on political agendas but that was not the case during most of the gas industry's 200-year history. Although Clean Air Acts were introduced in the mid-twentieth century to reduce the risk to health from smog, no serious consideration was given to the impact of burning fossil fuels on the atmosphere and climate.

What has become evident since entering the 2020s is not only that the UK needs the gas industry to play a major role in our energy future, but that to do so it

---

137 The US National Institute of Standards and Technology claimed in November 2022 that it had developed an aluminium formate material which works effectively for CCUS despite its simplicity, stability, and ease of preparation (Science Advances, 2022).

138 Hydrogen produced in this way but without carbon capture is usually referred to as 'grey' hydrogen. 'Pink' (or sometimes red or purple) hydrogen is a term used to describe hydrogen generated through a process of electrolysis powered by nuclear energy. 'Yellow' hydrogen is a term for hydrogen produced using solar power.

will have to introduce changes perhaps even greater in scale than those that were necessary when the UK embarked on the transition from coal gas to natural gas. The industry has to prepare for an ultimately hydrogen gas future in the long-term, as well as significantly reduce its own carbon footprint in the short term. For that reason, and until such time as sufficient supplies of green hydrogen are available, and homes and gas appliances are 'hydrogen ready', the industry is having to gear up to being able to blend natural gas with hydrogen to maintain supplies to customers whilst at the same time reducing its own impact on the environment. How extensively this blending process will be employed will not only depend on how quickly the industry can move to a 100 per cent hydrogen network but whether the blending process can be demonstrated to be cost-efficient, something which has been undermined by the recent, huge, worldwide increase in natural gas prices.

The programme of research and development into a purely hydrogen future began with a 2016 NGN feasibility study of whether it was technically possible and economically viable to convert the gas distribution network of a city the size of Leeds to hydrogen. When that study established that it was possible, it was followed by what became known as H21, a programme of wide-ranging research projects conducted by a consortium within the gas industry, led by NGN, with £9 million of OFGEM funding.[139] Its main initial concern was to establish the safety of using hydrogen within the industry's existing 176,000 miles of pipework, which is currently connected to 23 million homes and a huge number of industrial and commercial premises. Because of the explosive potential of the original coal gas, safety has always been a major concern of the industry but, as hydrogen molecules are smaller than the predominant molecules in natural gas, it has been necessary to investigate whether hydrogen might leak more easily from the existing gas network than natural gas. A second phase of projects then examined the potential consequences of a hydrogen leak. The reports of these two phases of H21 concluded that, although hydrogen is potentially more likely to leak from old metal piping (but not newer plastic piping), measures can be taken to make the network even safer than it is today.[140] Other studies involved technical issues such as metering and leak detection; identifying issues which might arise with industrial and commercial as distinct from residential customers, and social science surveys of public perceptions of hydrogen as a fuel.

---

139 The programme of research was backed by all the UK's gas distribution networks and the Health and Safety Executive and financed with OFGEM's Network Innovation Competition (NIC) and Network Innovation Allowance (NIA) funding.

140 The programme to replace metal gas piping with plastic is already over 50 per cent complete.

A hydrogen project was opened to the public in Low Thornley near Gateshead in July 2021. Two semi-detached houses were built by NGN in conjunction with Cadent (another major gas distribution company) and the government's Department of Business, Energy and Industrial Strategy. The houses are equipped with hydrogen gas cookers, fires, and boilers so that visitors can see the similarity of hydrogen appliances to natural gas appliances, with the only obvious difference being that hydrogen burns with an orange flame compared to the familiar blue flame of natural gas.[141]

More ambitious hydrogen trials and developments are planned, following the government's decision to support a 100 per cent hydrogen village trial by 2025, and a town trial by 2030, to establish the feasibility, cost, and convenience of using hydrogen in residential properties. OFGEM received three applications from gas distribution companies. Scottish Gas Networks (SGN) had hoped to attract continuing support for its H100 Fife project on the east coast of Scotland, but its bid was unsuccessful.[142] Two other trials were proposed with OFGEM support. In the north-east of England, NGN's plan was to supply around 2,000 homes and businesses in the Redcar area (part of the Teesside conurbation) with locally produced green hydrogen. Also planned for the north-east coast is a hydrogen storage facility in the salt caverns at Aldbrough in Humberside.[143] Previously used for storing natural gas, the facility is being developed in conjunction with a major carbon capture and storage power plant at Keadby, near Scunthorpe in North Lincolnshire. However, the second village trial planned for Whitby in Ellesmere Port was scrapped in July 2023 following local opposition.

Incongruously, it is *Scottish* Power which is planning to build a £150m green hydrogen plant at the Port of Felixstowe on the east coast of *England* to power trains, trucks, and ships, with proposals for a 100MW plant at the Suffolk port from 2026.[144] In the south-west, green hydrogen will be produced by the Institute of Advanced Automotive Systems (IAAPS) at the Bristol and Bath Science Park

---

141 In the case of central heating boilers, well-known manufacturers such as Baxi, Ideal, Vaillant, and Worcester Bosch already have hydrogen-ready models which run on current gas supplies but which with simple adjustments will run on hydrogen when it becomes available through gas mains.

142 There were unconfirmed newspaper reports in September 2022 that the project had fallen behind schedule.

143 A September 2023 report from the Royal Society concluded that to avoid power cuts the UK needs 900 such hydrogen storage caverns to compensate for variations in weather-dependent renewable energy sources.

144 To confuse matters a little further, but at the same time illustrate the complex nature of today's ownership of what appear to be British companies, Scottish Power is owned by the giant Spanish utilities company Iberdrola (which owns Europe's currently largest production site for green hydrogen for industrial use at Puertollano), and the Port of Felixstowe is owned by Hutchison Ports, part of the Hong Kong based multinational C. K. Hutchison.

from 2023 to both reduce the AAPS building's carbon footprint and conduct research on the use of green hydrogen in hard-to-electrify sectors of the economy such as aviation, shipping and heavy-duty transport. Also in the south-west, a consortium of ten companies (including Airbus, GKN Aerospace and EDF's subsidiary Hynamics) have set up Hydrogen South-West to develop a major hydrogen infrastructure across the region.

The government's *UK Hydrogen Strategy* (published in the month following the opening of the Gateshead hydrogen houses in 2021) began with the candid admission that as a country the UK starts 'with almost no low carbon production of hydrogen'. It follows that even meeting the initial target of 5GW of green hydrogen by the end of the decade (estimated to be the equivalent of the gas consumption of about 3 million UK households) would be a daunting task. Yet since then, in 2022, the 2030 target was raised to 10GW of green *and* blue hydrogen (produced by steam methane reformation with carbon capture).[145] Even with the lower target, the Strategy conceded that although the 'focus will be on promoting domestic production and supply chains … we would expect to be … utilising import opportunities as appropriate' (*Hydrogen Strategy*, p.32).

Given the uncertainties that remain over the supply of green (and blue) hydrogen, government and industry are also devoting a great deal of research and development into the use of a blend of natural gas with 20 per cent hydrogen. Some of the issues to be resolved await the final results of the HyDeploy projects which began with a testing of a blend of natural gas and hydrogen in the private gas network on the Keele University campus in Staffordshire. Laboratory tests were conducted on a range of gas appliances and extensive research carried out on the effects of hydrogen blends on a variety of the materials used in the gas network, and appliances found in homes and businesses. The results confirmed that up to 20 per cent blended hydrogen was safe to use within both gas network pipes and in gas boilers, hobs, cookers, and meters.

The success of Phase 1 paved the way for the more ambitious Phase 2, an 11-month trial by an NGN consortium in Winlaton (a community once supplied with coal gas by the Newcastle and Gateshead Gas Company, and one situated close to the Low Thornley hydrogen houses). Hydrogen blended with natural gas was supplied to 668 homes, a school, and some small businesses (*Hydrogen Strategy*, p.8). Although the improvement in emissions was not comparable to what could

---

145 Although these hydrogen targets are ambitious, to put them in perspective, in 2021 the UK was generating about 15GW of power from *onshore* wind turbines alone, and about 13.5 GW from solar power. Burning hydrogen at the rate of 1kg per second has the potential to produce 120+ MW of power, with 1,000 MW being the equivalent of 1GW (or 1 billion watts).

be achieved with a hydrogen only gas supply, it is estimated that if the Winlaton project were to be adopted nationally it could reduce carbon dioxide emissions by about six million tonnes annually: the equivalent of taking about 2.5 million vehicles off our roads.

Following the success of this second stage of the HyDeploy project, it has now moved on to Phase 3. At the time of writing, the consortium is working with industry to complete the collection of evidence on safety which the government will need before reaching a final decision on blending. The mix of natural gas and 20 per cent hydrogen has already been used successfully in the production of float glass by Pilkington, and consumer products such as washing powder and hair shampoo by Unilever. Further trials are continuing in the ceramics industry and with several other companies.[146] A different kind of trial is planned by Centrica. It intends to blend 3 per cent hydrogen produced by HiiROC into its existing 'peaking' gas plan in Brigg, North Lincolnshire.[147] If the 12-month project is successful, the hydrogen content will be increased in stages to 20 per cent.

* * *

The UK is on its way to an energy future in which green hydrogen gas will be a significant element. A final decision remains to be made on the proposed interim measure of blending natural gas with hydrogen. If it is introduced, the length of time it will be used in the network will depend on how quickly green hydrogen can be produced on a sufficient scale to replace it. Until that stage is reached, there will remain a need for natural gas both for that purpose and for the generation of blue hydrogen. Despite these uncertainties, the already 200-year-old UK gas industry undoubtedly has many years ahead of it. The product it distributes will be cleaner than either the coal gas it distributed in its first 150 years, or the natural gas it distributed in the subsequent 50 years. It will also operate with a business model markedly different from anything envisaged by such pioneers as Murdoch, Clegg, and Winsor. However, what those innovators set in motion has stood us in good stead and there is no doubt that the population of the UK will be growing up with gas into the foreseeable future.

---

146 Bosch, Duomo, Eastham Refinery Limited, Gas Fired Products UK Ltd (SpaceRay), Ideal Heating, Limpsfield Burners, Mantec Technical Ceramics Limited, and SAACKE Combustion services. Other hydrogen infrastructure projects either underway or planned include the HyNet hydrogen pipeline; INOVYN hydrogen storage; the East Coast Cluster hydrogen pipeline; and Aldbrough hydrogen storage; and hydrogen electrolyser capacity deployment.

147 A peaking plant operates only at peak times, typically for about three hours a day.

A perimeter wall of the Minton Lane gasworks and the remaining gasholder.

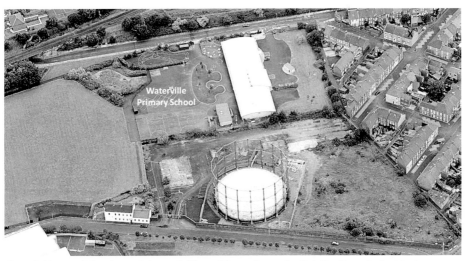

An aerial image of the sole remaining gasholder at Minton Lane, shortly before its vertical supports were removed. By then the gasworks house had been demolished. The surviving gasworks offices are now used by North Tyneside Council. The building in the upper part of the image is Waterville Primary School. Danny Lawrence's home from 1955-65 (then one of six terraced flats) is marked with a black cross in the top right hand corner. Copyright and courtesy of Microsoft's Bing Maps.

2016 image of the crown of the remaining Minton Lane gasholder, at ground level. Copyright and courtesy of Northern Gas Networks (NGN). With thanks to Mark Johnson.

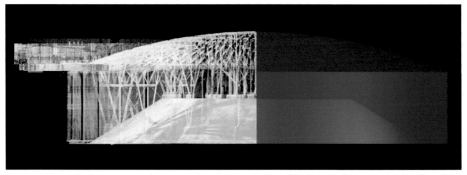

Sonar pulsing techniques were used to reveal these features that would otherwise have remained hidden. The concrete 'dumpling' can be seen at the base of the gasholder, along with the 'moat' around it which would have held water, and the predominantly wooden structure supporting the heavy metal crown when in its lowest position. Copyright and courtesy of NGN. With thanks to Mark Johnson.

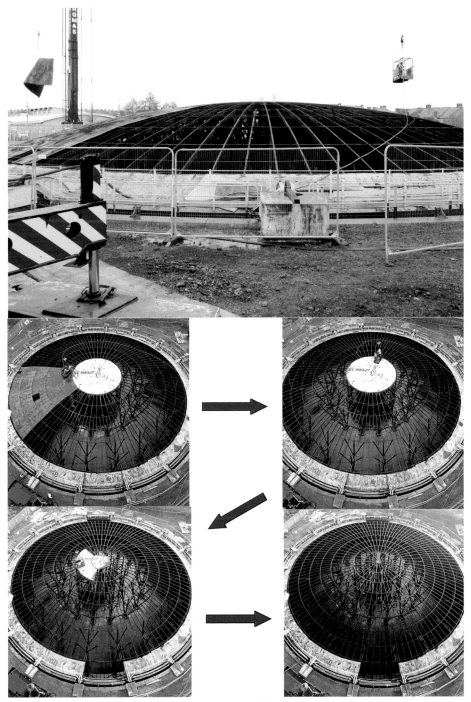

Above: The crane to the left is removing a section of the metal crown. The crane to the right is lowering an engineer towards the surface of the crown. Below: These four images, in addition to the image above, reveal the crown's predominantly wooden supporting structure. Copyright and courtesy of NGN. With thanks to Mark Johnson.

Later stages in the removal of the wooden supporting structure. Copyright and courtesy of Northern Gas Networks. With thanks to Mark Johnson.

The removal of the inner wall of the gasholder, revealing its outer metal wall. Copyright and courtesy of NGN. With thanks to Mark Johnson.

A caterpillar tracked crane on the 'dumpling', the domed concrete base of the gasholder, revealing the outer metal wall before the base itself was removed. Copyright and courtesy of NGN. With thanks to Mark Johnson.

The final stages in removing the domed base of the gasholder prior to infilling. Copyright and courtesy of NGN. With thanks to Mark Johnson.

The infilling of the site following the removal of the gasholder. Note the now clear view of the brick perimeter wall which has been retained with one section reinforced. Copyright and courtesy of NGN. With thanks to Mark Johnson.

An aerial image of Minton Lane after the removal of the final gasholder. The black X marks Danny Lawrence's home between 1955-65. Copyright and courtesy of Google Maps.

The ten Duncan children in their gasworks garden, c.1927 when the Tynemouth company was taken over by the Newcastle and Gateshead Gas company. In age order, from left to right, they are Alice, George, Ingram, Phyllis (the mother of Helen Lawrence), Mary, Elizabeth, Margaret, Jean, Joseph Henry and Lorna. The original black and white photo is courtesy of Hazel Iliffe. The enhanced and colourised version of the damaged original is courtesy of Hope Lawrence.

Left to right: Danny Lawrence, Helen Lawrence (daughter of Phyllis Duncan), Hazel Iliffe (daughter of Lorna Duncan) and Alan Iliffe at the Minton Lane gasworks site on 23 November 2016 (prior to the removal of the gasholder).

Appendix 1

James Robson's Gas Engines

THE TANGYES company of Birmingham had enjoyed considerable success with steam engines but was keen to innovate and between 1880 and 1900, thanks in part to James Robson, established themselves as manufacturers of gas and oil engines. It was not until the German Dr N. A. Otto built his successful four-stroke 'Silent Gas Engine' in 1876, after 20 years of development, that there was a sufficiently economical and efficient alternative to steam on the market. In the UK, the license to manufacture Otto's engine went to Crossley's of Manchester. However, attempts to produce a simpler two-stroke engine continued and Tangyes were actively searching for a design they could manufacture in quantity. Three concept engines, by Woolfe, Hurd and Robinson, looked promising but disappointed or failed to reach the working model stage. It was at that point that George Haswell, the managing director of another Midlands engineering firm, who had been born and raised in North Shields, drew their attention to the designs of James Robson.[148] He facilitated a meeting between the two parties and, on 4th January 1881, Robson signed an agreement giving Tangyes the sole rights to manufacture his gas-operated pump and gas hammer. His 1880 patent also included an engine designed on the spring-type atmospheric pressure principle, which Waygood's of London had begun to manufacture as the 'London' Gas Engine.

What had become a life-long preoccupation for Robson was prompted by his visit to the Great Exhibition in 1851. In trying to construct an incubator similar to one that had been demonstrated, he tried using town gas rather than paraffin, and began to experiment with a closed cylinder (24 in. long by 3 in. in diameter) and different proportions of coal gas and air. By 1857, after trying different forms of ignition, he had designed and built an experimental engine, in which a separate explosion drove each revolution of a crankshaft. That led to a second prototype, built in 1858-9, which developed three horse-power and was used to drive a circular saw in his father's workshop. An engine of a similar design was used for

---

148 Haswell was the President of the Midlands Tyneside Club.

driving the printing machinery of *The Shields Daily News* and another smaller engine at a printing works. Although Robson did not patent his designs, they were certainly innovative and incorporated water-cooling and electric spark ignition.[149]

He next began work compressing gases before ignition to improve the efficiency of his engines, whilst he had a shop in King Street, across the river in South Shields. However, during excavations to build a new theatre on the adjacent site in 1865, his premises collapsed, and his experimental engine and equipment were destroyed. That, coupled with the death of his uncle, took him back to North Shields to work with his father for most of the next ten years. However, that did not stop his experimentation. He worked on a vacuum type of engine, followed by a vertical spring-type atmospheric engine, before starting on his most important invention, the two-stroke (cycle) gas engine. The patent for it, which he took out in 1877, was genuinely innovative. His was the first two-cycle engine, in which compression took place in the same cylinder as ignition, combustion and gas expulsion, providing an impulse at every revolution of the crankshaft. It was a further improved engine, with an additional 1879 patent, that he took to Tangyes in 1881. The initial production model was a one horse-power engine, but later models produced up to four horse-power. About 300 Robson engines were exported to Scandinavia, Spain, Australia, and New Zealand.

Robson later returned to work on his gas forging hammer. It went into production in 1884 and, though it did not sell well during a period of depressed trading conditions, his work was again undoubtedly innovative.

---

149 During this period, he was listed in trade directories as Robson James, Ironmonger, Plumber, Brazier, Bellhanger and Gas Fitter, 9 Union Street, North Shields.

Appendix 2

Thomas Taylor

TAYLOR WAS born on 9 August 1898. He was the grandson of the lady he called mother and the man he referred to as 'the old man'. The three of them lived as a family at 21 Stanley Street, North Shields. On other occasions, for example, on the death of the 'old man', he refers to himself as an adopted child. He believed that he had gone to live with his grandmother after his brother Christopher Fawcett was born in 1900, but then remained there even though his mother went on to have two more children. Christopher died towards the end of WWI. He appears to have been a galley boy on a merchant vessel.

Thomas Taylor wrote to a friend after his grandmother's death in 1914:

> Granny was 94 – a great age. You will better understand my loss and just how I feel when I say that she was everything to me: and everything I have gained, every happiness I have known, I owe to her. She was a grand, dear old lady, who brought me up from babyhood. My younger brother (who lost his life in the War) was born when I was little more than two years old. Granny took care of me and I never returned to my own home.

Taylor joined the gas company in 1914. He subsequently served in the army and was demobbed in 1920. By 1939 he was living at 25 Cleveland Road in a household of three ladies and one person still with a closed record.[150] Given the views he expressed about women in his journals, it is ironic that after moving from 21 Stanley Street he should move into a household of three women: Melita M. Frier b. 1879, a widow; Florence H. Townsend b.1884, a widow; and Dorothy Townsend (later Thompson) b.1919, then a spinster. In 1939, 12 years after the takeover of the Tynemouth Gas Company by the Newcastle and Gateshead Company, Thomas was described as a costing clerk but before the takeover

---

150 The names of those who could still be alive are redacted from the 1939 Register unless proof of their death has been provided.

he appears to have played a significant administrative role in the Tynemouth company and, not unreasonably, thought of himself as the right-hand man to the manager Mr Duncan.

Appendix 3

Occupants of the Minton Lane Gasworks House

James Kemp 1876-1879
William Hardie 1879-1911
Frederick Willis 1911-1918
George Duncan 1918-1941
Ernest Wearne 1941-1955
Harold Jarmy 1955-1966
George Brigham 1967-1976

Appendix 4

Script of the 1942
BBC Radio Drama-documentary

For Gallantry. Lorna Duncan

What follows is the full text of the broadcast from the BBC's Newcastle Studios
on 9 May 1942, after four hours of rehearsals on 8 May 1942.

"FOR GALLANTRY" (3)
LORNA DUNCAN

OVERSEAS 12.30 – 12.45 GMT 9 May 1942 Eastern (Live)
From Newcastle

Rehearsals: Friday 8th May 6 p.m. – 10 p.m. (Studios 3, 4, Echo Room, D.C. panel)

Saturday 9th May 1 p.m. – 2 p.m. (Studios 3, 4, Echo Room, D.C. panel)

ANNOUNCER: This is London Calling!

We present the third in the series "For Gallantry" –
dramatised impressions showing how British men and
women have faced danger at home and overseas.

NARRATOR: Joseph Callaghan, Foreman, North Shields Gas Works –
George Medal.
George Duncan, Gasworks Manager – MBE.
Lorna Duncan, Commended for Gallantry!
(Trumpet fanfare – Col. DB 1671 – 1st band 2nd half)

ANNOUNCER: On the 10th of April 1941 the industrial district of
Tyneside suffered a heavy air attack, the brunt being

borne by the twin towns of North and South Shields. In the annals of the Merchant Navy the spirit of the men of Shields fills glorious pages; the spirit of the womenfolk was well typified that night by the bravery of a 20-year-old student.

But this is more than the tale of a young girl's courage: it is a story of great modesty. For only now has the real account come to light, and today is told for the first time the full story of the gallantry of Lorna Duncan. The story opens in the home of George Duncan, Gasworks Manager.

(Fade up clock chiming three-quarters)

JEAN:	I don't suppose it'll be much.
GEORGE:	Nothing happened yet, anyway! Anybody want a cigarette?
JEAN:	Yes. Me.
GEORGE:	Phyllis?
PHYLLIS:	No thanks.
GEORGE:	Mr. Duncan? You still keeping off them?
DUNCAN:	Aye, I'd better give this chest of mine a chance.
JEAN:	I'm glad I didn't go to bed when Lorna did. I don't mind a raid so much when I've got my clothes on, but I hate being hauled out of a nice warm bed.
GEORGE:	Me too!
PHYLLIS:	She's a long time coming down, Jean. Are you sure she heard the siren?
JEAN:	Yes. I shouted to her and she answered.
DUNCAN:	She's probably dozed off. She's been working pretty hard lately for her exams.

(Door opens)

JEAN:	(at door, shouting) Hey! Our Lorna! (Quieter) Oh, there you are! Not got your clothes on yet?!
LORNA:	(Approaching) No, I've just come down to see what time it is.

(Door shuts)

GEORGE: Quarter to twelve.

PHYLLIS: You should stay down here.

DUNCAN: Yes, get your things on, Lorna. It's freezing outside. You want something more than that thin dressing gown.

LORNA: But there's nothing happening, Father. We might just as well be in bed. I came home for a rest!

JEAN: What d'ye think they sound the sirens for, anyway?

LORNA: Oh, I know, but I … .

GEORGE: Quiet, everybody! I'm sure I heard a 'plane there.

(Faint "Rhum … Rhum" of bomber)

GEORGE: That's a Jerry all right!

(Tremendous bang, then heavy Ack-Ack and occasional bombs. Hold behind the following scene)

DUNCAN: Don't go out yet! It's too heavy.

LORNA: You mustn't go out at all, Daddy. You'll have your pneumonia back again.

JEAN: And you don't want to go out in your nightie, either, our Lorna!

GEORGE: We'll all be mugs if we go outside. There was a heavy frost when I came in.

(Few seconds of heavier Ack-Ack and bombs)

LORNA: This is going to be a raid, all right! Some of those bangs seem pretty near.

(Heavy rattle of incendiaries hitting ground)

LORNA: My! What was that? Sounded like a lot of tin cans!

JEAN: Perhaps it was a time bomb. There didn't seem to be any explosion.

GEORGE: (Fading) I didn't like the sound of that at all. I'm going out to have a look.

298

JEAN:	Be careful, George.
GEORGE:	(Yells) It's incendiaries – hundreds of 'em! They're all over the works!
DUNCAN:	Out, everybody! We've got to get them out quick!
LORNA:	Daddy, come here! You mustn't go out in that cold! You're not fit yet.
DUNCAN:	I must, Lorna. I'm the manager. I must.
GEORGE:	(Shouting) There's an incendiary every couple of feet!
	Use the sandbags from in front of the window.
DUNCAN:	The sandbags ... quick! Or the whole place'll be ablaze!
JEAN:	Lorna! Don't go out there in your dressing gown! Lorna! Come back! Come back!
	(Fade on this)
NARRATOR:	Hundreds of incendiaries hissed and exploded in a hideous firework display. The office block, the huge stacks of coal and coke, the furnaces, retorts, and the three great tanks of coal gas – 50 feet high, 100 feet broad – all were bathed in a vivid greenish white glare. Firefighters and ARP men fought frantically to smother the deadly magnesium bombs; in the yard and around the house, the Duncan family forgot the dangers of bomb and shell, forgot everything but the urgent need to kill those incendiaries.
	(Fade up background noise again, and:)
GEORGE:	Stick it! There's not many more.
DUNCAN:	Is the house all right?
GEORGE:	Yes, they've missed the house. I've sent Jean back there to look after things.
LORNA:	Bring some more sandbags!
GEORGE:	There's no more left.
LORNA:	Pull down the blast wall; use those.
GEORGE:	We've used them too. That's the lot.

LORNA:	Earth'll do. Dig the garden up! There's spades along the wall.
GEORGE:	O.K. The soil's pretty loose at this end. I'll do it.
LORNA:	(Shout of alarm) Oh, Daddy! Look! Look! No.1 holder's on fire!
DUNCAN:	I'll have to get that out! I'll have to get that out!
LORNA:	Get some of the men to … Oh my goodness! The wood shed's blazing! George! George! I'll take the stirrup pump: you bring the water.
GEORGE:	Right!
	(Fade on clatter of bucket handle)
NARRATOR:	For many minutes Lorna and George fought the flames together the least of a score of fires that blazed at Shields that night. By the riverside, a burning timber yard filled the sky with the blaze of a midsummer sunset.
	(Fade up background noise once more, and:)
GEORGE:	Phew! That was a warm job. Good work, lass!
LORNA:	Daddy must have gone in. (Shouts) Phyllis! Where's Daddy?
PHYLLIS:	(Distant shout) I dunno. Haven't seen him for a bit.
LORNA:	(Shouts) Father! … Father! (Quieter) Jean! Have you seen him?
JEAN:	He went back to the house once to get some whisky. He looked awful, but he went out again.
LORNA:	You should've made him stay in.
JEAN:	I tried to stop him … but you know what he is!
LORNA:	Well, where's he gone?
JEAN:	I don't know. He just dashed off again, and I was busy helping George.
GEORGE:	We'll have to get him in. He'll be ill again if he's not careful.

(Raid fills up few seconds)

LORNA: (Running up) Daddy! Daddy! Wherever have you been? You must go in and lie down.

DUNCAN: (Exhausted; almost incoherent) I've managed it … . it's out … . the fire … No.1 holder.

LORNA: (Horrified) Daddy! You haven't been up on top of the holder!

DUNCAN: Had to get it out … still a big escape … a big escape … have to be closed up … dangerous.

LORNA: Where is it? How can we seal it up?

DUNCAN: Far side … near the edge … there's clay in a bucket … on the top … gas escaping.

WORKMAN: (Approaching, eagerly) Anything I can do, sir?

DUNCAN: (On point of collapse) Big escape … get …

LORNA: (Shouts) Jean! Look after Daddy, here. Take him in. (Quieter, quickly) I know what he wants done. Quick! Come with me!

WORKMAN: O.K. Miss.

LORNA: Come on! Run! No.1 holder.

WORKMAN: (Approaching) I've been helping Mr Callaghan, Miss. There's been fires all over. Most of them's out now. Mr Callaghan's up on one of the holders that was bleezin'.

LORNA: That's what we've got to do with this one. My father says there's a big escape. It might take fire.

WORKMAN: You're never gonna climb this, Miss!

LORNA: I used to climb these gasholders when I was a kid.

WORKMAN: But it's nearly 50 feet!

LORNA: No time to argue. I'll go first.

(From here onwards both are talking in increasingly breathless shouts: Lorna close to mike; he is more distant (5 or 6ft below) but keeping his voice well up)

WORKMAN:	All right, Miss. But for Heaven's sake be careful.
LORNA:	Father's been up already. He's put the fires out. But he says there's still a big escape.
WORKMAN:	Whereabouts?
LORNA:	On the far side – near the edge …. We've got to seal it up.
WORKMAN:	What with?
LORNA:	There's clay … in a bucket on the top.
WORKMAN:	Be careful on these rungs, Miss. There's ice on them.
LORNA:	I'm all right. I've got slippers on …. Oh dear! I can't get any higher … there's a girder across. We must be on the wrong side of the ladder. Why didn't you tell me?
WORKMAN:	Sorry, Miss, but I'm new here. Should we go down again?
LORNA:	No … when you're up to here you'll have to get off the ladder, then climb over the girder, and get back again.
WORKMAN:	(Urgently) Don't do it, Miss Duncan! Ye'll kill yerself!
LORNA:	It's fairly easy, I think … … (Gasp!) Rightho! I'm over …. When you leave the ladder hold on to this cross piece with your left hand. Can you see it?
WORKMAN:	Aye!
LORNA:	Are you all right? Can you get over?
WORKMAN:	I suppose so! Ye beggor, I'll not forget this night in a hurry. It's a good job we can see what we're doing!
LORNA:	(Very breathless now) Nearly there! … I can see the clay bucket … there's a spade too …. Right! … I'm up!
WORKMAN:	(Climbing on to top) I'll carry the things.
LORNA:	Upsadaisy! There we are! (Both voices are now equally balanced)
WORKMAN:	By! Me heart hasn't beat like this since me weddin'.
LORNA:	You bring the clay. I'll carry the spade.
WORKMAN:	Round the far side, is it?

(Bucket handle rattles, and his heavy hobnails ring on the crown of the holder – like footsteps on the deck of a ship)

LORNA: Yes. Come on. Hang on to the rail.

WORKMAN: By gum! But there's not half some wind blowin' up here!

Goes right through ye … . Good Heavens, Miss! Have you not got yer clothes on?

LORNA: I've got my nightie and a dressing gown.

WORKMAN: Ye'll get yer death o' cold.

LORNA: I've been too busy to feel cold. Can you see where the escape is?

WORKMAN: Round here. I can hear it hissin'.

(Hiss increases as they approach)

Aye, that's it Miss! It's a long split, look! About 10 feet from the edge. I'll get over and seal it up. You can throw us the clay.

(A clatter as he falls and an exclamation of pain)

LORNA: Have you hurt yourself?

WORKMAN: I canna keep me feet. The crown's that steep and it's all frosty.

LORNA: Right! I'll do it. You pass me the clay.

WORKMAN: Don't get too near. Ye'll get gassed.

LORNA: No, I'll lie down at the side of it. The gas is just rushing straight up. Throw me some clay.

WORKMAN: Can you reach?

LORNA: Just throw it.

(Plonk of clay hitting metal. Second plonk as she claps it into place)

LORNA: Throw some more!

WORKMAN: Coming!

(More plonks)

By! I've done some daft things in me time, mind, but I never thought I'd be making mud pies on top of a gasometer in an air raid.

(More plonks. Hiss quietens as gap is closed)

WORKMAN: (Frantic yell) Look out, Miss! Duck!

(Scream of bomb, and then explosion)

WORKMAN: That was a near one! Over in the field there.

LORNA: Come on! More clay!

(More plonks)

LORNA: Another lot!

(Plonks. Hiss ends)

LORNA: That's it! There'd be no heat and light in Shields tomorrow if all that gas had escaped.

WORKMAN: Miss Duncan yer a grand lass!

LORNA: Thank goodness that's over. Just leave the bucket and spade here. Let's get down. It seems to be getting heavy again.

(Heavier background noise. Footsteps)

WORKMAN: And this time, Miss, we'll keep on the proper side of the ladder. That ruddy girder gave me the willies!

(Fade out on this)

NARRATOR: But Lorna Duncan's work did not end there. A few minutes later she was helping the firemen in another part of the yard. There was no rest that night for the Duncan family, and even when daylight came and the raid was over there was one more job to be done. No.1 holder had to be climbed again.

(Fade Up:)

LORNA: I dunno where it's got to. Has anybody seen the cord of my dressing gown?

JEAN: No, Lorna.

DUNCAN: It'll turn up somewhere.

PHYLLIS: Are you sure you've had enough breakfast, Father?

DUNCAN: Yes. I've got to get out. There's a lot to be done.

LORNA: Is Mr Callaghan all right, Daddy?

DUNCAN: He's badly gassed. I used the oxygen and got him round though. They've taken him to hospital. I think he'll be all right.

(Knock on door which opens)

WORKMAN: Mornin' Mr Duncan! Excuse me sir, but there's a streamer or a pennant or something flyin' from the top of No.1 holder.

DUNCAN: A pennant!? … Jean, hand me my glasses over!…. Aye, it's a pennant all right … and flying very bravely too! (Louder) Here you are Lorna! We've found the cord of your dressing gown!

(He laughs; the workman is the first to join in; then the others; and the laughter is covered by the fanfare which finishes full.)

ANNOUNCER: You've been listening to the story of how Lorna Duncan, a 20-year-old student, received her Commendation for Gallantry. The programme was written by John Polwarth and produced by Cecil McGivern. Listen at this time next week for the fourth in the series 'For Gallantry' and hear how Lieutenant Richard Wallace Annand won the Victoria Cross.

Appendix 5

Alice and Lorna Duncan's Recollections of their Gasworks Home

Alice: Our house was three-storied. There was an entrance lobby and an entrance hall. On the left-hand side was a sitting room with just one flat sash window, a white marble fireplace and, of course, a gas fire. There was a green carpet square and a white sheepskin hearth rug. There was the same piano, of course, and violin [that had been used so much in their previous Walton Avenue house], and a comfortable three-piece suite with quite a large occasional table. Next on the left-hand side was the dining room. Facing the door was a flat sash window looking onto the yard. Just within the door on the left-hand side, fixed to the floor, was a small heavy metal safe standing about 2-3 feet high. Opposite the door next to the window was the fireplace – a marble fireplace again. Around an upright gas fire was a brass fender, a foot and a half high, standing on brass feet. On the right-hand side of the fireplace was a built-in cupboard the length of the recess and, on the top of that, was a double glass door bookcase standing almost to the ceiling. … Adjoining this on the right-hand side was a large bay window looking onto the back area of the house: quite a large garden, which was bordered by a hedgerow and set with flower beds. On the same wall there was a shelf for the telephone. On the right-hand side of the room, behind the door, there was what was called a settle. It was neither a couch nor a sofa, with a high back and sides – not quite so high. There was also a rolled pillow on each end. The covering was dark green damask. This could seat four people. There was a large carpet square on the floor in tones of brown and fawn, and a woollen hearth rug. On the left-hand side of the door was a long walnut sideboard. It had a cupboard on each end and three deep drawers in the middle down to the floor. It also had a full-length high mirror at the back. Standing under the window directly opposite the door stood mother's treadle sewing machine, which was always in use – believe me – because most things were made not bought! There was a polished walnut dining table for which there were two separate leaves which could be inserted when necessary. There were dining chairs which were upholstered on the seat and the back in what was called plush velvet and there were two armchairs to match. Surrounding the carpet square was polished linoleum.

At the windows of the sitting room and dining room were long net curtains and venetian blinds. These venetian blinds were taken down every springtime and sometimes in between. The lathes were painted wood, slotted through wide linen tapes. Believe me they took some cleaning. The lathes were washed and polished and the tapes thoroughly scrubbed. I had to do those as one of my chores and always vowed that if I ever had a house it would never have venetian blinds! Furniture polish was well used – believe me – on piano, sideboard, and tables. The piano keys had to be – the piano was so well used that it had to have a daily rub with a wash-leather – that is the keys. In spite of being taught to have clean hands before using it, they still seemed to be a bit grubby, and so it had to be kept clean. … On the wall along the passage, by the side of the staircase, there were two rows of hot water pipes the length of the hall between the lobby door and the staircase. These were heated by gas on the outside. These continued up through the ceiling along the skirting board in the bedroom above. This was the only central heating. At the end of that passage, on the left, was a door leading onto the back of the premises. Outside that door was a sizeable concrete area between the house and leisure garden – the home produce garden was further away. On that area of the back of the house was a coal house and a very good size floor space of mosaic tiles with a flush lavatory. This was, of course, in addition to the one inside. Further around the side in that area there was a hefty wooden erection of a swing. Between this and the laid-out garden there was a short pathway leading to some steps down into what was the vegetable garden. As well as that, there was a wooden bungalow – at least a wooden chalet – which had been built for the previous manager's son who had been tubercular, and he lived there. It was built so that he needn't be in the house at all. Of course, that was a marvellous place to play. On the wall outside between the door and the bay window was a speaking tube which led up to the master bedroom. This was to be used in case of an emergency, which could be during the night, as father's job was a 24-hour one.

Straight ahead from the passage of the side entrance, a door led to the breakfast room. Just within the entrance on the right-hand side was a modern fireplace with a coal fire and on the right of that in the corner was a hinged wooden box seat which was always kept full of chopped sticks. This job was done by a jobbing gardener who also took care of the garden, providing plenty of fresh vegetable salads such as lettuce, tomatoes – red and yellow – cucumbers and mushrooms. On the floor was red tiled polished inlaid linoleum and by the fireplace was a hand-made 'hooky' mat.[151] On the left-hand side was a single sash window with net curtains and again venetian blinds. Under these was a sofa which served as part seating at mealtimes round the polished solid mahogany dining table, in addition to the polished wood chairs as well as a big highchair for the latest member of the family. That always stood in between mother and father at the table.

The wall directly ahead was taken up by a double height cupboard (it was called a press) but that really meant the bottom half was covered at each side by a cupboard with deep drawers in between. The top half was all cupboard shelves with two large doors almost to the ceiling. This housed most of the everyday china. Our shoes and odds and ends were kept in the cupboards on the bottom half and kitchen linen in the drawers.

On the right-hand side past the fireplace a door led into the kitchen. It was quite a big kitchen. On the left-hand side was the sink and bench which was scrubbed almost white with powdered bath brick mixed with dry soap powder, as was the bread trencher and pastry board. On the right-hand side of the sink, in the middle of that wall, was quite a large single window along which was a large kitchen table. From the ceiling hung five long rails which were clothes airers. At the right of this wall was the pantry, which had a concrete floor, where all the tinned food was kept. Perishable food was kept on the middle shelves and on the top shelf home-made jams and marmalade. There were shelves in the recess between the pantry and the next wall where most of the pans were kept. Then on the right of that wall was a walk-in pantry where all dry groceries were kept. Then next was quite a large gas cooker and a fireplace which provided an abundance of hot water. I never remember the kitchen fire actually being quite out because at night tea leaves and vegetable refuse were used to damp it down. There was always a high fire guard surrounding this fireplace. The floor was covered

---

151 Hooky and clippy mats were made from a sheet of hessian stretched over a wooden frame. Scraps of cloth, cut into small strips, were inserted into the hessian with 'proggers', metal spikes with a hook for a 'hooky' mat or a straight one for a 'clippy' mat. For a clippy mat, two holes were made, and the material pushed through. For a hooky mat, a longer length of material was woven through a line of holes. The clippy mat finished up with a shaggy pile. The hooky mat had a harder finish.

with inlaid linoleum and coconut matting mostly, I think, with a view to hygiene because, as mother said, that was picked up and given a good old shake outside and the dirt that fell onto the floor could be swept up and then washed so to keep it clean.

To that, Lorna added:

I believe that the kitchen was an addition to the house as there was quite a wide doorway between the breakfast room and the kitchen above which was a wooden covering. This cover had a gap along it so that we were able to jump up, grasp the wood and pull ourselves up, using it as wall bars. It was all great exercise and fun. Preparing food for 12 people took a great deal of time, so the kitchen was very well used. Washing dishes was a laborious task, although we always had plenty of hot water, heated by the boiler behind the fire. Drying, folding, and ironing the clothes took place in the kitchen too.

Although the gas company had long been promoting the use of gas fires, it is noteworthy that, as Lorna explained:

The fires [downstairs] were all open fires. We were extremely fortunate in that one of the many perks of Daddy being manager of the gasworks was that we received free coal, sticks with which to light the fires and, of course, as we lived at the gasworks, free gas: all the lights being gas lights. The fire in the breakfast room was lit on most mornings. There was a lovely inglenook by the side of this fire, and it was a favourite seat for us. The tiles around the grate were pictures of characters from classic novels, most of them from Sir Walter Scott's stories. I did not then know the stories, but I loved watching the pictures as I toasted my toes in front of a blazing fire. The box below the ingle housed the sticks which were delivered regularly by workmen from the yard. There the sticks were kept dry, ready for quick ignition each day.

Alice continued:

The floor of the hall and passage was covered with linoleum and carpet runners with a red Turkish design. The stair carpets were the same design. The sides of the stair treads were white, which were always kept clean and

polished with furniture cream after washing, and the carpet held in place
with brass stair rods which were always kept bright in spite of tarnishing
from the works' fumes.

This remark is a reminder that the Duncans new home was on the site of a
potentially dangerous chemical plant and that, both in the air and underfoot, there
were substances that they would never have encountered at their previous home in
Preston Village. Yet, although the Minton Lane house would hardly have pleased
those estate agents who insist that 'Location, Location, Location' is what matters
most about a property, it was still a house to impress those who lived in the small
upstairs or downstairs Tyneside flats that predominated in the neighbourhood.

Select Bibliography and Sources

Arapostathis, Stathis, Anna Carlsson-Hyslp, Peter J. G. Pearson, Judith Thornton, Maria Gradillas, Scott Laczay and Suzanne Wallis, 'Governing Transitions: Cases and Insights from Two Periods in the History of the UK Gas Industry', *Energy Policy* 52, 2013 pp.25-44.

Barty-King, R., *The New Flame: The Illustrated History of Piped Gas* (Tavistock: Graphmitre, 1984).

Bolger, Peter, *North Shields 173. The Wilkinson's Lemonade Factory Air Raid Disaster* (North Shields, 2019).

Boyce, A. O., *Records of a Quaker family: The Richardsons of Cleveland* (1889).

Chandler, D. and Lacey, A. D., *The Rise of the Gas industry in Britain* (London: British Gas Council, 1949).

Chittenden, Ruth and Alan Fidler., *The Response. The North East and the Great War 1914-1918* (2014).

Coates, Mike N., *Clifford's Fort, the Low Lights and High Lights of North Shields* (2016).

Coates, Mike N., *The Pow Burn North Shields* (2017).

Evans, Hayden., 'Aluminium formate, $Al(HCOO)_3$: An earth-abundant, scalable, and highly selective material for CO_2 capture.' *Science Advances* (journal of the American Association for the Advancement of Science, November 2022).

Falkus, M. E., 'The British Gas Industry Before 1850.' *The Economic History Review* Vol. 20 (3), pp. 494-508 (1967).

Gas Journal.

Gas Times (The).

Gas World (The).

Goodall, F., *The British Gas Appliance Industry 1875-1939.* Ph.D. Thesis (L.S.E., 1992).

Grace's Guide to British Industrial History at https://www.gracesguide.co.uk/Grace%27s_Guide

Hide, Katria, *Profession versus Trade. A defining episode in the development of the gas lighting industry in the late 19th century* (M.A. thesis, 2010). http://sas-space.sas.ac.uk/2816/1/Hide_-_Gas_Lighting__-_MA_2010.pdf

HM Government, Policy: The Ten Point Plan for a Green Industrial Revolution (18 November 2020) The ten point plan for a green industrial revolution – GOV. UK (www.gov.uk)

HM Government, UK Hydrogen Strategy, CP 475 (August 2021) UK Hydrogen Strategy (publishing.service.gov.uk)

Hovey, A. Clement. 'Constructional Details and Costs of recent Extension (1900-1902) With Notes on Working Results, at the Tynemouth Gas Works, North Shields', *Journal of Gas Lighting, Water Supply &c.*

Hunt, C., *A History of the Introduction of Gas Lighting* (London: Walter King, 1907).

Iliffe, Alan. 'Miss Lorna & the flaming holder'. *Historic Gas Times*, p.3 (September 2003).

Jackson, Dan. *The Northumbrians. North-East England and Its People* (London, Hurst, 2021).

Jackson, J. F., *A Short History of the Newcastle and Gateshead Gas Company* (Newcastle, 1945).

Lawrence, Danny, *Shiels to Shields. The Life Story of a North Tyneside Town* (Lancaster: Carnegie, 2016).

Lawrence, Danny, *Arthur Jefferson. Man of the Theatre and Father of Stan Laurel* (Studley: Brewin, 2017).

Macfarlan, J. 'George Dixon: Discoverer of Gas Light from Coal', *Transactions of the Newcomen Society*, vol.5 no.1, pp.53-55 (1924).

Morpeth Gas Company, *History of the Morpeth Gas Company. Centenary 1833-1933* (Morpeth, 1933).

Navigant, *Pathways to Net-Zero: Decarbonising the Gas Networks in Great Britain*, prepared for the Energy Networks Association (London: 21 October 2019).

Newcastle Courant.

Newcastle Daily Chronicle.

Newcastle Journal.

North & South Shields Gazette.

Northern Gas Networks, Environmental Assessment Site Investigation (2002).

Northern Gas Networks, Green Light for First Hydrogen Blending on a Public Gas Network (2021).

Northumberland Advertiser.

OFGEM, *Hydrogen Village Trial Detailed Design Studies Decision* (London: 6 May 2022).

Pears, Brian and Roy Ripley. *North-East Diary. 1939-1945. https://ne-diary.genuki.uk*

Peebles, M. W., *The Evolution of the Gas Industry* (London: Macmillan, 1980).

Jones, Carol, 'Coal, gas, and electricity' in Pope, Rex (Ed.), *Atlas of British Social and Economic History Since C.1700* (London: Routledge, 1989).

Port of Tyne Pilot.

Shields Daily Gazette.

Shields Daily News. }

Shields News. } These three bracketed titles are the

Shields Evening News. } changing titles of the same newspaper.[152]

Thomas, Russell. 'The History and Operation of Gasworks (Manufactured Gas Plants) in Britain', (14 February 2014).

Thomas, Russell. *The Manufactured Gas Industry: Volumes 1-5* (Historic England, Research Report Series, no.182, 2020).

Tomory, Leslie. 'Building the First Gas Network, 1812-1820', *Society for the History of Technology, Technology and Culture* (2011).

Tomory, Leslie. *Progressive Enlightenment, The Origins of the Gaslight Industry, 1780-1820* (M.I.T. Press, 2012).

Vitchev, D. (2021). 'A brief analysis of the physical requirements for converting coal-fired power plants to hydrogen.' *Academia Letters*, Article 2884, (August 2021). https://doi.org/10.20935/AL2884.

Westall, Robert, *The Making of Me. A Writer's Childhood* (London: Catnip Press, 2006).

Wilkinson, J. B., *Desk Study and Historical Report. Former Gasworks Site at Minton Lane, North Shields* (Leeds, 2002).

Williams, T. I. *A History of the British Gas Industry* (London: Oxford University Press, 1981).

---

152 In the British Newspaper Archive, all three are included under the same umbrella title *Shields Daily News.*

Index

314